North Somerset Enterprise and Technology College
Your vision Your future

CGP

Radiate Science knowledge with CGP...

OK, so there's a lot to learn in GCSE Combined Science — it is worth two GCSEs, after all.

Not to worry. This chunky CGP book explains all the facts, theory and practical skills you'll need, with essential exam practice questions on every page. It's a beautiful thing.

How to access your free Online Edition

This book includes a free Online Edition to read on your PC, Mac or tablet.
To access it, just go to **cgpbooks.co.uk/extras** and enter this code...

2439 5370 4903 9910

By the way, this code only works for one person. If somebody else has used this book before you, they might have already claimed the Online Edition.

CGP — still the best! ☺

Our sole aim here at CGP is to produce the highest quality books —
carefully written, immaculately presented and dangerously close to being funny.

Then we work our socks off to get them out to you
— at the cheapest possible prices.

Contents

Published by CGP.

Based on the classic CGP style created by Richard Parsons.

Editors: Robin Flello, Emily Forsberg, Emily Garrett, Emily Howe, Paul Jordin, Sharon Keeley-Holden, Duncan Lindsay, Ciara McGlade, Sarah Oxley, Rachael Rogers, Frances Rooney, Hayley Thompson, Sean Walsh, Charlotte Whiteley and Sarah Williams.

Contributor: Paddy Gannon.

ISBN: 978 1 78294 564 2

With thanks to Chris McGarry and Sophie Scott for the proofreading.

With thanks to Jan Greenway for the copyright research.

Data used for graph showing the prevalence of nonalcoholic fatty liver disease against the prevalence of obesity on page 19 from The Epidemiology of Nonalcoholic Fatty Liver Disease: A Global Perspective, Mariana Lazo, M.D., M.Sc.; Jeanne M. Clark, M.D., M.P.H Seminars in Liver Disease. 2008; 28(4): 339-350. www.thieme.com (reprinted by permission).

Data used for graph showing the risk of cardiovascular events against LDL levels on page 19 from P.M. Ridker, et al. Comparison of C-reactive protein and low density lipoprotein cholesterol levels in the prediction of first cardiovascular events. NEJM 2002; 347: 1557-65.

With thanks to HERVE CONGE, ISM/SCIENCE PHOTO LIBRARY for permission to reproduce the image on page 50.

Data provided to construct a graph on page 85 provided by The European Environment Agency.

Data provided to construct a graph on page 85 provided by the NASA GISS.

Graph to show trend in atmospheric CO_2 concentration and global temperature on page 160 based on data by EPICA community members 2004 and Siegenthaler et al 2005.

Printed by Elanders Ltd, Newcastle upon Tyne.
Clipart from Corel®

Cells and Genetic Material

When someone first peered down a microscope at a slice of cork and drew the boxes they saw, little did they know that they'd seen the <u>building blocks</u> of <u>every organism on the planet</u>...

Organisms can be Made from Eukaryotic or Prokaryotic Cells

1) <u>All living things</u> are made of <u>cells</u>.

2) Cells can be either <u>eukaryotic</u> or <u>prokaryotic</u>. Eukaryotic cells are <u>complex</u> and include all <u>animal</u> and <u>plant</u> cells. Prokaryotic cells are <u>smaller</u> and <u>simpler</u>, e.g. bacterial cells.

3) Both types of cell contain <u>genetic material</u> in the form of the chemical <u>DNA</u> — this contains <u>instructions</u> that control the <u>activities</u> of the <u>cell</u>, and allows the whole organism to <u>develop</u> and <u>function</u> as it should.

There's more about DNA on page 3.

4) Genetic material is <u>stored differently</u> in eukaryotic and prokaryotic cells (see below).

Eukaryotic Cells Have a Nucleus

Subcellular structures are also known as organelles.

The different parts of a cell are called <u>subcellular structures</u>. The diagram below shows a typical <u>animal cell</u>. Like most <u>eukaryotic</u> cells, it contains the following subcellular structures:

1) <u>Nucleus</u> — contains <u>genetic material</u>, which is arranged into <u>chromosomes</u> (see p.3).

2) <u>Cytoplasm</u> — gel-like substance where most of the <u>chemical reactions</u> happen. It contains <u>enzymes</u> (see page 25) that control these chemical reactions.

3) A <u>partially permeable cell membrane</u> — holds the cell together and controls what goes <u>in</u> and <u>out</u> (see page 30-31).

4) <u>Mitochondria</u> — contain the <u>enzymes</u> (see page 25) needed to control most of the reactions in aerobic <u>respiration</u>. Respiration transfers <u>energy</u> that the cell needs to work (see page 47).

5) <u>Ribosomes</u> — these are involved in the <u>synthesis of proteins</u>.

Nucleus

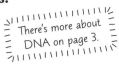

Plant cells usually have <u>all the bits</u> that <u>animal</u> cells have, plus a few <u>extra</u> things that animal cells <u>don't</u> have:

1) Rigid <u>cell wall</u> — made of <u>cellulose</u>. It <u>supports</u> the cell and strengthens it.

2) <u>Large vacuole</u> — contains <u>cell sap</u>, a weak solution of sugar and salts.

3) <u>Chloroplasts</u> — these are where <u>photosynthesis</u> occurs, which makes food for the plant (see page 27). They contain a <u>green</u> substance called <u>chlorophyll</u>.

Prokaryotic Cells Have No Nucleus

1) <u>Prokaryotic cells</u> (such as bacteria) <u>don't have a nucleus</u>. Instead they store their <u>genetic material</u> as:

- <u>One</u> long <u>circular chromosome</u>, which <u>floats free</u> in the <u>cytoplasm</u>.

- <u>Plasmids</u> — <u>small loops</u> of <u>extra DNA</u>. They contain genes for things like <u>drug resistance</u>, and can be <u>passed</u> between prokaryotic cells. Not all prokaryotic cells contain plasmids.

2) Prokaryotes also have other <u>subcellular structures</u>, such as:

Cell membrane   Cell wall   Ribosomes

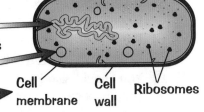

3) Unlike eukaryotic cells, prokaryotic cells <u>don't</u> contain <u>mitochondria</u> or <u>chloroplasts</u>.

Cell structures — become a property developer...

The main difference between eukaryotic and prokaryotic cells is that eukaryotic cells contain a nucleus and prokaryotic cells don't. Both types of cell contain subcellular structures though, which each have their own function.

Q1   Give two ways in which genetic information may be stored in a prokaryotic cell.   [2 marks]

 **PRACTICAL** # Cells and Microscopes

Without <u>microscopes</u> we would never have discovered cells. We can even use them to look <u>inside</u> cells.

You Need to Know How to View Cells Using a Light Microscope

Microscopes <u>magnify</u> images (make them look bigger) and allow things to be seen in more detail. <u>Light microscopes</u> work by passing <u>light</u> through the specimen (the sample you're looking at). They let you see subcellular structures, like <u>nuclei</u> and <u>chloroplasts</u>. This is how you'd use a light microscope to view cells:

1) Your specimen needs to <u>let light through it</u> so if your specimen is quite thick, you'll need to take a <u>thin slice</u> of it to start with.

2) Next, take a clean <u>slide</u> (a strip of clear glass or plastic) and use a <u>pipette</u> to put one drop of water or <u>mountant</u> (a clear, gloopy liquid) in the middle of it — this will <u>secure</u> the specimen in place.

3) Use <u>tweezers</u> to place your specimen on the slide.

4) Add a drop of <u>stain</u> if your <u>specimen</u> is completely <u>transparent</u> or <u>colourless</u> — this will make the specimen <u>easier to see</u>. <u>Different</u> stains are used to <u>highlight</u> different <u>structures</u>. For example, <u>eosin</u> is used to stain <u>cytoplasm</u> and <u>methylene blue</u> stains <u>DNA</u>.

5) Place a <u>cover slip</u> (a square of thin, transparent plastic or glass) at one end of the specimen, holding it at an <u>angle</u> with a <u>mounted needle</u>.

6) Carefully <u>lower</u> the cover slip onto the slide. Press it down <u>gently</u> with the <u>needle</u> so that no <u>air bubbles</u> are trapped under it.

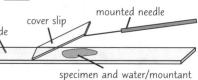

7) Clip the <u>prepared slide</u> onto the <u>stage</u> of the microscope.

8) Select the <u>lowest-powered objective lens</u> (i.e. the one that produces the lowest magnification).

9) Use the <u>coarse adjustment knob</u> to move the stage <u>up</u> so that the slide is <u>just underneath</u> the objective lens. Then, <u>looking</u> down the <u>eyepiece</u>, move the stage <u>downwards</u> (so you don't accidently crash it into the lens) until the specimen is <u>nearly in focus</u>.

10) Then <u>adjust the focus</u> with the <u>fine adjustment knob</u>, until you get a <u>clear image</u>.

11) If you need to see your specimen with <u>greater magnification</u>, swap to a <u>higher-powered objective lens</u> and <u>refocus</u>.

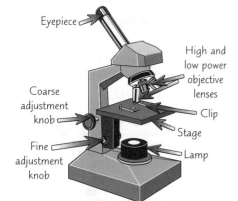

You Might Need to Produce a Scientific Drawing of a Specimen

1) You should draw what you see under the microscope using a <u>pencil</u> with a <u>sharp point</u>.

2) Make sure your drawing takes up <u>at least half</u> of the space available and that it is drawn with <u>clear, unbroken lines</u>.

3) Your drawing should not include any <u>colouring</u> or <u>shading</u>.

4) If you are drawing <u>cells</u>, the <u>subcellular structures</u> should be drawn in <u>proportion</u>.

5) Remember to include a <u>title</u> of what you were observing and write down the <u>magnification</u> that it was observed under.

6) You should also <u>label</u> the <u>important features</u> of your drawing (e.g. nucleus, chloroplasts), using <u>straight lines</u> drawn with a <u>ruler</u>. Make sure that none of these lines <u>cross each other</u> because this can make them hard to read.

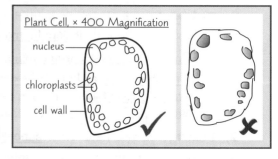

What, no colouring pencils? Scientists are spoilsports...

There's lots of important stuff here about how you use a light microscope to view specimens — so get learning.

Q1 A student prepares a slide with a sample of onion cells and places it on the stage of a light microscope. Describe the steps she should take to get a focused image of the cells. [4 marks]

Genomes and Characteristics

Right, time to find out exactly what this <u>genetic material</u> is all about and why it's so blummin' <u>important</u>...

Chromosomes are Really Long Molecules of DNA

1) The <u>genome</u> is the <u>entire genetic material</u> of an organism.

2) In <u>plant</u> and <u>animal</u> cells, genetic material is stored in the <u>nucleus</u> and is arranged into <u>chromosomes</u>.

3) The chromosomes normally come in <u>pairs</u> — e.g. humans have <u>23 pairs</u> (so 46 chromosomes in total).

4) Each chromosome is <u>one</u> very long <u>molecule of DNA</u> that's <u>coiled up</u>.

5) DNA is a <u>polymer</u> — a molecule that's made up of <u>smaller</u>, <u>repeating units</u> called <u>monomers</u>. DNA is made from monomers called <u>nucleotides</u>.

6) Each DNA molecule contains <u>two strands</u> of nucleotides, which coil together to form a <u>double helix</u> (a double-stranded spiral).

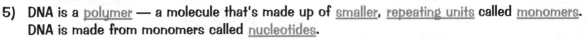

single chromosomes

A DNA molecule with a double helix structure

Genes are Instructions in the Genome

1) A <u>gene</u> is a <u>short length</u> of DNA on a chromosome.

2) Each gene <u>codes for</u> (tells the cells to make) a <u>particular sequence</u> of <u>amino acids</u>, which are put together to make a <u>specific protein</u>. This process of making a <u>big molecule</u> (e.g. a protein) from lots of <u>smaller molecules</u> (e.g. amino acids) is called <u>polymerisation</u>.

3) Proteins <u>control</u> the development of different <u>characteristics</u>, e.g. dimples, and how an organism <u>functions</u>.

4) Genes can exist in <u>different versions</u>. Each version gives a different form of a <u>characteristic</u>, like blue or brown eyes. The different versions of the same gene are called <u>alleles</u>.

5) Each chromosome in a pair carries the <u>same genes</u>, but they may each carry <u>different alleles</u>.

6) Different versions of a gene can also be called <u>genetic variants</u>.

The code carried by genes is known as the genetic code.

Genes and the Environment can Influence Characteristics

1) The combination of <u>alleles</u> an organism has for each <u>gene</u> is called its <u>genotype</u>. An organism's genotype is what makes its genome <u>unique</u>.

2) The <u>characteristics</u> the organism displays is called its <u>phenotype</u>.

3) It's <u>not only</u> genotype that can affect an organism's <u>phenotype</u> — interactions with the <u>environment</u> (the conditions in which the organisms lives) can modify a phenotype.

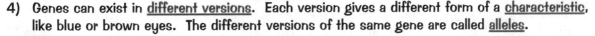

For example, a plant grown on a nice sunny windowsill could grow <u>luscious</u> and <u>green</u>. The same plant grown in darkness would grow <u>tall</u> and <u>spindly</u> and its leaves would turn <u>yellow</u> — so the characteristics it displays would be affected by its environment.

4) Most variation in phenotype is determined by a <u>mixture</u> of <u>genetic</u> and <u>environmental</u> factors. For example, the <u>maximum height</u> that an animal or plant could grow to is determined by its <u>genes</u>. But whether it actually grows that tall depends on its <u>environment</u> (e.g. how much food it gets).

Insert joke about genes and jeans here...

There are so many, I thought you could come up with your own as a bit of light relief. Make sure that you're clued up on this stuff about genomes, DNA, genes, genotypes and phenotypes before you move on.

Q1   What is an organism's genome?   [1 mark]

Q2   What is an organism's: a) genotype,   b) phenotype?   [2 marks]

Genetic Diagrams

This page is about how <u>characteristics</u> are <u>inherited</u> — it involves drawing little <u>diagrams</u> too, which is (a bit) fun.

Alleles are Different Versions of the Same Gene

1) In <u>sexual reproduction</u>, the mother and father produce <u>gametes</u> (reproductive cells), e.g. <u>sperm</u> and <u>eggs</u>. Each gamete only has <u>one copy</u> of <u>each chromosome</u> (rather than having pairs of chromosomes like other cells — see p.3). So gametes only have <u>one version of each gene</u> (i.e. <u>one allele</u>).

2) To produce an offspring, the chromosomes from a <u>male gamete</u> get <u>mixed together</u> with those from a <u>female gamete</u> — so the offspring ends up with <u>pairs of chromosomes</u> and <u>two alleles</u> for each gene.

3) If the alleles are <u>different</u>, then the organism has <u>instructions</u> for <u>two different versions</u> of a characteristic (e.g. freckles or no freckles) but it only <u>shows one version</u> of the two (e.g. freckles). The version of the characteristic that appears is caused by the <u>dominant allele</u>. The other allele is said to be <u>recessive</u>. The characteristic caused by the recessive allele only appears if <u>both alleles</u> are recessive.

4) In genetic diagrams, <u>letters</u> are used to represent <u>genes</u>. <u>Dominant alleles</u> are always shown with a <u>capital letter</u> (e.g. 'C') and <u>recessive alleles</u> with a <u>small letter</u> (e.g. 'c').

5) If you're <u>homozygous</u> for a trait, you have <u>two alleles the same</u> for that particular gene, e.g. <u>CC</u> or <u>cc</u>. If you're <u>heterozygous</u> for a trait, you have <u>two different alleles</u> for that particular gene, e.g. <u>Cc</u>.

6) Remember, an organism's <u>genotype</u> is the alleles it has. Its <u>phenotype</u> is the characteristics it displays.

Genetic Diagrams show the Possible Alleles in the Offspring

Some characteristics are controlled by a <u>single gene</u>, e.g. blood group — this is called <u>single gene inheritance</u>. Genetic diagrams help to <u>predict the phenotype</u> of the <u>offspring</u> when you know the <u>genotype</u> of the <u>parents</u>.

Let's say an allele that causes hamsters to have superpowers is <u>recessive</u> ("b"), and that normal (boring) hamsters don't have superpowers due to a <u>dominant</u> allele ("B").

1) A hamster with superpowers <u>must</u> have the <u>genotype bb</u> (i.e. it must be homozygous for this trait).

2) However, a <u>boring hamster</u> could have <u>two</u> possible genotypes — BB (homozygous) or Bb (heterozygous), because the dominant allele (B) <u>overrules</u> the recessive one (b).

3) Here's what happens if you breed from two <u>heterozygous</u> hamsters:

Parents' <u>phenotypes</u>:	boring	boring
Parents' <u>genotypes</u>:	Bb	Bb
Gametes' <u>genotypes</u>:	B b	B b
Offsprings' <u>genotypes</u>:	BB Bb	Bb bb
Offsprings' <u>phenotypes</u>:	boring boring	boring <u>superpowered!</u>

There's a <u>75% chance</u> of having a boring hamster, and a <u>25% chance</u> of one with superpowers. To put that another way... you'd expect a <u>3:1 ratio</u> of boring:superpowered hamsters. Or yet another way... out of 100 hamsters, the <u>proportion</u> of them you'd expect to have superpowers would be 25.

4) If you breed <u>two homozygous</u> hamsters there's only <u>one</u> possible offspring you can end up with. E.g. breeding BB and bb hamsters can only give offspring with a <u>Bb</u> genotype — and they'd all have a <u>boring</u> phenotype.

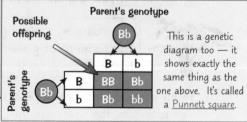

This is a genetic diagram too — it shows exactly the same thing as the one above. It's called a <u>Punnett square</u>.

However, it's not always quite this simple — <u>most</u> characteristics are actually controlled by <u>multiple genes</u>. (You don't need to be able to draw the genetic diagrams for these though.)

Your meanotype determines how nice you are to your sibling...

Remember, results like this are only probabilities. It doesn't mean it <u>will</u> happen.

Q1 The height of garden pea plants is controlled by a single gene with two alleles. The allele for tall plants (T) is dominant over the allele for dwarf plants (t). Two heterozygous pea plants are crossed. Draw a genetic diagram to find what proportion of the offspring would be expected to be dwarf plants. [3 marks]

More Genetic Diagrams

Here's another page of funny diagrams with squares, circles and lines going everywhere. And it's not the last...

Your Chromosomes Control Whether You're Male or Female

1) There are 23 pairs of chromosomes in every human body cell. The 23rd pair are labelled XY or XX. These are sex chromosomes — they decide whether you turn out male or female.

   - Males have an X and a Y chromosome: XY
   - Females have two X chromosomes: XX

2) Like other characteristics, sex is determined by genes.

3) The Y chromosome carries a gene which makes an embryo develop into a male as it grows, by stimulating the growth of testes. Females, who don't have a Y chromosome, don't have this gene and so they develop in a different way.

4) The genetic diagram for sex inheritance is fairly similar to a bog-standard one. It just shows the sex chromosomes rather than different alleles.

5) Sometimes, you might see a genetic diagram showing the inheritance of an allele on one of the sex chromosomes. The sex chromosome and the allele can be shown together like this: X^H or X^h.

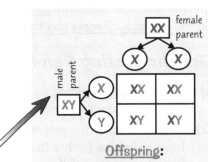

Offspring:
Two XX genotypes and two XY genotypes, so there's a 50% chance of having either a boy or a girl. This means there is a 50:50 ratio of boys to girls.

Family Trees Can Also Show Single Gene Inheritance

Knowing how inheritance works helps you to interpret a different type of genetic diagram called a family tree. Here's a worked example using cystic fibrosis — a genetic disorder of the cell membranes.

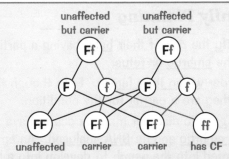

1) The allele which causes cystic fibrosis (CF) is a recessive allele, 'f', carried by about 1 person in 30.

2) Because it's recessive, people with only one copy of the allele won't have the disorder — they're known as carriers.

3) For a child to have a chance of inheriting the disorder, both parents must either have the disorder themselves or be carriers.

4) As the diagram shows, there's a 1 in 4 chance of a child having the disorder if both parents are carriers.

Below is a family tree for a family that includes carriers of cystic fibrosis. The lines on the family tree link the parents to each other (horizontal) and to their children (vertical).

1) You can see from the family tree that the allele for cystic fibrosis isn't dominant because plenty of the family carry the allele but don't have the disorder.

2) There is a 1 in 4 (25%) chance that the new baby will have cystic fibrosis and a 1 in 2 (50%) chance that it will be a carrier because both of its parents are carriers but don't have the disorder.

3) The case of the new baby is just the same as in the genetic diagram above — so the baby could be unaffected (FF), a carrier (Ff) or have the disorder (ff).

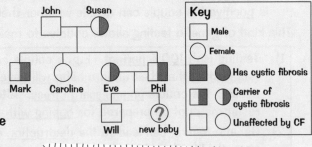

Key
- Male
- Female
- Has cystic fibrosis
- Carrier of cystic fibrosis
- Unaffected by CF

If a disorder is caused by a dominant allele, there will be no carriers shown on the family tree.

Have you got the Y-factor...

I bet you're sick of genetic diagrams by now. Still, that family tree makes a nice change. Umm... sort of.

Q1   Use the family tree above for the following question. Mark and his wife (who is not shown in the diagram) have a baby with cystic fibrosis. What are the possible genotypes of Mark's wife?   [1 mark]

Genome Research and Testing

Scientists might be able to use genes to predict diseases and provide us with new and better drugs. Cool innit?

Scientists Have Researched the Human Genome

Scientists have identified all of the genes found in the human genome. This has lots of potential uses in medicine — by comparing the genomes of people with and without a certain disease, scientists can try to identify the genetic variants that are involved in the disease. People can then be tested for the genetic variants that are linked to a particular disease.

Genetic Testing Can Help To Improve Healthcare

1) Some genetic variants put you at a higher risk of developing a certain disease, e.g. some types of cancer. If people knew they had a particular variant, they may be able to make lifestyle changes to reduce this risk.

2) In some cases, the presence of a particular genetic variant or variants means that a person will definitely have a disease (rather than just being more likely to get it). E.g. a person will have cystic fibrosis if they have two copies of the recessive CF allele. In the UK, newborn babies are routinely tested for certain genetic variants, so doctors can tell whether or not they've inherited a particular genetic disorder. If they have, treatment for the disorder can begin early.

3) It's now known that some common genetic variants make some drugs less effective. Genetic testing for these variants could help doctors to predict how their patient will respond to specific drugs and only prescribe the ones that will be most effective for the patient. This is called personalised medicine.

There are drawbacks with this kind of genetic testing though. For example, it could lead to:

1) Discrimination — employers may discriminate against people who are genetically likely to get a disease.

2) Increased stress — if people knew they were susceptible to a nasty brain disease, they could panic every time they get a headache (even if they never get the disease).

Genetic Testing May Also Help People With Family Planning

A couple wanting to have a baby could use genetic testing to identify the risk of their baby having a particular genetic disorder. This could involve testing of the parents and of the embryo or fetus.

1) Parent — one of the parents may know there is a genetic disorder within their family. Even though they may not have the disorder, genetic tests could reveal whether they are a carrier for the condition.

2) Embryo — a couple who know they are at risk of passing on a genetic disorder may choose to have their eggs fertilised in a lab. A cell can be taken from each resulting embryo and its DNA analysed. An embryo without the genetic variants linked to the disorder can be implanted into the womb to develop into a baby.

3) Fetus — once a woman is pregnant, it is possible to get some of the fetal DNA by taking a sample of the amniotic fluid, which surrounds the fetus in the womb. (This procedure carries a very small risk of miscarriage.) The fetal DNA can then be tested for the genetic variants linked to the disorder. If the test is positive the couple can decide whether they wish to continue with the pregnancy.

This kind of genetic testing allows couples to make informed decisions about family planning. But...

1) Testing isn't 100% perfect. E.g. a couple could receive a positive test result during pregnancy (suggesting that their unborn baby will have a genetic disorder) but the test result may be wrong, causing the couple unnecessary stress. Alternatively, a couple who incorrectly receive a negative test result may not be prepared for coping with their child's disorder when he or she is born.

2) Genetic testing can lead to the destruction of embryos or a termination. Some people think that any potential life should be allowed to survive, whatever disorders he or she may have. There's also a worry that genetic testing is a 'slippery slope' and that there may come a point where everyone wants to screen their embryos and choose one with the characteristics (e.g. hair colour) that they prefer.

Personalised medicine — write your name on the bottle...

Pfft... nothing's ever straight-forward is it. Make sure you know the pros and cons of using genetic testing.

Q1   Describe a test that could be carried out to determine whether a fetus has a genetic disorder.   [2 marks]

Genetic Engineering

Genetic engineering is an interesting area of science with <u>exciting possibilities</u>, but there might be <u>dangers</u> too...

Genetic Engineering Transfers Genes Between Organisms

The basic idea of genetic engineering is to <u>transfer</u> a <u>gene</u> from the <u>genome</u> of one organism to the genome of <u>another</u>. This gives the organism that receives the gene <u>new</u> and <u>useful characteristics</u>. For example:

- The <u>gene</u> for the <u>human insulin</u> protein has been inserted into <u>bacteria</u>. The bacteria are grown in large numbers to produce insulin for the <u>treatment</u> of <u>diabetes</u>.
- A <u>gene</u> that helps <u>fish</u> to survive in <u>cold water</u> has been inserted into <u>tomato plants</u> to help the plants <u>survive</u> at <u>low temperatures</u>.

Here's how it works:

Genetic engineering works because all organisms use the same molecule (DNA) to store their genetic material.

1) A useful gene is <u>isolated</u> (cut) from an organism's genome using <u>enzymes</u>. The gene is then <u>replicated</u> to produce lots of copies.

2) Each copy is then inserted into a <u>vector</u>. The vector is usually a <u>virus</u> or a <u>bacterial plasmid</u> (see page 1) depending on the type of organism that the gene is being transferred to.

3) The <u>vectors</u> are then <u>mixed with other cells</u>, e.g. bacteria. The idea is that the vectors (containing the desired gene) will be <u>taken up</u> by the cells, which will become <u>genetically modified</u>.

Plasmids are good vectors to use in the genetic engineering of bacteria as they're separate to the main chromosomal DNA and naturally pass between bacterial cells.

4) <u>Most</u> cells <u>don't</u> take up the vector and the desired gene, so the cells that have been modified need to be <u>identified</u> and <u>selected</u>.

5) The <u>selected cells</u> are then allowed to <u>replicate</u> — each new cell will contain the <u>desired gene</u> and produce the <u>protein</u> it codes for.

This can be done by adding a <u>marker gene</u> to the vectors, along with the desired gene. The marker gene allows cells that have taken up the vectors to be identified, e.g. some marker genes cause cells to <u>fluoresce</u> (glow) under UV light.

Genetic Engineering is Useful in Agriculture and Medicine

1) For example, in <u>agriculture</u>, <u>crops</u> can be genetically modified to be <u>resistant to herbicides</u> (chemicals that kill plants). Making crops <u>herbicide-resistant</u> means farmers can <u>spray</u> their crops to <u>kill weeds</u>, <u>without</u> affecting the crop itself. This can <u>increase crop yield</u>, helping us to produce <u>more food</u> for the growing human population.

2) In <u>medicine</u>, genetically engineering <u>bacteria</u> to produce human <u>insulin</u> has helped to improve healthcare. Researchers have also managed to transfer <u>human genes</u> that produce <u>useful proteins</u> into <u>sheep</u> and <u>cows</u>, e.g. human <u>antibodies</u> used in therapy for illnesses like <u>arthritis</u>. These proteins can then be <u>extracted</u> from the animal, e.g. from their <u>milk</u>.

3) However, there are <u>concerns</u> about the genetic engineering of animals. It can be hard to predict what <u>effect</u> modifying its genome will have <u>on the organism</u> — many genetically modified embryos <u>don't survive</u> and some genetically modified <u>animals</u> suffer from <u>health problems</u> later in life. There are also <u>moral concerns</u> about the use of the technology to modify <u>human genomes</u> — for example, there are fears it could lead to the creation of 'designer babies' and parents choosing their child's characteristics.

4) There are also <u>concerns</u> about growing genetically modified crops. One is that <u>transplanted genes</u> may get out into the <u>environment</u>. E.g. a herbicide resistance gene may be picked up by <u>weeds</u>, creating a new '<u>superweed</u>' variety. Another concern is that genetically modified crops could <u>adversely</u> affect <u>food chains</u> — or even <u>human health</u>. Some think that more <u>long-term studies</u> need to be carried out so the risks are more fully understood.

I say it's great.

If only there was a gene to make revision easier...

As with most new technologies there are benefits and risks to genetic engineering. Make sure you learn them.

Q1 Explain one benefit of being able to genetically engineer herbicide-resistant crops. [2 marks]

Revision Questions for Chapter B1

Hooray! You're at the end of the Chapter B1 — by now you should understand just how important DNA is.

- Try these questions and <u>tick off each one</u> when you <u>get it right</u>.
- When you've done <u>all the questions</u> for a topic and are <u>completely happy</u> with it, tick off the topic.

Cells, Genetic Material and Microscopy (p.1-2) ☑

1) State whether each of the following is a eukaryotic cell or a prokaryotic cell:
   a) animal cell   b) bacterial cell   c) plant cell. ☑

2) True or false? All cells contain genetic material. ☑

3) Where is genetic material stored in a eukaryotic cell? ☑

4) Why is it necessary to use thin samples of tissue when viewing cells using a light microscope? ☑

5) Why are samples sometimes stained before viewing under a light microscope? ☑

Genomes and Characteristics (p.3) ☑

6) Why is DNA described as a polymer? ☑

7) What is a gene? ☑

8) What is an allele? ☑

9) What interacts with an organism's genotype to determine its phenotype? ☑

Genetic Diagrams (p.4-5) ☑

10) In a genetic diagram, is a capital letter used to represent a dominant or recessive allele? ☑

11) What does it mean if an organism is
    a) homozygous for a gene?
    b) heterozygous for a gene? ☑

12) What are the 23rd pair of chromosomes labelled as in a female? ☑

13) How does the Y chromosome cause an embryo to develop into a male as it grows? ☑

14) A couple have a child.
    What's the probability that the child will have the XX combination of sex chromosomes? ☑

15) How are carriers shown on a family tree? ☑

Genome Research and Genetic Engineering (p.6-7) ☑

16) How has research on the human genome led to the potential development of personalised medicines? ☑

17) Give one potential drawback of genetic testing in healthcare. ☑

18) What does 'genetic engineering' mean? ☑

19) Explain how a useful gene from one organism is inserted into the genome of another organism. ☑

20) Describe two concerns people may have about using genetic engineering in agriculture. ☑

Health and Disease

If you're feeling <u>bright-eyed</u> and <u>bushy-tailed</u> then you might not be for much <u>longer</u>. Here's a page on <u>diseases</u>.

Organisms' Health Can be Affected by Disease

1) A <u>healthy</u> organism is one that is in a state of <u>well-being</u>
   — it's <u>functioning</u> just as it <u>should</u> be, both <u>physically</u> and <u>mentally</u>.

2) A <u>disease</u> is a condition that commonly damages cells of the host and <u>impairs</u> the <u>normal structures</u>
   or <u>functioning</u> of the organism. Most organisms will experience disease <u>at some point</u> in their lifetime.

3) There are many <u>causes</u> of <u>disease</u> and <u>ill health</u>. For example:

   - the organism may become <u>infected</u> by a <u>pathogen</u> (see below).
   - there may be a <u>mutation</u> (change) in the organism's <u>genes</u>.
   - the organism may be affected by <u>environmental conditions</u>,
     e.g. if a plant <u>doesn't get enough light</u> it won't grow properly.
   - an organism may experience <u>trauma</u> (an <u>emotional shock</u> or a <u>physical injury</u>) which can
     affect their health, e.g. the sudden death of a loved one may cause <u>anxiety</u> and <u>depression</u>.
   - the organism's <u>lifestyle</u> may affect their health, e.g. eating too much food can lead to <u>obesity</u>.

Diseases Can be Communicable or Non-Communicable

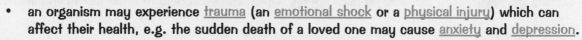
Communicable diseases are also known as infectious diseases.

1) A <u>communicable</u> disease is a disease that can <u>spread</u> between organisms.
   They are caused by <u>pathogens</u> infecting the organism. A <u>pathogen</u> is a type of <u>microorganism</u> that
   causes <u>disease</u>. Types of pathogen include <u>bacteria</u>, <u>viruses</u>, <u>protists</u> and <u>fungi</u> (see next page).

2) <u>Non-communicable</u> diseases <u>cannot</u> be passed from one organism to another, e.g. cardiovascular and
   respiratory diseases, cancers and diabetes. They generally last for a <u>long time</u> and <u>progress slowly</u>.
   They are associated with <u>genetic mutations</u>, <u>lifestyle</u> and <u>environmental factors</u> (see pages 17-18).

3) Both communicable and non-communicable diseases cause <u>symptoms</u> — <u>changes</u> in the organism
   that indicates disease is present. E.g. a symptom of <u>multiple sclerosis</u> (a disease that damages
   <u>nerve cells</u>) can be a <u>temporary loss of vision</u>.

4) However, symptoms may not <u>always</u> be obvious, especially in the early stages of a disease.
   For example, chicken pox is caused by a <u>virus</u>. Its main symptom is a <u>spotty rash</u>. Once a person
   has been <u>infected</u> with the virus, it takes around <u>14 days</u> for any spots to <u>appear</u> — this <u>time</u> between
   being <u>infected</u> with a pathogen and <u>showing</u> symptoms of the disease is called the <u>incubation period</u>.

Diseases May Interact With Each Other

Sometimes having <u>one disease</u> can make it <u>more or less likely</u> that you will suffer from <u>another disease</u>. E.g.

1) <u>HPV</u> (human papillomavirus) is a <u>virus</u> that can infect the <u>reproductive system</u>.
2) An <u>infection</u> by the virus <u>doesn't always</u> cause <u>symptoms</u> and often clears up on its own
   within a couple of months.
3) However, some <u>HPV infections</u> can cause <u>cell changes</u> resulting in the development of certain
   types of <u>cancer</u>. It's thought that <u>nearly all</u> cervical cancer cases result from HPV infections.

1) <u>Helminths</u> are a type of worm. If certain helminths get inside the human body, they can cause <u>disease</u>.
2) <u>Trichinosis</u> is a disease caused by infection by the helminth, *Trichinella spiralis*.
3) However, it's thought that infection by *Trichinella spiralis* may <u>reduce the development</u>
   of some <u>autoimmune diseases</u>, e.g. <u>Crohn's disease</u>.

Autoimmune diseases are diseases in which the body's immune system recognises the body's own cells as foreign, and attacks them.

I have a communicable disease — it's telling me to go to bed...

Communicable diseases can be <u>passed</u> between people because they involve <u>pathogens</u>.

Q1   What is meant by the term 'non-communicable' disease?   [1 mark]

How Disease Spreads

Well, here are loads of ways you can catch diseases. As if I wasn't feeling paranoid enough already...

Communicable Diseases are Caused by Pathogens

As you saw on the previous page, pathogens are microorganisms that cause communicable diseases. There are four types:

1) **BACTERIA** — very small cells (about 1/100th the size of your body cells), which can reproduce rapidly. They make you feel ill by producing toxins (poisons) that damage your cells and tissues.

2) **VIRUSES** — these are not cells. They're really tiny, about 1/100th the size of a bacterium. They replicate themselves inside the infected organism's cells. These cells then burst, releasing the viruses.

3) **PROTISTS** — these are eukaryotic (see page 1), usually single-celled and vary in size.

4) **FUNGI** — some fungi are single-celled while others have a body, which is made up of thread-like structures called hyphae. These hyphae can grow and penetrate human skin and the surface of plants, causing diseases. They can also produce spores, which can be spread to other plants and animals.

Communicable Diseases are Transmitted in Different Ways

Pathogens infect both animals and plants and can spread in different ways. For example:

Water	• Some pathogens can be picked up by drinking or bathing in dirty water. E.g. Cholera is a bacterial infection that causes diarrhoea and dehydration. It's spread when drinking water is contaminated with the diarrhoea of other sufferers.
Air	• Some pathogens are carried in the air. E.g. *Hymenoscyphus fraxineus* is a fungus which infects ash trees and causes Chalara ash dieback disease. It is transmitted from infected plants, through the air, by the wind. • Airborne pathogens can be carried in droplets produced when you cough or sneeze — so other people can breathe them in. E.g. the influenza virus that causes flu is spread this way.
On Surfaces	• Some pathogens can be picked up by touching contaminated surfaces. E.g. tobacco mosaic disease affects many species of plants, e.g. tomatoes. It's caused by a virus called tobacco mosaic virus (TMV) that makes the leaves of plants mottled and discoloured. The discolouration means the plant can't photosynthesise as well, so the virus affects growth. It's spread when infected leaves rub against healthy leaves. • Athlete's foot is a fungal disease which affects humans — it makes skin on the feet itch and flake off. It's most commonly spread by touching the same things as an infected person, e.g. shower floors and towels.
Body fluids	• Some pathogens are spread by body fluids such as blood (e.g. by sharing needles to inject drugs or by contaminated blood transfusions), breast milk (through breast feeding) and semen (through unprotected sex — diseases that are spread through sexual contact are known as sexually transmitted infections or STIs). HIV is a virus spread by exchanging body fluids. It initially causes flu-like symptoms for a few weeks, but after that, the person doesn't usually experience any symptoms for several years. The virus enters the lymph nodes and attacks the immune cells. If the immune system isn't working properly, it can't cope with other infections or cancers. At this stage, the virus is known as late stage HIV, or AIDS.
Animal vectors	• Animals that spread disease are called vectors. E.g. malaria is caused by a protist. Part of the malarial protist's life cycle takes place inside a mosquito. Mosquitoes act as vectors — they pick up the malarial protist when they feed on an infected animal. Every time the mosquito feeds on another animal, it infects it by inserting the protist into the animal's blood vessels. Malaria causes repeating episodes of fever. It can be fatal.
Soil	• Some pathogens can live in the soil, so plants in the contaminated soil may be infected. E.g. the bacteria, *Agrobacterium tumefaciens*, that cause crown gall disease, are able to live freely in some soils and on the roots of some plants. If the bacteria enter a plant, they can cause growths or tumours called galls on roots, stems and branches. The galls can damage the plant tissue, restricting the flow of water through the plant. This causes the plant to become weaker and it may eventually die.
Food	• Some pathogens are picked up by eating contaminated food. E.g. *Salmonella* bacteria are found in some foods, e.g. raw meat. If these foods are kept too long or not cooked properly the bacteria can cause food poisoning.

Ahh...Ahh... Ahhhhh Chooooooooo — urghh, this page is catching...

Pathogens are usually really small — you often need a microscope to see them — but they don't half get about...

Q1   Give three ways in which communicable diseases can be spread.   [3 marks]

Defending Against Pathogens

Pathogens can be <u>anywhere</u>, so our bodies have to be <u>on guard</u> at all times to make sure they don't get in.

Humans Have a Pretty Sophisticated Defence System

1) The human body has got features that <u>stop</u> a lot of nasties entering the <u>blood</u>.

2) These are <u>non-specific</u> defences (they aren't produced in response to a <u>particular</u> pathogen) and they're <u>always present</u>.

3) These can be <u>physical</u> (if they act as a physical <u>barrier</u> to pathogens), <u>chemical</u> (if they involve chemicals which <u>kill</u> pathogens) or <u>microbial</u> (if they involve <u>other</u> microorganisms). Here are some examples:

Physical Defences

1) The whole <u>respiratory tract</u> (nasal passage, trachea and lungs) is lined with <u>mucus</u> and <u>cilia</u> (hair-like structures) — the mucus <u>traps</u> particles that could contain pathogens and the cilia <u>waft the mucus</u> up to the back of the throat where it can be <u>swallowed</u>.

2) The <u>skin</u> acts as a <u>barrier</u> to pathogens. If it gets <u>cut</u>, pathogens could enter the <u>bloodstream</u> through the <u>wound</u>. This is where platelets come in...

3) <u>Platelets</u> in the blood clump together to 'plug' the wound. This is known as <u>blood clotting</u>. Blood clots <u>stop you losing</u> too much <u>blood</u> and help to prevent <u>microorganisms</u> from entering the blood.

Platelets are <u>tiny fragments of cells</u>. They contain lots of <u>different substances</u> that are needed to help form the <u>clot</u>. They also have <u>proteins</u> on their surface which help them stick together and to the site of the wound.

platelets

Chemical Defences

1) <u>Eyes</u> produce (in <u>tears</u>) an enzyme called <u>lysozyme</u>, which breaks down <u>bacteria</u> on the surface of the eye.

2) <u>Saliva</u> (produced in the <u>mouth</u>) contains molecules which <u>kill</u> pathogens that enter the mouth, so they don't reach the <u>stomach</u>.

3) The <u>stomach</u> produces <u>hydrochloric acid</u>. This <u>kills pathogens</u>.

Microbial Defences

1) <u>Some</u> pathogens manage to make it past the <u>saliva</u> in the mouth and the <u>acid</u> in the stomach and enter the <u>gut</u>.

2) Here, they have to compete with the <u>bacteria</u> which <u>naturally live in the gut</u> (intestines), in order to <u>survive</u>.

And even if pathogens <u>do</u> manage to make it past all of these defences to <u>enter the blood</u>, there's still a complex <u>immune system</u>, involving <u>antibodies</u> and <u>immune cells</u> (see next page) that they have to deal with.

Drowning pathogens in soda — my preferred fizzy kill defence...

You'll find out more about defences against pathogens on the next page. But don't get too excited — before you move on, you need to learn the forms of defence shown here and be able to answer this question.

Q1   Explain how platelets help to defend the body against pathogens.   [2 marks]

The Human Immune System

This page is all about <u>white blood cells</u>, or the <u>ninjas</u> of your body, as I like to call them. These little fellows can sneak up on pathogens in your blood, and <u>kill them</u> before they have a chance to cause you serious problems.

Your Immune System Can Attack Pathogens

1) If pathogens do make it into your body, your <u>immune system</u> kicks in to destroy them.

2) The most important part of your immune system is the <u>white blood cells</u>. They travel around in your <u>blood</u> and crawl into every part of you, constantly patrolling for <u>pathogens</u>.

3) Every cell has <u>molecules</u> on its surface called <u>antigens</u>. Each antigen is <u>unique</u> to the specific cell type that it's found on. White blood cells have special <u>receptors</u> in their membrane which help them to identify antigens on <u>pathogens</u>.

4) In a <u>healthy person</u>, white blood cells recognise antigens on <u>pathogens</u> as <u>non-self</u> (foreign) and antigens on <u>normal</u> body cells as <u>self</u>.

5) When they come across <u>non-self antigens</u> the immune system is triggered to <u>destroy</u> any invading pathogens. There are <u>three</u> main lines of attack:

1. Consuming Them

Some white blood cells (<u>phagocytes</u>) have a <u>flexible membrane</u> and contain lots of <u>enzymes</u>. This enables them to <u>engulf</u> (<u>ingest</u>) foreign cells and <u>digest</u> them. This is called <u>phagocytosis</u>.

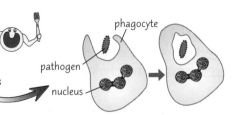

phagocyte

pathogen

nucleus

Some white blood cells (eosinophils) release enzymes that break down pathogens.

2. Producing Antibodies

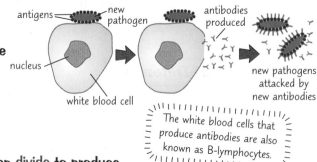

antigens — new pathogen

antibodies produced

nucleus

white blood cell

new pathogens attacked by new antibodies

The white blood cells that produce antibodies are also known as B-lymphocytes.

1) When white blood cells come across a <u>foreign antigen</u> on a pathogen, receptors in the membrane bind to the antigen. The white blood cells then start to produce <u>proteins</u> called <u>antibodies</u> which lock onto the antigens on the invading cells. The antibodies produced are <u>specific</u> to that type of antigen — they won't lock on to any others.

2) The white blood cells that detect the pathogen then <u>divide</u> to produce <u>more copies</u> (<u>clones</u>) of the <u>same</u> white blood cell, so that <u>more antibodies</u> can be produced.

3) Antibodies are produced <u>rapidly</u> and are carried around the body to <u>lock on</u> to all similar pathogens.

4) The <u>antibodies</u> may <u>disable</u> the pathogen or 'tag' the pathogens, which <u>helps</u> the phagocytes <u>find</u> them so they can <u>engulf</u> them.

5) Some white blood cells <u>stay around</u> in the blood after the pathogen has been fought off — these are called <u>memory cells</u>. If the person is <u>infected</u> with the <u>same pathogen again</u>, the memory cells will <u>trigger</u> the rapid production of the antibodies needed to destroy it, before the pathogen causes the disease — the person is <u>naturally</u> immune to that pathogen and won't get ill.

3. Producing Antitoxins

Some pathogens can cause problems for the body by the <u>toxins</u> which they produce. Some white blood cells also produce <u>antitoxins</u> which <u>counteract</u> these toxins and so <u>limit</u> any damage done by the <u>invading pathogens</u>.

Fight disease — give your nose a blow with boxing gloves...

The <u>body</u> makes <u>antibodies</u> against the <u>antigens</u> on <u>pathogens</u>. There, don't say I never help you. Right, tea...

Q1   Give one role of antibodies in the immune response.   [1 mark]

Q2   Describe the role of memory cells in the immune response.   [2 marks]

Reducing and Preventing the Spread of Disease

The best way of dealing with disease is sometimes to just <u>avoid any contact</u> with pathogens in the first place...

The Spread of Disease Can Be Reduced or Prevented in Animals...

If a disease spreads <u>uncontrollably</u>, it can result in huge <u>loss</u> of <u>life</u> and <u>food sources</u> (if animals reared for food are affected). It's important that we take measures to prevent this from happening — including:

1) <u>Being hygienic</u> — basic hygiene measures (e.g. <u>washing hands</u> regularly to <u>remove pathogens</u>) can be very effective at preventing the spread of disease.

Many diseases are spread when a person touches a source of pathogens (e.g. door handle) and then touches their eyes, nose or mouth.

2) <u>Sterilising wounds</u> in the <u>skin</u> — this <u>kills</u> microorganisms (including pathogens) near the wound so stops them entering the blood.

3) Living in <u>sanitary conditions</u> — having access to <u>clean drinking water</u> and a good system for disposing of <u>sewage</u> are both <u>very effective</u> measures for reducing the transmission of <u>water-borne</u> pathogens, such as cholera (see page 10), and pathogens in the urine or faeces of infected people. However, the <u>initial cost</u> to a <u>society</u> of creating sanitary conditions can be <u>high</u>.

4) <u>Destroying infected animals</u> — infected animals may pass on the disease to other individuals, so in some cases, such as on farms with <u>large herds</u> of animals, it might be necessary to <u>kill</u> the infected individuals to prevent <u>large numbers</u> of other animals from <u>getting the disease</u>. However, this is very <u>costly</u> and the disease may still spread if it is present in other individuals <u>without symptoms</u>.

5) <u>Isolating infected individuals</u> — this <u>prevents</u> them from <u>passing it on</u> to anyone else. In some cases, individuals should also be prevented from <u>travelling</u>, and <u>spreading</u> it even further. Although this <u>benefits</u> society, it can be difficult for an infected person as they can't be with their loved ones — sometimes it can be difficult to <u>balance</u> the needs of an <u>individual</u> while doing what is best for <u>society</u>.

6) <u>Vaccination</u> (see next page) — vaccinating people and animals against communicable diseases means that they <u>won't</u> develop the infection and then <u>pass it on</u> to others.

7) The use of <u>contraception</u> — using <u>condoms</u> prevents <u>sexually transmitted infections</u>, (e.g. HIV — see p.10) from being transmitted between people during <u>sex</u>.

...And in Plants

Plant <u>diseases</u> can <u>reduce food sources</u> for many organisms and can <u>damage habitats</u> for other organisms in an <u>ecosystem</u>. Here are some ways that the spread of disease in plants can be <u>controlled</u>:

1) <u>Regulating movement of plant material</u> — this makes sure that <u>infected</u> plants don't come into <u>contact</u> with <u>healthy</u> plants, e.g. plant nurseries are not allowed to sell plants which have <u>crown gall disease</u>.

2) <u>Destroying infected plants</u> — this stops them being <u>sources</u> of infection, but can be costly to a farmer.

3) Only using sources of <u>healthy</u> seeds and plants — this stops the disease from being introduced into a population.

4) <u>Crop rotation</u> — many pathogens are <u>specific</u> to a particular plant. <u>Changing</u> the <u>type of plants</u> that are grown stops the pathogens becoming <u>established</u> in an area. However, it may limit how <u>profitable</u> a farm is if it has to change <u>farming practices</u> for a different crop each year.

5) <u>Polyculture</u> (growing <u>different types</u> plants in a <u>single area</u> at the <u>same time</u>) — if a pathogen <u>specific</u> to a single plant enters one plant, it's less likely to infect <u>neighbouring</u> plants because they are <u>different species</u> — <u>limiting</u> the <u>spread</u> of the pathogen through the crop.

6) <u>Chemical control</u> — for example, <u>fungicides</u> can be used to kill <u>fungal</u> pathogens. This can be an effective method but may also lead to the evolution of <u>resistant strains</u> of the pathogen (see page 70).

7) <u>Biological control</u> — this is when <u>another organism</u> is used to control a pest or pathogen. For example, ladybirds eat aphids (an insect pest) so ladybirds can be released into an area to reduce aphid numbers. However, in some cases, the <u>control organism</u> may become a <u>pest</u> itself and cause more problems.

The spread of disease — mouldy margarine...

Make sure you understand how each method above can be effective in preventing the spread of disease. However, you should also be aware of any costs associated with them, whether to an individual or to society as a whole.

Q1   Give one benefit and one cost to a farmer of using a crop rotation system.   [2 marks]

Vaccinations

Before you get cracking on this page, take a look back at p.12 to remind yourself about the <u>immune response</u>.

Vaccinations Stop You Getting Infections

1) When you're infected with a <u>new</u> pathogen it can take your white blood cells a while to produce the <u>antibodies</u> to deal with it. In that time you can get <u>very ill</u>, or maybe even die.

2) To avoid this you can be <u>vaccinated</u> (immunised) against some diseases, e.g. polio or measles.

3) Vaccination involves injecting <u>dead, inactive or weakened</u> pathogens into the body. These carry <u>antigens</u>, so even though they're <u>harmless</u> they still trigger an <u>immune response</u> — your white blood cells produce <u>antibodies</u> to attack them.

4) Some of these white blood cells will remain in the blood as <u>memory cells</u>, so if <u>live</u> pathogens of the <u>same type</u> ever appear, the antibodies that <u>help destroy them</u> will be produced immediately.

5) Big outbreaks of disease — called <u>epidemics</u> — can be prevented if a <u>large percentage</u> of the population is vaccinated. That way, even the people who aren't vaccinated are <u>unlikely</u> to catch the disease because there are <u>fewer</u> people able to <u>pass it on</u>. But if a significant number of people <u>aren't</u> vaccinated, the disease can <u>spread</u> quickly through them and lots of people will be <u>ill</u> at the same time.

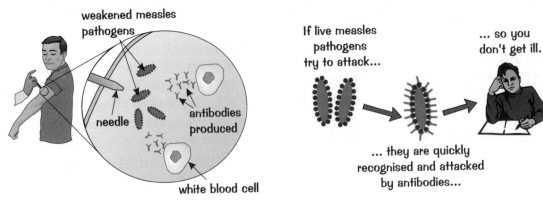

There are Pros and Cons of Vaccination

<u>PROS</u>

Vaccines have helped <u>control</u> lots of communicable diseases that were once <u>common</u> in the UK (e.g. polio, measles, whooping cough, rubella, mumps, tetanus...). <u>Smallpox</u> no longer occurs at all, and <u>polio</u> infections have fallen by 99%.

<u>CONS</u>

1) Vaccines don't always work — sometimes they <u>don't</u> give you <u>immunity</u>.

2) You can sometimes have a <u>bad reaction</u> to a vaccine (e.g. swelling, or maybe something more serious like a fever or seizures). But bad reactions are very <u>rare</u>.

3) It can be <u>expensive</u> to make vaccines and carry out <u>vaccination programmes</u> — if a disease occurs only very <u>rarely</u> or the vaccine isn't very <u>effective</u>, the cost of carrying out the programme may <u>outweigh</u> any benefits to society.

> Some people are concerned that using whole pathogens in vaccines (even though they are dead, weakened or inactive) could still cause disease. Some vaccines therefore only use parts of cells, to avoid these concerns.

Take that, you evil antigen...

Deciding whether to have a vaccination means balancing risks — the risk of catching the disease if you don't have a vaccine, against the risk of having a bad reaction if you do. As always, you need to look at the evidence. For example, if you get measles (the disease), there's about a 1 in 15 chance that you'll get complications (e.g. pneumonia) — and about 1 in 500 people who get measles actually die. However, the number of people who have a problem with the vaccine is more like 1 in 1 000 000.

Q1   Explain how white blood cells respond to vaccinations.

[2 marks]

Culturing Microorganisms PRACTICAL

Here's how you can <u>grow microorganisms</u> and test how effective different <u>antibiotics</u> are at killing them.

You Can Grow Bacteria in the Lab

1) Bacteria (and some other microorganisms) are grown (cultured) in a "<u>culture medium</u>", which contains the <u>carbohydrates</u>, <u>minerals</u>, <u>proteins</u> and <u>vitamins</u> they need to grow.

2) The culture medium used can be a <u>nutrient broth solution</u> or solid <u>agar jelly</u>.

3) Bacteria grown on agar 'plates' will form visible <u>colonies</u> on the <u>surface</u> of the jelly, or will <u>spread out</u> to give an even covering of bacteria.

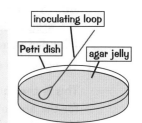

- To make an agar plate, <u>hot</u> agar jelly is poured into a shallow round plastic dish called a <u>Petri dish</u>.
- When the jelly's cooled and set, an <u>inoculating loop</u> (wire loop) can be used to <u>transfer</u> microorganisms to the culture medium. Alternatively, a <u>sterile dropping pipette</u> and <u>spreader</u> can be used to get an <u>even covering</u> of bacteria.
- The microorganisms then <u>multiply</u>.

4) In the <u>lab at school</u>, cultures of microorganisms are not kept <u>above 25 °C</u>, because <u>harmful pathogens</u> are more likely to grow above this temperature.

5) In <u>industrial conditions</u>, cultures are incubated at <u>higher temperatures</u> so that they can grow a lot faster.

You Can Investigate the Effect of Antibiotics on Bacterial Growth

Antibiotics are substances which <u>kill</u> or <u>reduce</u> the <u>growth</u> of bacteria. You can test the action of <u>antibiotics</u> on <u>cultures</u> of bacteria:

1) Place <u>paper discs</u> soaked in different <u>types</u> (or different <u>concentrations</u>) of <u>antibiotics</u> on an agar plate that has an <u>even covering</u> of bacteria. Leave some <u>space</u> between the discs.

2) The antibiotic should <u>diffuse</u> (soak) into the agar jelly. <u>Antibiotic-resistant</u> bacteria (i.e. bacteria that <u>aren't affected</u> by the antibiotic — see p.70) will continue to <u>grow</u> on the agar around the paper discs, but <u>non-resistant</u> strains will <u>die</u>. A <u>clear zone</u> will be left where the bacteria have died.

3) Make sure you use a control. This is a paper disc that has <u>not been soaked</u> in an antibiotic. Instead, soak it in <u>sterile water</u>. You can then be sure that any <u>difference</u> between the <u>growth</u> of the bacteria around the <u>control</u> disc and around one of the <u>antibiotic</u> discs is due to the <u>effect</u> of the antibiotic <u>alone</u> (and not, e.g. something in the paper).

4) Leave the plate for <u>48 hours</u> at <u>25 °C</u>.

5) The <u>more effective</u> the antibiotic is against the bacteria, the <u>larger</u> the <u>clear zone</u> will be — see next page.

no bacteria growing (clear zone)

bacteria growing

paper disc — control

paper disc — with antibiotic

You Need to Use Aseptic Techniques

<u>Aseptic techniques</u> are used to <u>prevent contamination</u> of cultures by <u>unwanted microorganisms</u>. This would <u>affect your results</u> and could potentially result in the growth of <u>pathogens</u>. To <u>avoid</u> this:

1) The Petri dishes and culture medium must be <u>sterilised</u> before use (e.g. by heating to a high temperature) to <u>kill</u> any <u>unwanted microorganisms</u> that may be lurking on them.

2) If an <u>inoculating loop</u> is used to transfer the bacteria to the culture medium, it should be <u>sterilised</u> first by carefully <u>passing it through a hot flame</u>.

3) Work near a <u>Bunsen flame</u>. Hot air <u>rises</u>, so any microorganisms in the <u>air</u> should be drawn <u>away</u> from your culture.

inoculating loop

4) After transferring the bacteria, the lid of the Petri dish should be <u>lightly taped on</u> — to stop microorganisms from the air getting in.

5) The Petri dish should be stored <u>upside down</u> — to <u>stop</u> drops of <u>condensation</u> falling onto the agar surface.

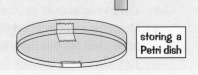

storing a Petri dish

Chapter B2 — Keeping Healthy

Culturing Microorganisms

Calculate the Sizes of the Clear Zones to Compare Results

1) You can <u>compare</u> the <u>effectiveness</u> of different antibiotics on bacteria by looking at the <u>relative sizes</u> of the <u>clear zones</u>.

2) The <u>larger</u> the clear zone around a disc, the <u>more effective</u> the antibiotic is against the bacteria.

3) You can do this <u>by eye</u> if there are large differences in size. But to get more accurate results it's a good idea to calculate the <u>area</u> of the clear zones using their <u>diameter</u> (the distance <u>across</u>).

Don't open the Petri dish to measure the clear zones — they should be visible through the bottom of the dish.

4) To calculate the area of a clear zone, you need to use <u>this equation</u>:

This is the equation for the area of a circle. You're likely to use the units cm^2 or mm^2.

$$\text{Area} = \pi r^2$$

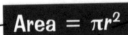

r is the radius of the clear zone — it's equal to half the diameter.

π is just a number. You should have a button for it on your calculator. If not, just use the value 3.14.

The diagram below shows the clear zones produced by antibiotics A and B. Use the areas of the clear zones to compare the effectiveness of the antibiotics.

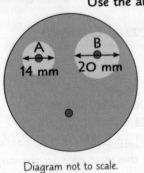

Diagram not to scale.

1) Divide the diameter of zone A by <u>two</u> to find the <u>radius</u>.

2) Stick the radius value into the <u>equation</u> area = πr^2.

3) <u>Repeat</u> steps 1 and 2 for zone B.

4) <u>Compare</u> the <u>sizes</u> of the <u>areas</u>. 314 mm^2 is just over twice 154 mm^2, so you could say that:

Radius of A = 14 ÷ 2 = 7 mm

Area of A = $\pi \times 7^2$ = 154 mm^2

Radius of B = 20 ÷ 2 = 10 mm

Area of B = $\pi \times 10^2$ = 314 mm^2

The clear zone of antibiotic B is roughly twice the size of the clear zone of antibiotic A.

You Can Also Find the Area of a Colony

The equation above can also be used to calculate the <u>area</u> of a bacterial <u>colony</u>. You just need to measure the <u>diameter</u> of the colony you are interested in first.

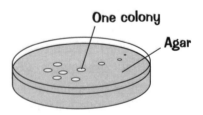

One colony

Agar

Agar — my favourite jelly flavour after raspberry...

Microorganisms might be the perfect pets. You don't have to walk them, they won't get lonely and they hardly cost anything to feed. But whatever you do, do not feed them after midnight.

Q1 A researcher was investigating the effect of three different antibiotics on the growth of bacteria. The diagram on the right shows the results.

a) Which antibiotic was most effective against the bacteria? [1 mark]

b) Calculate the size of the clear zone for Antibiotic C. Give your answer in mm^2. [2 marks]

c) Describe a control that could have been used for this investigation. [1 mark]

d) Explain why a control should be used. [1 mark]

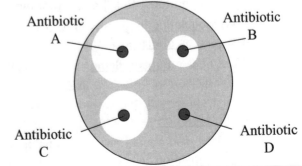

Antibiotic A

Antibiotic B

Antibiotic C

Antibiotic D

Non-Communicable Diseases

You may remember non-communicable diseases from page 9. Well, here's a bit more about them...

Lots of Factors Interact to Cause Non-Communicable Diseases

1) All diseases have risk factors — things that increase a person's chance of getting that disease. Risk factors are often aspects of a person's lifestyle (e.g. how much exercise they do). They can also be the presence of certain substances in the environment (e.g. a person's work may mean they are more exposed to certain pollutants in the air, which could increase the risk of getting lung cancer) or a person's genes (specific genetic variants — see page 3 — may make it more or less likely for a person to get a particular disease).

2) Many non-communicable diseases (such as some cancers, cardiovascular disease (CVD) (diseases of the heart or blood vessels, see p.22), some lung diseases, liver diseases, and some nutrition-related diseases, e.g. type 2 diabetes, see p.67) are caused by several different risk factors interacting with each other rather than one factor alone. For example:

> Normally, when cells have divided enough times to make enough new cells, they stop. But if there's a mutation in a gene that controls cell division, the cells can grow out of control. The cells keep on dividing by mitosis to make more and more cells, which form a tumour. Cancer is a tumour that invades surrounding tissue.

> Sometimes you can inherit genetic variants that make you more susceptible to cancer. The genes alone don't mean you will get cancer but the chance is increased if you have other risk factors too, such as poor diet, high alcohol consumption and smoking (see below and next page).

> Loads of things are known to be risk factors for cancer, e.g. HPV (see p.9), UV exposure, radiation, etc.

3) Risk factors are identified by scientists looking for correlations in data, but correlation doesn't always equal cause (see p.228). Sometimes a risk factor is linked to another factor, and it's this other factor that actually causes the disease. For example, a lack of exercise and a high fat diet are heavily linked to an increased chance of CVD, but they can't cause it directly. It's the resulting high blood pressure and high 'bad' cholesterol levels (see below) that can actually cause it.

4) There are some examples where scientists have found evidence to support a risk factor being a cause of a disease though, e.g. the fact that smoking can cause lung disease and lung cancer (see next page).

Lifestyle Factors Can Affect the Risk of Non-Communicable Diseases

Exercise

1) Exercise increases the amount of energy used by the body and decreases the amount of stored body fat. It also builds muscle, which helps to boost your metabolic rate — a higher metabolic rate means that energy from food is used more quickly. So people who exercise regularly are less likely to suffer from health problems such as obesity (see below) and CVD.

> There's more on the beneficial effects of regular exercise on page 20.

2) A lack of exercise increases the risk of CVD because it increases blood pressure.

Diet

1) Eating too much can lead to obesity. Obesity is linked to type 2 diabetes, high blood pressure and CVD. It's also a risk factor for some cancers.

> Obesity is defined as being >20% over the maximum recommended body mass.

2) Too much saturated fat in your diet can increase your blood cholesterol level. Too much of a certain type of cholesterol (known as 'bad' or LDL cholesterol) in the blood can cause fatty deposits to form on the inside wall of arteries, which can lead to coronary heart disease (see p.22).

> People whose diet is badly out of balance are said to be malnourished.

3) Eating too little can also cause problems. Malnutrition caused by a lack of food can lead to issues such as fatigue and poor resistance to infection. Some diseases (called deficiency diseases) can be caused by a lack of certain vitamins or minerals. E.g. scurvy is caused by a lack of vitamin C — it leads to problems with the skin, joints and gums.

4) However, eating a healthy, balanced diet that is rich in fruit and vegetables can reduce your risk of getting many non-communicable diseases, such as CVD and obesity.

Best put down that cake and go for a run...

If you're amazed at all the different risk factors for non-communicable diseases then you'll just love the next page.

Q1   Give two lifestyle factors that can increase the risk of obesity.   [2 marks]

More on Non-Communicable Diseases

Unfortunately, you're not finished with risk factors for non-communicable diseases yet. Here are some more...

Alcohol and Smoking Can Also Lead to Non-Communicable Diseases

Alcohol

1) Alcohol is poisonous. It's broken down by enzymes in the liver and some of the products are toxic. If you drink too much alcohol over a long period of time these toxic products can cause the death of liver cells, forming scar tissue that stops blood reaching the liver — this is called cirrhosis.

2) Drinking too much alcohol increases blood pressure which can lead to CVD.

3) Many cancers including those of the mouth, throat, bowels and liver have all been linked to alcohol consumption because the toxic products damage DNA and cause cells to divide faster than normal.

Smoking

Burning cigarettes produce nicotine, which is what makes smoking addictive. They also produce carbon monoxide, tar, and particulates — which can all cause illness and other problems. E.g.

1) CVD — carbon monoxide reduces the oxygen carrying capacity of the blood. If the cardiac muscle doesn't receive enough oxygen it can lead to a heart attack (see page 22). Nicotine increases heart rate. The heart contracts more often increasing blood pressure, which also increases the risk of CVD.

2) Lung, throat, mouth and oesophageal cancer — tar from cigarette smoke is full of toxic chemicals, some of which are carcinogens (cause cancer). Carcinogens make mutations in the DNA more likely, which can lead to uncontrolled cell division (see previous page).

3) Lung diseases, such as chronic bronchitis — cigarette smoke can cause inflammation of the lining of the bronchi and bronchioles (tubes in the lungs), which can result in permanent damage. Symptoms of chronic bronchitis include a persistent cough and breathing problems.

4) Smoking when pregnant can cause lots of health problems for the unborn baby.

Lifestyle Factors Cause Different Trends

Global

Non-communicable diseases are more common in developed countries, where people generally have a higher income, than in developing countries. However, these diseases are now becoming much more common in developing countries too. Different lifestyle factors contribute to these trends, but a lot of it is to do with income. For example:

- Lack of exercise and higher alcohol consumption are associated with higher income.

- Smoking varies massively between countries, but smoking-related deaths are more common in poorer countries.

- In both developed and developing countries, obesity is associated with higher incomes as people are able to afford lots of high-fat food. However, obesity is now associated with lower incomes too, as people are eating cheaper, less healthy foods.

National

Non-communicable diseases are the biggest cause of death in the UK. However, there are differences across the country. For example:

- People from deprived areas are much more likely to smoke, have a poor diet, and not take part in physical activity than those who are better off financially. This means that the incidence of heart disease, obesity, type 2 diabetes, and cancers is higher in those areas. People from deprived areas are also more likely to suffer from alcohol-related disorders.

Local

Individual lifestyle choices affect the incidence of non-communicable diseases at the local level — if you choose to smoke, drink, not take part in exercise or have a poor diet, then the risk increases.

Too many exams are a risk factor for stress...

Trends in non-communicable diseases are often to do with income, because it can have a big effect on lifestyle.

Q1   Suggest what kind of impact increasing cigarette prices may have on the prevalence of lung cancer at a national level. Explain your answer.   [2 marks]

Interpreting Data on Disease

In the exam, you could be given some data about the <u>causes</u>, <u>spread</u>, <u>effects</u> or <u>treatment</u> of disease. You'll need to be able to <u>interpret</u> the data (i.e. work out what it's showing) — this page should help you.

You Need to be Able to Interpret a Scatter Diagram

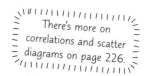
There's more on correlations and scatter diagrams on page 226.

In a <u>scatter diagram</u>, <u>one variable</u> is plotted against a <u>second variable</u>, allowing you to easily spot if there's a <u>correlation</u> (a relationship) between the two variables. Both variables have to be <u>numbers</u>. For example:

1) This scatter diagram shows the <u>prevalence of nonalcoholic fatty liver disease (NAFLD)</u> plotted against the <u>prevalence of obesity</u> for the general population of <u>nine different countries</u>.

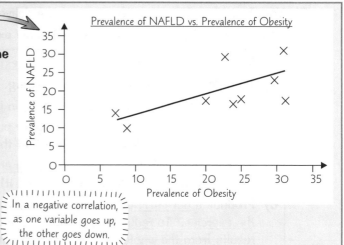

2) The two variables are <u>positively correlated</u> with each other, as the values for both variables go in the <u>same direction</u> — i.e. as the prevalence of NAFLD goes up, so does the prevalence of obesity. The <u>line of best fit</u> helps to show this relationship (the <u>closer</u> the points are to the line, the <u>stronger</u> the correlation).

3) However, the golden rule to remember is that <u>correlation does not equal cause</u> (see p.228).

In a negative correlation, as one variable goes up, the other goes down.

Data Can be Illustrated in Lots of Ways

Level of LDL cholesterol in blood (mg/dl)	>97.6- 115.4	>115.4- 132.2	>132.2- 153.9	>153.9
Relative risk of cardiovascular event	0.9	1.1	1.3	1.5

1) There are lots of different ways that data can be <u>displayed</u>, e.g. data might be shown in a <u>numerical</u> form and displayed in a <u>table</u>, as shown here.

2) The <u>same</u> data can also be shown on a <u>graph</u>, e.g. a bar graph.

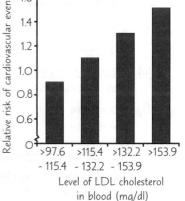

3) In the exam you might have to <u>translate</u> between different forms of data. For example, you might be given a <u>table</u> of data and be asked to <u>draw a graph</u> using the data. Or you might be <u>shown a graph</u> and be asked to give <u>numerical</u> data from it. You could also be given <u>frequency tables</u> or <u>histograms</u>.

A histogram looks a bit like a bar chart, but you need to calculate the area of each bar to interpret it, rather than just look at its height.

4) Whatever you're asked to do, make sure you pay close attention to any <u>titles</u> in the table or <u>axes labels</u> on the graph, and to the <u>units</u> used.

Health Data Has to be Collected Carefully

1) When studying issues about <u>health and disease</u>, e.g. risk factors for non-communicable diseases, it isn't possible to collect all of the <u>potential data</u> (data can't be collected from <u>every</u> member of the population). Instead data has to be collected from a <u>sample</u> that <u>represents</u> the full <u>potential</u> data set.

2) The <u>bigger</u> the sample <u>size</u> the <u>better</u>, as it's <u>more likely</u> that more of the different <u>characteristics</u> present in the <u>whole</u> population will be <u>included</u> in the sample. The sample should also be <u>random</u> to <u>avoid bias</u>. E.g. in a study looking at the effect of an <u>unhealthy diet</u> on the risk of <u>CVD</u>, it would be no good collecting the data by questioning people as they leave the <u>gym</u> (as gym-goers may not <u>represent</u> the whole population).

I thought illustrating data just meant colouring in the table...

Don't be frightened by any questions where you need to interpret data — just take your time and make sure you really understand what the data's showing you before you answer the questions.

Q1   Explain why a large sample size is better than a small one when collecting health data.   [1 mark]

Investigating Pulse Rate

So, a fun experiment to do now — grab your headband and leg warmers and let's get started...

You Can Investigate The Effect of Exercise on Pulse Rate

1) When you exercise, more energy is needed by your muscles to allow them to contract more.

2) This means your rate of respiration has to increase, so you need to get more oxygen into your cells.

Respiration is the process that transfers energy to your cells — it usually requires oxygen (see p.47).

3) Your heart rate increases to speed up the delivery of oxygenated blood to muscles.

4) You can do an experiment to investigate how exercise affects heart rate. E.g.

Your pulse rate is a way of measuring your heart rate. You can find it by putting two fingers on the inside of your wrist or your neck and counting the number of pulses in 1 minute.

1) Measure and record your pulse rate at rest.

2) Then do 3 minutes of gentle exercise, e.g. walk around your school field.

3) Measure and record your pulse rate again immediately after the exercise.

4) Then take regular measurements of your pulse rate until it has returned to its resting rate. Record the time that this takes — this is called the recovery rate.

5) Repeat steps 2-4 two times more, but increase the intensity of the exercise each time (e.g. jog round the field, then run round it).

6) Produce a bar chart of your results to show how pulse rate is affected by the intensity of the exercise. To reduce the effect of random errors on the results, collect anonymised results from the whole class and plot the average percentage change in pulse rate for each exercise. Do the same to show how recovery rate is affected by the intensity of exercise.

7) Remember to control any variables during the experiment, e.g. if you're using results from the whole class, make sure everyone's done the same exercise activities and for the same length of time.

Regular Exercise Can Reduce the Risk of Some Non-Communicable Diseases

1) A high resting heart rate and a slow recovery rate have both been linked to an increased risk of developing some non-communicable diseases, such as CVD.

2) Regular exercise can reduce a person's resting heart rate and speed up their recovery rate, and so could help to reduce the chance of them developing some non-communicable diseases.

3) Scientists are able to investigate the link between regular exercise and a lower resting heart rate and faster recovery rate using long term studies. For example, scientists could:

1) Recruit a large number of volunteers that do not exercise regularly.

2) Record the resting heart rate for each volunteer, then ask the volunteers to all do the same exercise activity and record the recovery rate of each of the volunteers.

3) Split the group in half, and ask one group to continue with their normal lifestyles and the other group to exercise regularly for 3 months — e.g. take a brisk 30 minute walk, 5 times a week.

4) At the end of the trial period, ask the volunteers to come back and then repeat step 2.

5) Analyse the data.

4) Studies such as this can help scientists to determine what kind of exercise or length of training programme is most effective for improving a person's resting heart rate and recovery rate, allowing them to make lifestyle recommendations to people.

If looking at what you truly love can make your heart beat faster...

...then chocolate cake must be really good for me. Unless you've been living in a cave for the past few years, you should be well aware that regular exercise is a good thing. Make sure you know how you can investigate the effect of exercise on pulse rate and recovery rate.

Q1   What is meant by the term 'recovery rate'?   [1 mark]

Treating Disease

Your body does lots of things to try and fight against diseases, but sometimes it needs a little help...

Some Medicines Just Relieve Symptoms...

1) <u>Painkillers</u> (e.g. aspirin) are drugs that relieve pain (no, really). However, they don't actually tackle the <u>cause</u> of the disease or <u>kill</u> pathogens, they just help to <u>reduce</u> the <u>symptoms</u>.

2) Other drugs do a similar kind of thing — reduce how severe the <u>symptoms</u> are or <u>how long</u> the symptoms last for, without tackling the underlying <u>cause</u>. For example, lots of "cold remedies" don't actually <u>cure</u> colds.

3) Although these drugs don't help to <u>cure</u> the disease, they can still be used to <u>ease</u> a sick person's <u>suffering</u> while their body <u>fights it off</u>.

...And Some Medicines Can Treat the Disease

1) Sometimes the body might not be able to <u>fight off</u> a disease on its <u>own</u>. In this case, it might be necessary to use <u>medicines</u> that target the <u>underlying cause</u> of a disease (rather than just helping to relieve the symptoms).

2) For example, drugs which <u>kill</u> or <u>disable</u> pathogens can be used to <u>treat</u> or <u>control diseases</u>, e.g.:

Antibiotics

1) <u>Antibiotics</u> are chemicals that kill <u>bacteria</u> without killing your own body cells. Many are produced <u>naturally</u> by <u>fungi</u> and other <u>microorganisms</u>, e.g. penicillin is made by a type of mould. Pharmaceutical companies can grow them on a <u>large scale</u> in a lab and extract the antibiotics.

2) They can also sometimes be used to <u>prevent</u> bacterial infections from happening. E.g. people in close contact with a person with <u>bacterial meningitis</u> may be given the antibiotic <u>rifampin</u>, as this stops the disease from <u>spreading</u> to them from the <u>infected person</u>.

Antivirals

1) <u>Antivirals</u> can be used to treat viral infections. They are <u>difficult</u> to produce because viruses use the <u>host cells</u> to <u>replicate</u> — it's hard to target the virus <u>without</u> damaging the cell.

2) Most antivirals don't <u>kill</u> the viruses but <u>stop</u> them from <u>reproducing</u>.

3) Some medicines can cause <u>adverse reactions</u> in a person, e.g. some people have an <u>allergic</u> reaction to <u>penicillin</u>. Some medicines can also be very <u>expensive</u>, especially if they'll need to be taken for a <u>long time</u>, and they may <u>not</u> be <u>fully effective</u>. Doctors need to <u>weigh up</u> the potential <u>benefits</u> of medicines against the <u>risks</u> and <u>costs</u> associated with them when they're deciding what to prescribe.

Overuse of Antibiotics May Make Some Diseases Difficult to Treat

1) Some bacteria are <u>naturally resistant</u> to certain antibiotics.

2) The <u>misuse</u> of antibiotics can increase the <u>rate of development</u> of these <u>resistant strains</u>. For example, if a person is prescribed a <u>course</u> of antibiotics for a <u>bacterial infection</u> and they <u>don't complete</u> the full course, resistant bacteria can become <u>more common</u>. This is because the bacteria with the <u>most resistance</u> may <u>survive the antibiotic treatment</u>. Once all the non-resistant bacteria have been killed, the resistant strains will have <u>less competition</u> and will be able to <u>grow and reproduce</u>.

3) Because of the <u>misuse</u> of antibiotics, <u>very resistant strains</u> of bacteria have developed, e.g. <u>MRSA</u> (the hospital 'superbug') is a well-known example of an antibiotic-resistant strain. The development of these very resistant strains means that the antibiotics we currently use are becoming <u>less effective</u>.

> The spread of antibiotic resistant bacteria is an example of evolution by natural selection, see p.70.

4) Since superbugs like MRSA can be very <u>dangerous</u>, doctors have to balance their patient's <u>well-being</u> with the well-being of <u>other people</u> in society when they decide whether or not to prescribe antibiotics — e.g. they may not prescribe antibiotics if they're <u>not really needed</u>, such as for only <u>minor infections</u>.

GCSEs are like antibiotics — you have to finish the course...

Kapow, down with you nasty pathogens — we will kill you all. Ahem, sorry. You best learn this lot.

Q1   Explain why many antibiotics are becoming less effective as treatments for infections.   [3 marks]

Treating Cardiovascular Disease

Cardiovascular disease is a big, big problem in the UK. The good news is there are lots of ways to treat it.

Cardiovascular Disease Affects The Heart and Blood Vessels

See p.57-58 for more on the heart and blood vessels.

Cardiovascular diseases (CVD) are diseases to do with your heart and blood vessels. E.g.

1) High blood pressure and lots of LDL cholesterol can lead to the build up of fatty deposits inside arteries, narrowing them. Over time the fatty deposits harden, forming atheromas. CORONARY HEART DISEASE is when the arteries that supply the heart muscle with blood (coronary arteries) have lots of atheromas in them, which restricts blood flow to the heart.

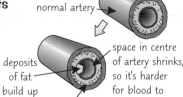

normal artery

deposits of fat build up

thickness of artery wall unchanged

space in centre of artery shrinks, so it's harder for blood to pass through

2) Sometimes bits of atheromas can break off or damage the blood vessel, causing a blood clot. Complete blockage of an artery by atheromas or blood clots can lead to a HEART ATTACK, where part of the heart muscle is deprived of oxygen. If the blockage occurs in the brain, it can cause a STROKE.

There are Different Ways of Treating CVD

See pages 17-18 for more about risk factors for CVD.

Healthy Lifestyle

1) Making changes to your lifestyle, such as eating a healthy diet that is low in saturated fat, reducing stress, exercising regularly and quitting smoking, can reduce the risk of developing CVD in the first place — which avoids the complications of treating it after it has already developed.

2) However, even if you've already had problems, e.g. a heart attack, having a healthy lifestyle can still help. Lifestyle changes can also help other forms of treatment (see below) be more effective.

Medicines

Sometimes medicines are needed to help control the effects of CVD. For example:

1) Statins can reduce the amount of cholesterol present in the bloodstream, which can slow down the rate of fatty deposits forming. However, statins can sometimes cause serious side effects, e.g. kidney failure, liver damage and memory problems.

2) Anticoagulants are drugs which make blood clots less likely to form. However, this can cause excessive bleeding if the person is hurt.

3) Antihypertensives reduce blood pressure. This reduces the risk of atheromas and blood clots forming. Their side effects can include headaches or fainting.

Surgical Procedures

If the heart or blood vessels are too badly damaged then surgery may be needed.

1) Stents are tubes that are inserted inside arteries. They keep them open, making sure blood can pass through to the cardiac muscle, lowering the risk of heart attack. But over time, the artery can narrow again as stents can irritate the artery and make scar tissue grow.

fatty deposit

stent pushes artery wall out, squashing fatty deposit

more space in the centre of the artery

2) If part of a blood vessel is blocked, a piece of healthy vessel taken from elsewhere can be used to bypass the blocked section. This is known as coronary bypass surgery.

3) The whole heart can be replaced with a donor heart (a heart donated after a person has died). However, the new heart does not always start pumping properly. The new heart can also be rejected because the body's immune system recognises it as 'foreign'.

Heart surgery is a major procedure and, as with all surgeries, there is risk of bleeding, clots and infection.

If treatment for cardiovascular disease is needed, doctors must weigh up the likely effectiveness of each treatment against the cost and risks involved for each one, before deciding on which one to use.

Treatments can be risky and expensive, so it's much better to stop CVD from developing in the first place. The same is true for other non-communicable diseases.

Look after yerselves me hearties...

...and make sure you're aware of the drawbacks as well as the advantages for the above ways of treating CVD.

Q1   Anticoagulants make blood clots less likely. Give a disadvantage of their use in treating CVD.   [1 mark]

Developing New Medicines

New medicines are constantly being developed and this nifty little page tells you all about how that happens.

Potential New Medicines Have to be Discovered First

1) In order to develop a new drug, a target that the drug will act upon needs to be identified.

2) The target is likely to be a gene or protein that is linked to the development or progression of the disease. E.g. the target for an anti-cancer drug might be an enzyme (a protein) that is linked to tumour formation.

3) Studying the genomes and proteins of plants and animals can help to identify targets. E.g. studying the genomes of people with and without Alzheimer's disease might lead to the discovery of certain gene variants that contribute to the disease. These gene variants or the proteins they code for can then be the targets for new Alzheimer's drugs. Similarly, the genomes and proteins of pathogens can be studied to identify targets for new drugs, which could help to stop the pathogens from causing disease.

4) Once a target has been identified, scientists then have to find a chemical substance that will have the effect they want on the target (e.g. stop an enzyme from working). To do this, large libraries of chemical substances have to be screened (using very high-tech processes) to assess their likely effectiveness.

5) The result of the screening is unlikely to find a chemical substance that will work exactly in the way the scientists want. Instead the most promising chemicals are selected and modified, and then undergo further tests.

Then There are Lots of Tests to Help Develop Potential Drugs

Preclinical testing:

1) In preclinical testing, drugs are first tested on cultured human cells (cultured means that they've been grown in a lab). However, you can't use human cells to test drugs that affect whole or multiple body systems, e.g. a drug for blood pressure must be tested on a whole animal.

2) The next step is to test the drug on live animals. Both of these steps are used to test that the drug is effective (produces the effect you're looking for) and to find out how safe it is.

Clinical testing:

1) If the drug passes the tests on animals then it's tested on human volunteers in a clinical trial.

2) First, the drug is tested on healthy volunteers to make sure that it is safe, i.e. that it doesn't have any harmful side effects when the body is working normally. Then, successful drugs can be tested on people that have the disease, to test its effectiveness and safety.

3) For many clinical tests, patients are randomly put into two groups. One is given the new drug, the other is given a placebo. This is to allow for the placebo effect (when the patient expects the treatment to work and so feels better, even though the treatment isn't doing anything).

> A placebo is a substance that looks like the drug being tested but doesn't do anything, e.g. a sugar pill

4) However, there are ethical issues around giving a placebo to people with the disease instead of a potential treatment, especially if the disease has severe symptoms (so in some trials they don't use placebos at all).

5) Clinical trials may be blind — the patient in the study doesn't know whether they're getting the drug or the placebo. In fact, they're often double-blind — neither the patient nor the doctor knows until all the results have been gathered. This is so the doctors monitoring the patients and analysing the results aren't subconsciously influenced by their knowledge.

6) Trials can also be open-label — the doctor and the patient are aware of who is receiving the drug. These might be used when comparing the effectiveness of two very similar drugs.

All new medicinal drugs have to go through testing before they can be widely used to treat patients.

The placebo effect doesn't work with revision...

Testing, retesting and then...yep, more testing. You'd know all about that anyway, it's just like being in school...

Q1   Explain how a double-blind trial would be carried out.   [2 marks]

Revision Questions for Chapter B2

Well that's <u>health and disease</u> for you — you've met some heroes and some villains, now time to learn it.

- Try these questions and <u>tick off each one</u> when you <u>get it right</u>.
- When you've done <u>all the questions</u> for a topic and are <u>completely happy</u> with it, tick off the topic.

Health and the Spread of Disease (p.9-10) ☑

1) What is a pathogen? ☑
2) What is meant by the 'incubation period' of a pathogen? ☑
3) Give an example of a disease that is spread through the air. ☑

Defence Against Pathogens and the Immune System (p.11-12) ☑

4) Describe how the skin acts as a defence against pathogens. ☑
5) What are platelets? ☑
6) Give an example of a chemical defence against pathogens found in humans. ☑
7) How do white blood cells recognise specific pathogens? ☑
8) Give three ways in which white blood cells help to defend the body against pathogens. ☑

Reducing and Preventing the Spread of Disease (p.13-14) ☑

9) Explain why isolating infected individuals can help to prevent the spread of disease. ☑
10) Give one method for preventing the transmission of HIV. ☑
11) Give one benefit and one cost of using biological control to prevent the spread of a disease in a crop. ☑
12) Give one potential risk of using vaccinations as a way of protecting people from diseases. ☑

Culturing Microorganisms (p.15-16) ☑

13) What does it mean if there is a clear zone around a disc containing an antibitotic on an agar plate of bacteria? ☑
14) There are ways in which you can make sure an experiment testing the effect of antibiotics on bacteria does not become contaminated. Give three of these ways. ☑

Non-Communicable Diseases (p.17-18) ☑

15) What is meant by a risk factor for a non-communicable disease? ☑
16) Apart from lifestyle factors, give an example of a risk factor that might be associated with a non-communicable disease. ☑
17) Give one non-communicable disease which may be associated with smoking. ☑

Interpreting Data on Disease and Investigating Pulse Rate (p.19-20) ☑

18) What is meant by a positive correlation? ☑
19) Briefly describe how you could investigate the effect of exercise on pulse rate. ☑

Treating Disease (p.21-23) ☑

20) What do antiviral drugs do? ☑
21) Give an example of a surgical procedure which can help to treat cardiovascular disease. ☑
22) How can genome sequences help in the discovery of new drugs. ☑

Enzymes

Chemical reactions are what make you work. And enzymes are what make them work.

Enzymes Are Catalysts Produced by Living Things

> A catalyst is a substance which increases the speed of a reaction, without being changed or used up in the reaction.

1) Living things have thousands of different chemical reactions going on inside them all the time.

2) These reactions need to be carefully controlled — to get the right amounts of substances.

3) You can usually make a reaction happen more quickly by raising the temperature. This would speed up the useful reactions but also the unwanted ones too... not good.

4) So... living things produce enzymes which act as biological catalysts. Enzymes reduce the need for high temperatures and we only have enzymes to speed up the useful chemical reactions in the body.

5) Enzymes catalyse reactions in both animals and plants — including photosynthesis in plants (see p.27).

Enzymes Have Special Shapes So They Can Catalyse Reactions

1) Chemical reactions usually involve things either being split apart or joined together.

2) The substrate is the molecule changed in the reaction.

3) Every enzyme has an active site — the part where it joins on to its substrate to catalyse the reaction.

4) Enzymes usually only work with one substrate. They are said to have a high specificity for their substrate.

5) This is because, for the enzyme to work, the substrate has to fit into the active site. If the substrate's shape doesn't match the active site's shape, then the reaction won't be catalysed. This is called the 'lock and key' model, because the substrate fits into the enzyme just like a key fits into a lock.

enzyme-substrate complex
active site
products
enzyme   substrate
enzyme unchanged after reaction

Temperature, pH and Substrate Concentration Affect the Rate of Reaction

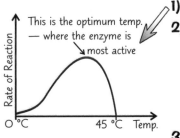
This is the optimum temp. — where the enzyme is most active
Rate of Reaction
0 °C   45 °C   Temp.

1) Changing the temperature changes the rate of an enzyme-catalysed reaction.

2) Like with any reaction, a higher temperature increases the rate at first. The enzymes and substrate have more energy, so they move about more and are more likely to collide and form enzyme-substrate complexes. But if it gets too hot, some of the bonds holding the enzyme together break. This changes the shape of the enzyme's active site, so the substrate won't fit any more. The enzyme is said to be denatured.

3) All enzymes have an optimum temperature that they work best at.

4) The pH also affects enzymes. If it's too high or too low, the pH interferes with the bonds holding the enzyme together. This changes the shape of the active site and denatures the enzyme.

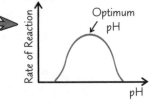
Optimum pH
Rate of Reaction
pH

5) All enzymes have an optimum pH that they work best at. It's often neutral pH 7, but not always.

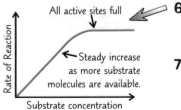
All active sites full
Rate of Reaction
Steady increase as more substrate molecules are available.
Substrate concentration

6) Substrate concentration also affects the rate of reaction — the higher the substrate concentration, the faster the reaction. This is because it's more likely that the enzyme will meet up and react with a substrate molecule.

7) This is only true up to a point though. After that, there are so many substrate molecules that the enzymes have about as much as they can cope with (all the active sites are full), and adding more makes no difference.

If the lock and key mechanism fails, get in through a window...

Make sure you use the special terms like 'active site' and 'denatured' — the examiners will love it.

Q1   Explain why enzymes have an optimum pH.   [3 marks]

PRACTICAL # More on Enzymes

You'll soon know how to investigate the effect of a variable on the rate of enzyme activity... I bet you're thrilled.

You Can Investigate How Temperature Affects Enzyme Activity

There are a couple of different ways to investigate how temperature affects enzyme activity. You can also adapt these experiments to measure variables other than temperature. For example:

1) To investigate the effect of pH, add a buffer solution with a different pH level to different tubes containing the enzyme-substrate mixture.

A buffer solution is able to resist changes in pH.

2) Vary the initial concentration of the substrate to investigate the effect of substrate concentration.

3) Vary the initial concentration of the enzyme to investigate the effect of enzyme concentration.

You Can Measure How Fast a Product Appears...

1) The enzyme catalase catalyses the breakdown of hydrogen peroxide into water and oxygen.

2) You can collect the oxygen and measure how much is produced in a set time.

3) Use a pipette to add a set amount of hydrogen peroxide to a boiling tube. Put the tube in a water bath at 10 °C and wait about five minutes.

4) Then set up the rest of the apparatus as shown. Add a source of catalase (e.g. a cube of potato) to the hydrogen peroxide and quickly attach the bung.
(Keep the boiling tube in the water bath.)

5) Record how much oxygen is produced in the first minute.

6) Repeat steps 3-5 three times and calculate the mean. Then repeat the whole experiment with the water bath at 20 °C, 30 °C and 40 °C.

There's more on variables and fair tests on p.222.

7) Control any variables (e.g. pH, the potato used, the size of potato pieces, etc.) to make it a fair test.

8) After the experiment you can calculate the mean rate of reaction at each temperature to analyse your results. Rate is a measure of how much something changes over time. To calculate a rate you need to divide the amount that something has changed by the time taken for the change to happen. So for this experiment, you calculate the mean rate of reaction by dividing the mean volume of oxygen produced in cm³ (this is the change) by the time taken (i.e. 60 s). The units will be cm³/second.

Figure labels: water bath at constant temperature; measuring cylinder; delivery tube; amount of oxygen produced per minute is measured; source of catalase (e.g. potato); hydrogen peroxide solution

...Or How Fast a Substrate Disappears

1) The enzyme amylase catalyses the breakdown of starch to maltose.

2) It's easy to detect starch using iodine solution — if starch is present, the iodine solution will change from browny-orange to blue-black.

3) Set up the apparatus as in the diagram. Put a drop of iodine solution into each well on the spotting tile. Use continuous sampling to record how long it takes for the amylase to break down all of the starch. To do this, take a fresh sample of the mixture every ten seconds and put a drop into a new well. Once the iodine solution does not turn blue-black, it means all the starch has been converted to maltose.

To calculate the rate for this experiment, use the formula: 1 ÷ time taken (in s). The units will be s⁻¹.

Figure labels: mixture placed in water bath at constant temperature; mixture sampled every 10 seconds; dropping pipette; starch solution and amylase enzyme; drop of iodine solution; spotting tile

4) Repeat with the water bath at different temperatures to see how it affects the time taken for the starch to be broken down. Remember to control all of the variables each time.

If only enzymes could speed up revision...

The key thing with experiments is to only change the thing you're testing — and absolutely nothing else. Sorted.

Q1   An enzyme-controlled reaction was carried out at 25 °C. After 60 seconds, 33 cm³ of product had been released. Calculate the rate of reaction in cm³/s.   [1 mark]

Photosynthesis

You don't know <u>photosynthesis</u> 'til you know its <u>equation</u>. It's in a nice <u>green box</u> so you can't possibly miss it.

Plants are Able to Make Their Own Food by Photosynthesis

1) During photosynthesis, <u>photosynthetic organisms</u>, such as <u>green plants</u> and <u>algae</u>, use <u>energy</u> from the Sun to make <u>glucose</u>.

Some prokaryotes can also photosynthesise, although they don't have chloroplasts (see below).

2) Some of the glucose is used during cellular <u>respiration</u> (see page 47) and some is converted to <u>starch</u> and <u>stored</u>. Some glucose is also used to make <u>larger</u>, <u>complex molecules</u> that the plants or algae need to <u>grow</u>, e.g. <u>lipids</u>, <u>proteins</u>, and <u>carbohydrates</u> besides starch. These make up the organism's <u>biomass</u>.

3) Photosynthesis happens inside subcellular structures called <u>chloroplasts</u> (see page 1). These contain the <u>enzymes</u> that <u>catalyse</u> reactions in photosynthesis, as well as <u>chlorophyll</u>, which <u>absorbs light</u>. Energy is <u>transferred</u> to the <u>chlorophyll</u> from the environment by <u>light</u>. This is the <u>equation</u> for photosynthesis:

$$\text{carbon dioxide} + \text{water} \xrightarrow[\text{chlorophyll}]{\text{LIGHT}} \text{glucose} + \text{oxygen}$$
$$6CO_2 + 6H_2O \xrightarrow[\text{chlorophyll}]{\text{LIGHT}} C_6H_{12}O_6 + 6O_2$$

4) Photosynthesis is <u>endothermic</u> — <u>energy</u> is transferred from the <u>environment</u> during photosynthesis.

5) <u>Lots</u> of <u>chemical reactions</u> happen during photosynthesis, but it takes place in <u>two main stages</u>. First, energy transferred by <u>light</u> to the chlorophyll is used to split <u>water</u> into <u>oxygen gas</u> and <u>hydrogen ions</u> — the oxygen is released as a <u>waste product</u>.

6) <u>Carbon dioxide gas</u> then combines with the <u>hydrogen ions</u> to make <u>glucose</u>.

The Starch Test Shows Whether Photosynthesis is Taking Place | PRACTICAL

Remember, <u>glucose</u> is <u>stored</u> by plants as <u>starch</u>. If a plant can't <u>photosynthesise</u>, it can't make <u>starch</u> — you can use this to show that <u>light</u> and <u>CO₂</u> are needed for photosynthesis.

First, you need to know how to <u>test a leaf</u> for starch. Start by dunking the leaf in <u>boiling water</u> (hold it with tweezers or forceps). This <u>stops</u> any <u>chemical reactions</u> happening inside the leaf. Now put the leaf in a boiling tube with some <u>ethanol</u> and heat it gently in an electric water bath — this gets rid of any <u>chlorophyll</u> and makes the leaf a <u>white-ish</u> colour. Finally, <u>rinse</u> the leaf in <u>cold water</u> and add a few drops of <u>iodine solution</u> — if <u>starch</u> is <u>present</u> the leaf will turn <u>blue-black</u>. Now for the experiments themselves...

Ethanol is highly flammable — keep it away from naked flames, e.g. Bunsen burners.

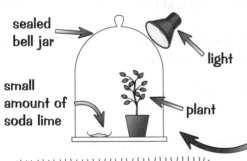

sealed bell jar

light

small amount of soda lime

plant

For both of these tests, it's important that any variables that could affect the results, e.g. the temperature, are controlled.

1) Start by <u>destarching</u> some plants (i.e. leave them in the dark for 48 hours so they use up their starch stores).

2) To show that <u>light</u> is <u>required</u> for <u>photosynthesis</u>, keep one plant <u>in the dark</u> and move the other one <u>into the light</u> for a while — then perform the <u>starch test</u> on a leaf from each plant. The leaf from the plant moved to the <u>light</u> should turn <u>blue-black</u>, but the leaf from the plant kept in the dark <u>won't</u>. This shows that <u>light is needed</u> for photosynthesis, as no starch has been made in the leaf grown without light.

3) A similar investigation can be conducted (using the apparatus shown on the left) to show that <u>CO₂</u> is needed for <u>photosynthesis</u>. Soda lime <u>absorbs CO₂</u> out of the air — so if you leave a plant in the jar for a while and then <u>test</u> a leaf for starch, it <u>won't</u> turn <u>blue-black</u>. This shows that <u>no starch</u> has been made in the leaf, which means that <u>CO₂ is needed</u> for photosynthesis to happen.

I'm working on sunshine — woah oh...

You must learn the photosynthesis equation. Learn it so well that you'll still remember it when you're 109.

Q1   Explain how the starch test can be used to show that plants need light to photosynthesise.   [4 marks]

Investigating the Rate of Photosynthesis

If you've always wanted to investigate how <u>different factors</u> affect the <u>rate</u> of photosynthesis, you're in luck...

Oxygen Production Shows the Rate of Photosynthesis | PRACTICAL

1) The rate of photosynthesis can be affected by <u>light intensity</u>, <u>concentration of CO_2</u> and <u>temperature</u>. Any of these can become <u>limiting factors</u>, meaning they can stop photosynthesis from happening any <u>faster</u>.

2) You can <u>investigate</u> how each of the different factors affect the <u>rate of photosynthesis</u>. A classic way to do this is to use <u>pondweed</u> and to measure <u>oxygen production</u> over <u>time</u>.

3) The rate at which the pondweed produces <u>oxygen</u> corresponds to the rate at which it's photosynthesising — the <u>faster</u> the rate of oxygen production, the <u>faster</u> the rate of photosynthesis.

4) The box below describes the <u>basic method</u> you could use — the ways in which you could alter the experiment to test the different factors are shown on the next page.

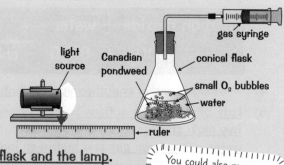

1) The <u>apparatus</u> is <u>set up</u> according to the <u>diagram</u>. This gas syringe should be empty to start with.

2) A set amount of <u>sodium hydrogencarbonate</u> (which gives off CO_2) may be added to the water in the conical flask to <u>control</u> the amount of <u>CO_2</u> the pondweed receives. You could also use a <u>heat shield</u> (e.g. a beaker of water) to stop the heat from the lamp affecting the results. Put the conical flask <u>in the beaker of water</u> or put the beaker <u>between</u> the <u>flask and the lamp</u>.

3) The pondweed is left to photosynthesise for a <u>set amount of time</u>.

4) As it photosynthesises, the oyxgen released will collect in the <u>gas syringe</u>. This allows you to <u>accurately measure</u> the <u>volume</u> of oxygen produced.

You could also measure how much oxygen is being produced by counting the bubbles, but it's not as accurate (see p.224).

5) The results are recorded in a table, and the experiment is then <u>repeated</u> to test a <u>range</u> of values for the <u>factor being investigated</u>, e.g. a range of different distances from the light source.

6) Variables other than the one being investigated should be kept the <u>same</u>, e.g. the other limiting factors, the time the pondweed is left for.

You Can Calculate Rate from a Graph

Once you've written your results in a table, you can <u>plot</u> them in a <u>graph</u>. (There's more on plotting graphs on p.225.) Graphs aren't just nice to look at — they're useful for spotting patterns in your results. You can carry out <u>calculations</u> from them too. If you want to calculate the rate of photosynthesis from a graph of your results, <u>volume of oxygen</u> should go on the <u>y-axis</u> and <u>time</u> should go on the <u>x-axis</u>.

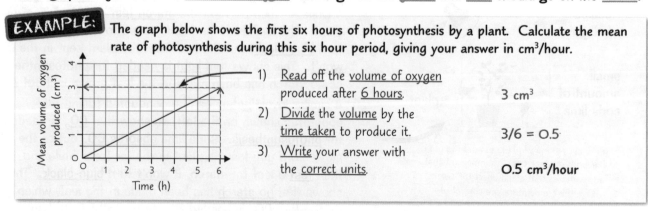

EXAMPLE: The graph below shows the first six hours of photosynthesis by a plant. Calculate the mean rate of photosynthesis during this six hour period, giving your answer in cm^3/hour.

1) <u>Read off</u> the <u>volume of oxygen</u> produced after <u>6 hours</u>. — $3 \ cm^3$

2) <u>Divide</u> the <u>volume</u> by the <u>time taken</u> to produce it. — $3/6 = 0.5$

3) <u>Write</u> your answer with the <u>correct units</u>. — $0.5 \ cm^3$/hour

That was intense — but I see light at the end of the tunnel...

The investigation above can be varied to see how different factors affect the rate of photosynthesis. The next page has more on this (bet you can't wait) but it's best to understand what's happening here before moving on.

Q1   Explain how the rate of oxygen production corresponds to the rate of photosynthesis.   [2 marks]

Limiting Factors of Photosynthesis

Before you start on this page, make sure you've read the photosynthesis experiment from the last page. OK...

Here Are Three Important Graphs for Rate of Photosynthesis

Not Enough LIGHT Slows Down the Rate of Photosynthesis

1) Light transfers the energy needed for photosynthesis.
2) As the light level is raised, the rate of photosynthesis increases steadily — but only up to a certain point.
3) Beyond that, it won't make any difference — it'll be either the temperature or the CO_2 level which is the limiting factor.
4) In the lab you can investigate light intensity by moving a lamp closer to or further away from your plant.

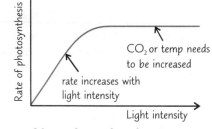

5) But if you just plot the rate of photosynthesis against "distance of lamp from the plant", you get a weird-shaped graph. To get a graph like the one above you either need to measure the light intensity at the plant using a light meter or do a bit of nifty maths with your results. Here's why:

The distance from the lamp and light intensity are inversely proportional to each other — this means that as the distance increases, the light intensity decreases. However, light intensity decreases in proportion to the square of the distance. This is called the inverse square law and is written like this:

Putting one over the distance shows the inverse.

$$\text{light intensity (i)} \propto \frac{1}{\text{distance (d)}^2}$$

Halving the distance → intensity is $2 \times 2 = 4$ times greater
Tripling the distance → intensity is $3 \times 3 = 9$ times smaller

Too Little CARBON DIOXIDE Also Slows it Down

1) CO_2 is one of the substrates needed for photosynthesis.
2) This means that increasing the concentration of CO_2 will increase the rate of photosynthesis — but only up to a point. After this the graph flattens out — CO_2 is no longer the limiting factor.
3) If CO_2 is in plentiful supply, then the factor limiting photosynthesis must be light or temperature.
4) In the experiment on the previous page, dissolving different amounts of sodium hydrogencarbonate in the same volume of water will vary the CO_2 concentration.

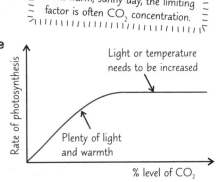

The TEMPERATURE has to be Just Right

1) Usually, if the temperature is the limiting factor it's because it's too low — the enzymes needed for photosynthesis work more slowly at low temperatures.
2) But if the plant gets too hot, the enzymes it needs for photosynthesis and its other reactions will be denatured — the rate of reaction decreases dramatically.
3) This happens at about 45 °C (pretty hot for outdoors, but greenhouses can get that hot if you're not careful).
4) Experimentally, you can vary the temperature of the conical flask (see p.28), using a water bath.

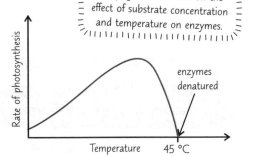

Don't blame it on the sunshine, don't blame it on the CO_2...

...don't blame it on the temperature, blame it on the plant. And now you'll never forget these three limiting factors. in photosynthesis. No... well, make sure you read these pages over and over again 'til you're sure you won't.

Q1   Describe the relationship between increasing light intensity and the rate of photosynthesis.   [2 marks]

Diffusion, Osmosis and Active Transport

Substances can move in and out of cells by <u>diffusion</u>, <u>osmosis</u> and <u>active transport</u>...

Diffusion — Don't be Put Off by the Fancy Word

1) <u>Diffusion</u> is simple. It's just the <u>gradual movement</u> of particles from places where there are <u>lots</u> of them to places where there are <u>fewer</u> of them. That's all it is — just the <u>natural tendency</u> for stuff to <u>spread out</u>. Here's the fancy <u>definition</u>:

> <u>DIFFUSION</u> is the <u>net (overall) movement</u> of <u>particles</u> from an area of <u>higher concentration</u> to an area of <u>lower concentration</u>.

If something moves from an area of higher concentration to an area of lower concentration it is said to have moved down a concentration gradient.

2) Diffusion happens in both <u>liquids</u> and <u>gases</u> — that's because the particles in these substances are free to <u>move about</u> randomly.

3) Diffusion continues until the <u>concentration</u> of the diffusing particles is <u>even</u> in both areas. This is what's happening when the smell of perfume diffuses through the air in a room:

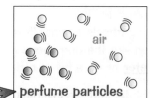

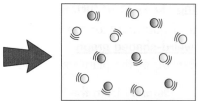

perfume particles diffused in the air

4) <u>Cell membranes</u> are <u>partially permeable</u>. This means that only very <u>small</u> molecules can move through them — things like <u>glucose</u>, <u>amino acids</u>, <u>water</u> and <u>oxygen</u>. <u>Big</u> molecules like <u>starch</u>, <u>sucrose</u> and <u>proteins</u> can't fit through the membrane.

Osmosis is a Special Case of Diffusion, That's All

> <u>OSMOSIS</u> is the <u>net movement of water molecules</u> across a <u>partially permeable membrane</u> from a region of <u>higher water concentration</u> to a region of <u>lower water concentration</u>.

1) The water molecules actually pass <u>both ways</u> through the membrane during osmosis. This happens because water molecules <u>move about randomly</u> all the time.

2) But because there are <u>more</u> water molecules on one side than on the other, there's a steady <u>net flow</u> of water into the region with <u>fewer</u> water molecules, i.e. into the <u>stronger</u> sugar solution.

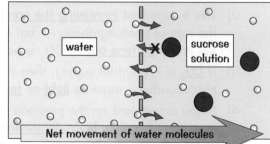

water | sucrose solution

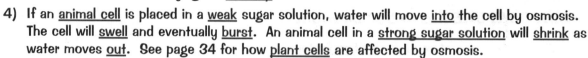

Net movement of water molecules

3) This means the <u>strong sugar</u> solution gets more <u>dilute</u>. The water acts like it's trying to "<u>even up</u>" the concentration either side of the membrane.

4) If an <u>animal cell</u> is placed in a <u>weak</u> sugar solution, water will move <u>into</u> the cell by osmosis. The cell will <u>swell</u> and eventually <u>burst</u>. An animal cell in a <u>strong sugar solution</u> will <u>shrink</u> as water moves <u>out</u>. See page 34 for how <u>plant cells</u> are affected by osmosis.

Active Transport Works Against a Concentration Gradient

> <u>ACTIVE TRANSPORT</u> is the <u>movement of particles</u> across a membrane against a concentration gradient (i.e. from an area of <u>lower</u> to an area of <u>higher concentration</u>) <u>using energy</u> transferred during respiration.

1) Active transport is a bit <u>different from diffusion</u> because particles are moved <u>up a concentration gradient</u> rather than down. The process also requires <u>energy</u> (unlike diffusion, which is a passive process).

2) There's an example of active transport at work on the next page.

Revision by diffusion — you wish...

Hopefully there'll have been a net movement of information from this page into your brain...

Q1 Give two differences between the processes of diffusion and active transport. [2 marks]

Transport in Plants and Prokaryotes

Diffusion, osmosis and active transport are at work in all living organisms, including plants and prokaryotes.

Exchanging Substances is Trickier in Multicellular Organisms

1) All cells need to exchange substances with their environment. They need to take in substances in order to function and get rid of waste. Their partially permeable cell membranes allow them to do this.

2) Single-celled organisms, including prokaryotes (see p.1), are only one cell big — therefore substances can diffuse straight into and out of them across their cell membranes.

3) In multicellular organisms, such as animals and plants, diffusion across the outer surface is more difficult because some cells are deep inside the organism — it's a long way from them to the outside environment and so specialised exchange surfaces are needed.

CO_2 and O_2 move through Stomata and Cell Membranes in Plants

When plants photosynthesise they use up CO_2 from the atmosphere and produce oxygen as a waste product. These gases move in and out of plants and their cells by diffusion.

> E.g. when a plant is photosynthesising it uses up lots of CO_2, so there's hardly any inside the leaf. This makes more CO_2 move into the leaf by diffusion.

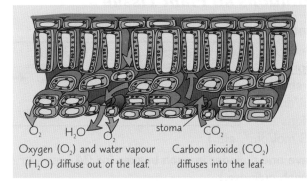

O_2 H_2O O_2 stoma CO_2
Oxygen (O_2) and water vapour   Carbon dioxide (CO_2)
(H_2O) diffuse out of the leaf.   diffuses into the leaf.

1) In plants, the lower surface of a leaf is full of tiny pores called stomata (see p.34).

2) The stomata are there to let gases like CO_2 and O_2 diffuse in and out. They also allow water vapour to escape — which is known as transpiration (see p.33).

3) These gases diffuse between air spaces inside the leaf and the plant's cells through the cells' partially permeable outer membrane.

Root Hairs Take in Water and Mineral Ions

> Molecules can only cross a membrane when they're right next to it, so a large surface area means loads more molecules are close to the membrane.

1) Plants need water for photosynthesis (amongst other things) and mineral ions for growth. They take both water and ions in through their roots.

2) The cells on plant roots grow into long 'hairs' which stick out into the soil.

3) Each branch of a root will be covered in millions of these microscopic hairs.

4) This gives the plant a big surface area for absorbing water and mineral ions from the soil:

- There's usually a higher concentration of water in the soil than there is inside the plant, so the water is drawn into the root hair cell across the partially permeable cell membrane by osmosis.

- Plants need nitrogen to make proteins. They get nitrogen from nitrate ions (NO_3^-). These mineral ions move into root cells by active transport, since the concentration of mineral ions in the root hair cells is usually higher than in the soil. The cells use molecules of ATP (see p.47) to provide energy to actively transport the ions through the cell membrane.

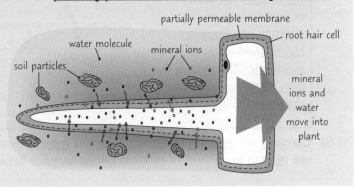

partially permeable membrane
root hair cell
water molecule   mineral ions
soil particles
mineral ions and water move into plant

Active transport — get on yer bike...

All cell membranes are partially permeable — this allows control over what goes in and out of the cell.

Q1   How are plant roots adapted to be able to absorb lots of water and mineral ions from the soil?   [2 marks]

Investigating Diffusion and Osmosis

For all you non-believers — here are a few experiments you can do to see diffusion and osmosis in action.

You Can Investigate Diffusion in a Non-Living System

Phenolphthalein is a pH indicator — it's pink in alkaline solutions and colourless in acidic solutions. You can use it to investigate diffusion in agar jelly:

1) First, you need some agar jelly made up with phenolphthalein and dilute sodium hydroxide. Dilute sodium hydroxide is an alkali, so the jelly should be a lovely shade of pink.

2) Now add some dilute hydrochloric acid to a beaker. Measure out and cut some cubes from the jelly — then put them in the beaker of acid.

3) If the cubes are left they'll eventually turn colourless as the acid diffuses into the agar jelly and neutralises the sodium hydroxide — use a stopwatch to time how long it takes.

4) You could investigate how varying the concentration of the acid (e.g. between 0.1 and 1 M) affects the rate of diffusion. Keep everything apart from the concentration of acid the same.

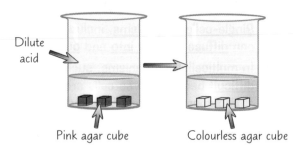
Dilute acid
Pink agar cube   Colourless agar cube

You can Observe the Effect of Sugar Solutions on Plant Tissue

There's a fairly dull experiment you can do to show osmosis at work.

1) You cut up an innocent potato into identical cylinders, and get some beakers with different sugar solutions in them. One should be pure water and another should be a very concentrated sugar solution (e.g. 1 mol/dm^3). Then you can have a few others with concentrations in between (e.g. 0.2 mol/dm^3, 0.4 mol/dm^3, 0.6 mol/dm^3, etc.)

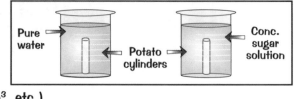
Pure water   Potato cylinders   Conc. sugar solution

2) You measure the mass of each cylinder, then leave one cylinder in each beaker for 24 hours or so. (Alternatively, you could measure the length of each cylinder.)

3) After taking the cylinders out, dry them with a paper towel and measure their masses again.

4) The only thing that you should change in this experiment is the concentration of the sucrose solution. Everything else (e.g. the volume of solution, the time the cylinders are left for, the temperature, etc.) must be kept the same or your results won't be valid (see p.222).

5) Once you've got your results you can calculate the percentage change in mass for the cylinders in each beaker, plot a graph and analyse your results.

By calculating the percentage change (see p.35), you can compare the effect of sugar concentration on cylinders that didn't have the same initial mass.

At the points above the x-axis, the water concentration of the sucrose solutions is higher than in the cylinders. The cylinders gain mass as water is drawn in by osmosis.

% change in mass / Concentration of sucrose solution (M)

Where there is no change in mass (where the curve crosses the x-axis) the fluid inside the cylinders and the sucrose solution have the same water concentration.

At the points below the x-axis, the water concentration of the sucrose solutions is lower than in the cylinders. This causes the cylinders to lose water so their mass decreases.

6) Carrying out repeats and calculating the mean percentage change in mass will reduce the effect of random errors on your experiment (see page 224).

So that's how they make skinny fries...

The experiment above used sucrose as a solute, but you could do the experiment with different solutes (e.g. salt).

Q1   Potato cylinders in a salt solution with a concentration of 0.3 mol/dm^3 do not change mass. What does this tell you about the concentration of the solution in the potato cells? Explain your answer.   [3 marks]

Xylem and Phloem

Instead of blood vessels, plants have <u>two</u> types of transport vessel (<u>xylem</u> and <u>phloem</u>) for transporting stuff around. <u>Both</u> types of vessel go to <u>every part</u> of the plant in a <u>continuous system</u>, but they're totally <u>separate</u>.

Phloem Tubes Transport Food Substances

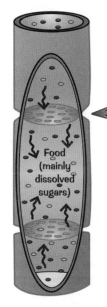

1) <u>Phloem tubes</u> are made of <u>columns</u> of <u>living cells</u> called <u>sieve tube elements</u>. These have <u>perforated end-plates</u> to allow stuff to flow through.

2) Sieve tube elements have <u>no nucleus</u>. This means that they <u>can't survive</u> on their own, so each sieve tube element has a <u>companion cell</u>. These cells carry out the <u>living functions</u> for both themselves and their sieve cells.

3) Phloem vessels transport <u>food substances</u> (mainly <u>sugars</u>) both <u>up</u> and <u>down</u> the stem to growing and storage tissues.

4) This <u>movement</u> of food substances around the plant is known as <u>translocation</u>. Sugars are usually <u>translocated</u> from <u>photosynthetic tissues</u>, e.g. the leaves, to <u>non-photosynthetic tissues</u>, e.g. the roots.

5) The <u>sugars</u> enter the phloem by <u>active transport</u>. They are then pushed around by <u>water</u>, which enters the phloem by <u>osmosis</u>.

Xylem Tubes Take Water and Ions UP

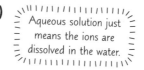

1) <u>Xylem tubes</u> are made of <u>dead cells</u> joined end to end with <u>no</u> connecting cell walls between them (to create a long tube) and a hole (<u>lumen</u>) down the middle.

2) The <u>thick side walls</u> are made of <u>cellulose</u>. They're <u>strong</u> and <u>stiff</u>, which gives the plant <u>support</u>. The cell walls are also strengthened with a material called <u>lignin</u>.

3) Xylem tubes carry <u>water</u> and <u>mineral ions</u> (e.g. nitrates) in <u>aqueous solution</u> from the roots <u>up the stem</u> to the leaves in the <u>transpiration stream</u> (see below).

Aqueous solution just means the ions are dissolved in the water.

Transpiration is the Loss of Water from the Plant

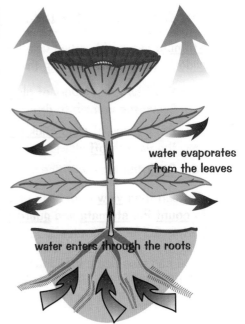

1) Transpiration is caused by the <u>evaporation</u> and <u>diffusion</u> of water from a plant's surface. Most transpiration happens at the <u>leaves</u>.

2) This evaporation and diffusion creates a slight <u>shortage</u> of water in the leaf, and so more water is drawn up from the rest of the plant through the <u>xylem vessels</u> to replace it.

3) This in turn means more water is drawn up from the <u>roots</u>, and so there's a constant <u>transpiration stream</u> of water through the plant.

Head back to page 31 to see how root hair cells are adapted for taking up water.

water evaporates from the leaves

Transpiration is just a <u>side-effect</u> of the way leaves are adapted for <u>photosynthesis</u>. They have to have <u>stomata</u> in them so that gases can be exchanged easily (see page 31). Because there's <u>more water inside</u> the plant than in the <u>air outside</u>, the water escapes from the leaves through the stomata by diffusion.

water enters through the roots

Don't let revision stress you out — just go with the phloem...

Phloem goes up and down, whereas xylem just goes up. You could remember it as xy to the sky... it sort of rhymes.

Q1 Explain why there is a continuous upward flow of water in plants. [3 marks]

Stomata

You've not learnt about <u>transpiration</u> 'til you've learnt about stomata (sadly)...

Stomata Open and Close Automatically

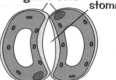

It's one stoma, but two or more stomata.

You should remember from p.31 that stomata are <u>tiny pores</u> on the surface of a plant, which allow <u>CO_2</u> and <u>oxygen</u> to <u>diffuse</u> directly in and out of a leaf. They also allow <u>water vapour</u> to escape during transpiration (see previous page). Stomata are able to open and close to control the amount of water lost from the leaves.

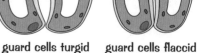

guard cells
stoma

guard cells turgid
— stoma <u>open</u>

guard cells flaccid
— stoma <u>closed</u>

1) Stomata are surrounded by <u>guard cells</u>, which <u>change shape</u> to control the size of the pore.

2) When the guard cells are <u>turgid</u> (swollen with water) the stomata are <u>open</u>, and when the guard cells are <u>flaccid</u> (low on water and limp) the stomata are <u>closed</u>.

3) <u>Stomata</u> close <u>automatically</u> when supplies of water start to <u>dry up</u> — they're also <u>sensitive to light</u> and <u>close at night</u> to <u>save water</u> without losing out on photosynthesis.

4) <u>Changes</u> in the <u>concentration of ions</u> inside the guard cells help to open and close the stomata:

- In response to stimuli like <u>light</u>, <u>potassium ions</u> (K^+) are pumped <u>into guard cells</u>.
- This <u>increases</u> the <u>solute concentration</u> of the guard cells, which <u>decreases</u> the concentration of <u>water molecules</u>.
- <u>Water</u> then moves <u>into</u> the guard cells by <u>osmosis</u>. This makes the guard cells <u>turgid</u> and the stoma <u>opens</u>.
- When potassium ions <u>leave</u> the guard cells, the <u>concentration of water molecules</u> in the cell <u>increases</u>.
- <u>Water</u> then moves <u>out</u> by <u>osmosis</u>, the guard cells become <u>flaccid</u> and the stoma <u>closes</u>.

K^+ pumped across guard cell membrane

Movement of water into guard cell by osmosis

5) If the plant's really short of water, the <u>cytoplasm</u> inside its cells starts to <u>shrink</u> and the membrane <u>pulls away</u> from the cell wall. A cell in this condition is said to be <u>plasmolysed</u>.

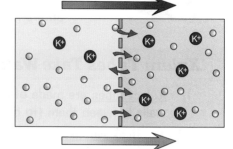

You Can View Stomata, Xylem and Phloem Under a Microscope

<u>Stomata</u> can be observed using a <u>light microscope</u>. You can prepare a <u>slide</u> to view them on using the following (ridiculously easy) method:

PRACTICAL

1) Paint two thin layers of <u>clear nail varnish</u> onto the leaf you want to look at. Leave the varnish to <u>dry</u> in between each coat.

2) Put a piece of <u>clear sticky tape</u> over the top of the painted leaf and use it to <u>peel</u> the varnish <u>off</u> slowly. The varnish will have an <u>impression</u> of the leaf's <u>surface</u>.

3) <u>Stick</u> the tape with the varnish onto a <u>microscope slide</u>.

You can then <u>view</u> your slide under the microscope (see p.2 for how to do this). You should be able to <u>count</u> the <u>stomata</u> and <u>guard cells</u> from the impression on the varnish. If you <u>compare</u> the top and bottom surfaces of a leaf you should find that there are <u>more stomata</u> on the <u>bottom</u> of the leaf.

You can also use a light microscope to observe the <u>structure</u> of <u>xylem</u> and <u>phloem</u> in <u>thin sections</u> of a plant's stem. If a stem is left upright in a beaker of <u>eosin dye</u>, the dye will travel up the stem, staining the <u>xylem</u> red. A thin section of the stem can then be taken and viewed on a slide under a microscope.

See p.2 for how to prepare a slide.

I say stomaaarta, you say stomaaayta...

A tree can lose around 1000 litres of water from its leaves every day. That's about as much water as the average person drinks in a year. No wonder the stomata close when the soil's dry or it's too dark to photosynthesise.

Q1   Explain how the stomata open in response to light.   [4 marks]

Transpiration Rate

If you thought that stuff on <u>transpiration</u> was <u>interesting</u>, you're in luck — here's another page all about it...

Transpiration Rate is Affected by Three Main Things

1) <u>AN INCREASE IN LIGHT INTENSITY</u> — the <u>brighter</u> the light, the <u>greater</u> the transpiration rate. Bright light <u>increases</u> the rate of <u>photosynthesis</u>. This increases the <u>demand for water</u> in the <u>leaves</u>, so more is drawn up from the roots. Bright light also causes the <u>stomata</u> to <u>open</u> to let CO_2 in, allowing more water vapour to diffuse out. <u>Stomata</u> begin to <u>close</u> as it gets darker because photosynthesis can't happen in the dark. When the stomata are closed, <u>water can't escape</u>.

2) <u>AN INCREASE IN TEMPERATURE</u> — the <u>warmer</u> it is, the <u>faster</u> transpiration happens. That's because when it's warm the water particles have <u>more energy</u> to evaporate and diffuse out of the stomata. An increase in temperature also <u>increases</u> the <u>rate of photosynthesis</u> and therefore the <u>demand for water</u> — so more is drawn up from the roots.

3) <u>AN INCREASE IN AIR MOVEMENT</u> — if there's <u>lots</u> of air movement (wind) around a leaf, transpiration happens <u>faster</u>. If the air around a leaf is very still, the water vapour just <u>surrounds the leaf</u> and doesn't move away. This means there's a <u>high concentration</u> of water particles outside the leaf as well as inside it, so <u>diffusion</u> doesn't happen as quickly. If it's windy, the water vapour is <u>swept away</u>, maintaining a <u>low concentration</u> of water in the air outside the leaf. Diffusion then happens quickly, from an area of higher concentration to an area of lower concentration.

You Can Measure Loss of Mass to Estimate Transpiration Rate

You can do an <u>experiment</u> to show this:

1) Add some <u>damp soil</u> to a <u>plastic sandwich bag</u>. Take a <u>small plant</u> and plant it in the soil, then <u>tie the bag shut</u> around the stem (leaving the leaves <u>out</u> of the bag).

2) <u>Measure</u> the <u>mass</u> of the wrapped up plant and <u>record</u> it.

3) <u>Leave</u> the plant in a well-lit place for <u>24 hours</u>, then <u>measure its mass again</u>.

4) You should notice that the plant has <u>decreased in mass</u>. It's assumed this is equal to the mass of the <u>water lost</u> through <u>transpiration</u>.

5) <u>Dividing</u> the <u>mass lost</u> (in grams) by the <u>time taken</u> to lose it (in days) will give you an <u>estimate</u> of the <u>transpiration rate</u> (in g/day).

6) You can <u>compare</u> how much water a plant loses under <u>different conditions</u>, e.g. in the <u>light</u> versus in the <u>dark</u>. To compare them fairly, you need to <u>calculate</u> the <u>percentage change in mass</u>.

> The plant could actually lose a small amount of mass in other ways, e.g. it loses oxygen during photosynthesis.

 **EXAMPLE:** A plant weighed 250 g at the start of the experiment. After being exposed to light for 24 hours it weighed 225 g. Calculate the percentage change in mass.

To find the <u>percentage change in mass</u>, use the following <u>formula</u>:

$$\text{percentage change} = \frac{\text{final mass} - \text{initial mass}}{\text{initial mass}} \times 100$$

$$\text{percentage change} = \frac{225 - 250}{250} \times 100 = -10\%$$

It's a negative result because the plant lost mass. If the result was positive the plant would have gained mass.

You can also <u>estimate transpiration</u> rate by <u>measuring water uptake</u> by a plant. There's more on this on the next page.

> If you're asked to calculate the percentage <u>loss</u> in mass, then you don't need to include the minus sign in your answer (because you've already been told that mass was lost).

Transpiration — the plant version of perspiration...

A really handy way to remember the three factors that affect the rate of transpiration is to think about drying your washing. A good day for drying your clothes is when it's sunny, warm and windy. It's the same — fancy that.

Q1 A plant was left in a warm room for 24 hours. It had an initial mass of 262 g and an final mass of 217 g. Calculate the percentage change in mass over the 24 hour period. [2 marks]

Using a Potometer

It's time for another <u>experiment</u> — you get to use a piece of equipment you've probably never heard of...

A Potometer can be Used to Measure Water Uptake

A <u>potometer</u> is a special piece of apparatus used to <u>measure water uptake</u> by a plant. This gives an <u>estimate</u> of <u>transpiration rate</u> because <u>water uptake</u> by the plant is <u>related</u> to <u>water loss</u> from the leaves (transpiration). It's <u>not</u> a completely <u>accurate</u> estimate though, because the water <u>taken up</u> by a plant is <u>not all lost</u> through transpiration (e.g. some is used up in <u>photosynthesis</u> and some may be lost from parts of the potometer that aren't <u>sealed</u>). Here's how to use a potometer:

1) <u>Cut</u> a shoot <u>underwater</u> to prevent air from entering the xylem. Cut it at a <u>slant</u> to increase the surface area available for water uptake.

2) <u>Assemble</u> the potometer <u>in water</u> and insert the shoot <u>under water</u>, so no <u>air</u> can enter.

3) Remove the apparatus from the water but keep the end of the capillary tube <u>submerged</u> in a beaker of water.

4) Check that the apparatus is <u>watertight</u> and <u>airtight</u>.

5) <u>Dry</u> the leaves, allow time for the shoot to <u>acclimatise</u> and then <u>shut</u> the tap.

6) Remove the end of the capillary tube from the beaker of water until <u>one air bubble</u> has formed, then put the end of the tube <u>back into the water</u>.

7) Record the <u>starting position</u> of the air bubble.

8) Start a <u>stopwatch</u> and record the <u>distance moved</u> by the bubble per unit time, e.g. per hour. Calculating the <u>speed</u> of <u>air bubble movement</u> allows you to <u>measure water uptake</u>.

9) Keep the <u>conditions constant</u> throughout the experiment, e.g. the <u>temperature</u> and <u>air humidity</u>.

Setting up a potometer is tough — if there are air bubbles in the apparatus or the plant's xylem it will affect your results.

Potometers can be set up in different ways. You might see one in the exam that's a bit different to this one but they're all used to estimate transpiration rate.

reservoir of water

Tap is shut off during experiment.

As the plant takes up water, the air bubble moves along the scale.

Water moves this way.

Bubble moves this way.

capillary tube with a scale

Beaker of water.

EXAMPLE:
A potometer was used to measure the rate of water uptake of a plant cutting. The bubble moved 25 mm in 10 minutes. Calculate the rate of water uptake.

Divide the <u>distance</u> the bubble moved by the <u>time taken</u>.

$$\frac{\text{distance moved}}{\text{time taken}} = \frac{25}{10} = 2.5 \text{ mm / minute}$$

You Can See How Environmental Conditions Affect Water Uptake

You can use a potometer to <u>estimate</u> how different factors affect the <u>rate of water uptake</u>. The set up above will be your <u>control</u> — you can <u>vary</u> an <u>environmental condition</u> (see below), run the experiment again and <u>compare</u> the results to the <u>control</u> to see how the change <u>affected</u> the rate of water uptake.

1) <u>Light intensity</u> — You could use a <u>lamp</u> to <u>increase</u> the <u>intensity of light</u> that hits the plant — this should <u>increase</u> the transpiration rate, and therefore the rate of water uptake. To <u>decrease</u> the light intensity, put the potometer in a <u>cupboard</u> (this should <u>decrease</u> the rate of water uptake).

2) <u>Temperature</u> — You could increase or decrease the temperature by putting the potometer in a <u>room</u> that's <u>warmer</u> or <u>colder</u> than where you did the control experiment. An <u>increase</u> in temperature should <u>increase</u> the rate of water uptake and a <u>decrease</u> in temperature should <u>lower</u> it.

3) <u>Air movement</u> — You could use a <u>fan</u> to <u>increase</u> the air movement around the plant — this should <u>increase</u> the transpiration rate, and therefore the rate of water uptake.

Potometer — a surprisingly useless tool for measuring crockery...

The tricky bit of using a potometer is setting it up — keeping air out and water in is harder than it sounds.

Q1   Give two variables you should keep constant if investigating the effect of temperature on the rate of water uptake.

[2 marks]

Ecosystems and Interactions Between Organisms

It's tough in the wild — there's always competition for food and other resources. So if the environment changes, e.g. there's not enough food or it's too hot, it can be the last straw for some organisms...

Ecosystems are Organised into Different Levels

A habitat is the place where an organism lives, e.g. a rocky shore or a field.

A species is a group of similar organisms that can reproduce with each other to give fertile offspring.

Ecosystems have different levels of organisation:
1) Individual — A single organism.
2) Population — All the organisms of one species in a habitat.
3) Community — All the organisms (different species) living in a habitat.
4) Ecosystem — A community of organisms along with all the non-living (abiotic) conditions (see below).

Organisms Compete for Resources to Survive

Organisms need things from their environment and from other organisms in order to survive and reproduce:
1) Plants need light, space, water and minerals from the soil, as well as seed dispersers (e.g. animals that eat fruit and spread the seeds in their droppings) and pollinators (e.g. bees).
2) Animals need space (territory), shelter, food, water and mates.

The size of a population is limited by competition for these factors as well as predation (see below). Organisms compete with other species (and members of their own species) for the same resources. E.g. red and grey squirrels live in the same habitat and eat the same food. Competition with the grey squirrels for these resources in some areas means there's not enough food for the reds — so the population of red squirrels is decreasing, partly as a result of this.

Environmental Changes Affect Communities in Different Ways

The environment in which plants and animals live changes all the time. These changes are caused by abiotic (non-living) and biotic (living) factors and affect communities in different ways — for some species population size may increase, for others it may decrease, or the distribution of populations (where they live) may change. Here are some examples of the effects of changes in abiotic and biotic factors:

Abiotic Factors Affect Communities...

1) Environmental conditions — e.g. the distribution of bird species in Germany appears to be changing because of a rise in average temperature. Other environmental conditions that affect the abundance and distribution of organisms include light intensity (plants only), moisture level and soil pH.
2) Toxic chemicals — e.g. chemical pesticides or fertilisers. Pesticides can build up in food chains through bioaccumulation — this is where, at each stage of the food chain, concentration of the pesticide increases, so organisms at the top of the chain receive a toxic dose. Excess fertilisers released into lakes and ponds cause increased growth of algae. This is called eutrophication. The algae block sunlight from plants, which die. Microorganisms feeding on the dead plants use up O_2 in the water, leading to the death of other organisms (e.g. fish).

... and so do Biotic Factors

1) Availability of food — e.g. in a bumper year for berries, the population of blackbirds might increase because there'll be enough food for all of them, so they're more likely to survive and reproduce.
2) Number of predators — e.g. if the number of lions (predator) decreases then the number of gazelles (prey) might increase because fewer of them will be eaten by the lions.
3) Presence of pathogens — e.g. if a new pathogen was introduced into the community then populations may decrease due to illness.

The presence of competitors is also a biotic factor that affects the population size and distribution of species.

Revision — an abiotic factor causing stress in my community...

Organisms like everything to be just right — temperature, light, food... I'd never get away with being that fussy.

Q1   Give two abiotic factors that could affect the community in an ecosystem.   [2 marks]

PRACTICAL Investigating Ecosystems

Here's how to study the <u>distribution</u> and <u>abundance</u> of organisms. First up, using <u>quadrats</u>...

Use a Quadrat to Study The Distribution of Small Organisms

A <u>quadrat</u> is a <u>square</u> frame enclosing a <u>known area</u>, e.g. 1 m². To compare <u>how common</u> an organism is in <u>two sample areas</u>, just follow these simple steps:

1) Place a <u>1 m² quadrat</u> on the ground at a <u>random point</u> within the <u>first</u> sample area. E.g. divide the area into a grid and use a random number generator to pick coordinates. Otherwise, if all your samples are in <u>one spot</u> and everywhere else is <u>different</u>, the results you get won't be <u>representative</u> of the <u>whole sample area</u>. For more about <u>random sampling</u> take a look at page 241.

2) <u>Count</u> all the organisms you're interested in <u>within</u> the quadrat.

3) <u>Repeat</u> steps 1 and 2 lots of times. (The <u>larger</u> the <u>sample size</u> the better, see p.223.)

4) <u>Work out</u> the <u>mean</u> number of organisms per quadrat within the first sample area.

5) <u>Repeat</u> steps 1 to 4 in the <u>second</u> sample area.

6) Finally <u>compare</u> the two means. E.g. you might find 2 daisies per m² in the shade, and 22 daisies per m² (lots more) in an open field.

A quadrat

$$\text{Mean} = \frac{\text{total number of organisms}}{\text{number of quadrats}}$$

Estimate Population Sizes by Scaling Up from a Small Sample Area

To work out the <u>population size</u> of an organism in one sample area, you need to work out the <u>mean number of organisms per m²</u> (if your quadrat has an area of 1 m², this is the same as the mean number of organisms per quadrat, worked out above). Then just <u>multiply the mean</u> by the <u>total area</u> of the habitat:

EXAMPLE: Students used 0.25 m² quadrats to randomly sample daisies in a field. They found a mean of 10 daisies per quadrat. The field's area was 800 m². Estimate the population of daisies in the field.

1) Work out the <u>mean number of organisms per m²</u>. 1 ÷ 0.25 = 4 4 × 10 = 40 daisies per m²

2) Multiply the <u>mean per m²</u> by the <u>total area</u> (in m²) of the habitat. 40 × 800 = 32 000 daisies in the field

Use Capture-Mark-Release-Recapture to Estimate Population Sizes

1) <u>Capture</u> a <u>sample</u> of the population and <u>mark</u> the animals in a <u>harmless</u> way.

2) <u>Release</u> them back into the environment (and give the animals time to redistribute into the population).

3) <u>Recapture</u> another sample of the population. <u>Count</u> how many of this sample are marked.

4) Then <u>estimate</u> population size with this equation:

$$\text{Population Size} = \frac{\text{number in first sample} \times \text{number in second sample}}{\text{number in second sample previously marked}}$$

EXAMPLE: 30 woodlice were caught in a pitfall trap in an hour and marked before being released back into the environment. The next day, 35 woodlice were caught in an hour, only 5 of which were marked. Estimate the population size.

All you need to do is put the numbers into the population size equation (shown above).

Population size = (30 × 35) ÷ 5 = 210 woodlice

number in the first sample   number in the second sample   number in the second sample previously marked

A pitfall trap is a steep-sided container, with an open top, which is sunk into the ground. It's used to trap ground-dwelling insects.

When using the capture-mark-release-recapture method, you have to make a number of <u>assumptions</u>. These include: there has been <u>no change</u> in the <u>population size</u> between the samples (e.g. births and deaths) and the <u>marking</u> hasn't affected individuals' <u>chance of survival</u> (e.g. making them more visible to predators).

Drat, drat and double drat — my favourite use of quadrats...

Choosing which sampling method to use often depends on the type of organism. E.g. quadrats are great for organisms that don't move such as plants, but nets and traps are better for organisms that move around, like insects.

Q1   Capture-mark-release-recapture was used to estimate a population of crabs. In the first sample 22 were caught. A second sample had 26 crabs, 4 of which were marked. Estimate the population size.   [2 marks]

More on Investigating Ecosystems PRACTICAL

Yep, there's still some more to learn about this stuff. Coming up we have <u>keys</u> and <u>transects</u> — lovely.

Keys are Used to Identify Creatures

1) A <u>key</u> is a <u>series of questions</u> that you can use to figure out what an <u>unknown organism</u> is.

2) Keys are useful when carrying out sampling as they help you to <u>correctly identify</u> organisms you find.

3) To use a key you start at question 1, and the answer to that question (which you know by looking at your mystery organism) is used to <u>narrow down</u> your options of what it could be.

4) Sometimes keys will just have <u>statements</u>, rather than questions, that are followed by a number of options — e.g. 'number of legs' followed by some different options (see below).

5) As you answer more and more questions you <u>narrow down your options further</u> until eventually you're just <u>left with one</u> possible species your organism could be.

<u>Part of a key</u> is shown on the right. It can be used to identify <u>types of organisms</u> that might be found <u>on the ground</u> in a <u>woodland</u>.

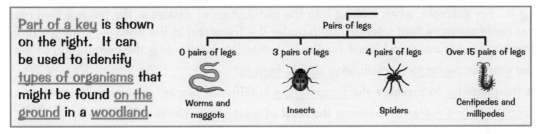

Pairs of legs

0 pairs of legs — Worms and maggots
3 pairs of legs — Insects
4 pairs of legs — Spiders
Over 15 pairs of legs — Centipedes and millipedes

Transects are Used to Investigate Distribution

1) You can investigate how the <u>distribution</u> of an organism <u>gradually changes</u> across an area (e.g. from a hedge towards the middle of a field) using <u>lines</u> called <u>transects</u>.

2) When you sample along the length of a transect using a <u>quadrat</u> (see previous page) this is called a <u>belt transect</u>.

3) To do a <u>belt transect</u> follow the steps below:

> 1) Mark out a <u>line</u> in the area you want to study using a <u>tape measure</u>.
>
> 2) Place a <u>quadrat</u> at the <u>start</u> of the <u>line</u> and <u>count</u> and <u>record</u> the organisms you find in the quadrat.
>
> 3) Then, instead of picking a second sampling site at random (which you'd do if you were sampling a whole area with a quadrat), you take samples by <u>moving</u> your quadrat <u>along the line</u>, e.g. placing the quadrat at <u>intervals</u> of every <u>2 m</u>.
>
> 4) You could even take samples along the <u>entire length</u> of your transect by placing your quadrats right <u>next to each other</u>. This might take <u>ages</u> if you have a long transect though.
>
> 5) <u>Repeat</u> your transect at least <u>twice</u> more at different places within the area you want to study.

4) If it's difficult to count all the individual organisms in the quadrat (e.g. if they're grass) you can calculate the <u>percentage cover</u>. This means estimating the percentage <u>area</u> of the quadrat covered by a particular type of organism, e.g. by <u>counting</u> the number of little squares covered by the organisms.

Measuring % cover

Organism Type A
42 squares = 42%

Organism Type B
47 squares = 47%

You count a square if it's more than half covered.

5) Taking <u>measurements</u> of <u>abiotic factors</u> (see next page) at points along the transect can show how changes in these affect the distribution and abundance of organisms in the habitat.
E.g. in a coastal habitat, changes in <u>salinity</u> and <u>soil depth</u> result in zones where different plants grow.

Identification keys — not much use in the world of home security...

Keys help you identify organisms you've found when sampling. This is pretty important when you want to talk about the different organisms that you've seen — it's not much use saying you found six slimy things in a pond...

Q1   Describe how to carry out a belt transect.   [3 marks]

Investigating Factors Affecting Distribution

The way organisms are distributed depends on a number of different factors. Prepare to learn all about them.

The Distribution of Organisms is Affected by Abiotic and Biotic Factors

1) The distribution of organisms is affected by abiotic factors such as temperature, moisture level, light intensity and soil pH (see page 37). For example, in a playing field, you might find that daisies are more common in the open than under trees, because there's more light available in the open.

2) Biotic factors can also affect the distribution of organisms (see p.37). E.g. competition between species might result in a different distribution of these species than if this competition didn't exist.

You Need to Know How to Measure Abiotic Factors | PRACTICAL

If you find there's a difference in the distribution of organisms, you can investigate the factors that might be causing it. For example, when looking into the distribution of daisies in the playing field mentioned above, you could measure light intensity both under the trees and in the open — finding a difference in light intensity could provide evidence for the idea that this is affecting the distribution of daisies.

Here's how you can measure the following abiotic factors:

There's more on measuring temperature on p.235 and pH on p.236.

1) Use a thermometer to measure the temperature in different places.
2) Use a soil moisture meter to measure the level of moisture in some soil.
3) Use an electronic device called a light meter to measure light intensity. Hold the meter at the level of the organisms you're investigating (ground level for daisies) and make sure it's at the same height and angle for every reading you take.
4) Measure soil pH using indicator liquid — water is added to a soil sample and then an indicator liquid (e.g. Universal indicator) is added that changes colour depending on the pH. The colour is compared to a chart to find out the pH of the soil. Electronic pH monitors can also be used to produce a more accurate pH value for the sample being tested.

The Distribution of Indicator Species Can Be Used to Assess Pollution

Some organisms are very sensitive to changes in their environment and can be studied to see how polluted an area is — these organisms are known as indicator species.

PRACTICAL

- Some invertebrate animals, like stonefly larvae and freshwater shrimps are good indicators for water pollution because they're very sensitive to the concentration of dissolved oxygen in the water — If you find stonefly larvae in a river, it indicates that the water is clean.
- Other invertebrate species have adapted to live in polluted conditions — so if you see a lot of them you know there's a problem. E.g. blood worms and sludge worms indicate highly polluted water.

Polluted water can lead to eutrophication (see p.37) — this reduces the concentration of dissolved oxygen in the water.

- Air pollution can be monitored by looking at particular types of lichen that are very sensitive to the concentration of sulfur dioxide in the atmosphere. (Sulfur dioxide is a pollutant released from car exhausts, power stations, etc.) E.g. the air is clean if there are lots of lichen — especially bushy lichen, which need cleaner air than crusty lichen.

When investigating indicator species, you need to sample them. Sampling methods will vary depending on the species you're interested in and where it is found. For example, aquatic organisms could be caught with a net which is swept through the water. Lichens (which grow on trees and rocks and don't move about) could be sampled using quadrats or transects (see pages 38-39).

Teenagers are an indicator species — not found in clean rooms...

Don't forget that the absence of an indicator species could mean the opposite of what they indicate. E.g. the absence of stonefly larvae could indicate polluted water. Nice and simple, innit?

Q1   Bushy lichen grows on trees in the local park. Explain what this indicates about the air quality.   [2 marks]

Food Chains and Food Webs

If you like <u>food</u>, and you like <u>chains</u>, then <u>food chains</u> might just blow your mind. Strap yourself in and prepare for some 'edge of your seat' learning, because the show is about to begin...

Food Chains Show What's Eaten by What in an Ecosystem

1) <u>Food chains</u> always start with a <u>producer</u>.
   Producers <u>make</u> (produce) <u>their own food</u> using energy from the Sun.

2) Producers are usually <u>green plants</u> — they make <u>glucose</u> by <u>photosynthesis</u> (see p.27).

3) When a green plant produces glucose, some of it is used to make <u>other biological molecules</u> in the plant. These biological molecules are the plant's <u>biomass</u> — the <u>mass</u> of <u>living material</u>. Biomass can be thought of as <u>energy stored</u> in a plant.

4) <u>Biomass</u> is <u>transferred</u> through living organisms in an ecosystem when organisms <u>eat</u> other organisms — this means that these photosynthetic organisms <u>support nearly all life on Earth</u>.

5) Producers are eaten by <u>primary consumers</u>. Primary consumers are then eaten by <u>secondary consumers</u> and secondary consumers are eaten by <u>tertiary consumers</u>. Here's an example of a food chain:

Producers   Primary consumers   Secondary consumer

<u>5000</u> dandelions... feed... <u>100</u> rabbits... which feed... <u>1</u> fox.

Consumers are organisms that eat other organisms.

Food Webs Show How Food Chains are Linked

1) There are many different species within an environment — which means <u>lots of different</u> possible <u>food chains</u>. You can draw a <u>food web</u> to show them.

2) All the species in a food web are <u>interdependent</u> — they <u>depend</u> on each other for survival.

3) The <u>transfer of biomass</u> is one way in which organisms are <u>interdependent</u>. The <u>direction</u> of biomass transfer is shown by the <u>arrows</u> in a food chain or web.

4) <u>Interdependence</u> means that a change in the size of one population will affect the sizes of other populations in the community.

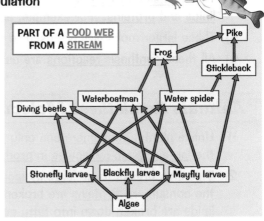

PART OF A <u>FOOD WEB</u> FROM A <u>STREAM</u>

> <u>For example</u>, in the food web on the right, if lots of <u>water spiders died</u>, then:
> * There would be <u>less food</u> for the <u>frogs</u>, so their numbers might <u>decrease</u>.
> * The number of <u>mayfly larvae</u> might <u>increase</u> since the water spiders wouldn't be eating them.
> * The <u>diving beetles</u> wouldn't be <u>competing</u> with the water spiders for food, so their numbers might <u>increase</u>.

Food webs — nothing to do with ordering pizza online, I'm afraid...

Food webs are handy for looking at relationships between individual species. Unfortunately you hardly ever see simple food webs in the real world — they're normally as tangled together and interlinked as a bowl of spaghetti.

Q1   The diagram on the right shows part of a food web. Using the diagram, suggest what might happen to the other species if the population of mice increased.

[4 marks]

Making and Breaking Biological Molecules

Organisms can break big molecules down into smaller ones and build small molecules back up into bigger ones. It's pretty clever stuff, and all given a helping hand by our good friends, enzymes (see p.25).

Carbohydrates, Lipids and Proteins are Organic Molecules

Organic molecules are molecules that contain carbon. Carbohydrates, lipids and proteins are all organic molecules and so are the smaller molecules they're made up from:

1) Long-chain carbohydrates, e.g. starch are made from simple sugars.

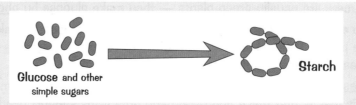

Glucose and other simple sugars → Starch

2) Proteins are made from amino acids.

Amino acids → Proteins

3) Lipids are made by joining fatty acids and glycerol.

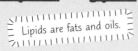

Lipids are fats and oils.

Glycerol & fatty acids → Lipid

Plants Build Up Organic Molecules in their Biomass

1) Producers take in the elements they need to survive from their environment, e.g. plants take in carbon from the air and nitrogen compounds from the soil.

2) Producers use carbon (along with oxygen and hydrogen) to make glucose during photosynthesis (see page 27).

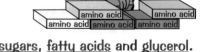

3) Glucose is then used to make other small organic molecules, e.g. other sugars, fatty acids and glycerol. Glucose and nitrate ions (see page 31) are combined to make amino acids.

4) These small molecules are then used by the producer to create long-chain carbohydrates, lipids and proteins. For example, amino acids are joined together to make proteins.

5) These larger molecules are used to build structures like cell membranes and organelles.

6) All these synthesis reactions are catalysed by enzymes.

Animals Break these Molecules Down, then Build them Up Again

1) Unlike plants, consumers can only get carbon and nitrogen compounds by eating and digesting the large organic molecules in producers or other consumers in the food chain.

2) Digestion breaks these large molecules down into smaller ones, which can be more easily absorbed by the consumer. Proteins are broken down into amino acids, starch is broken down into simple sugars, and lipids are broken down into fatty acids and glycerol. Digestion reactions are also catalysed by enzymes.

3) The small molecules are then transported to the consumer's cells (usually in the blood supply) to be built up into larger molecules (proteins, etc.) again. These form the biomass of the consumer.

What do you call an acid that's eaten all the pies...

Make sure you learn the diagrams at the top of the page really well (I mean, really, really well). And remember that when the bigger organic molecules get broken down, the arrow just goes the opposite way.

Q1   Name the molecules that result from the breakdown of: a) carbohydrates, b) proteins.   [2 marks]

Testing for Biological Molecules

You need to know how you can <u>test</u> for <u>biological molecules</u> using <u>different chemicals</u>. The tests are all <u>qualitative</u> — you can tell <u>whether or not</u> a substance is <u>present</u> in a sample, but <u>not how much</u> is present.

You Can Test for Sugars Using Benedict's Reagent

There are lots of different types of <u>sugar molecules</u>. Due to their <u>chemical properties</u>, many sugars (e.g. glucose) are called <u>reducing sugars</u>. You don't need to know exactly what reducing sugars are, but you do need to know how to <u>test</u> for them:

1) Add <u>Benedict's reagent</u> (which is <u>blue</u>) to a sample and <u>heat</u> it in a water bath that's set to <u>75 °C</u>. If the test's <u>positive</u> it will form a <u>coloured precipitate</u> (solid particles suspended in the solution).

2) The <u>higher</u> the <u>concentration</u> of reducing sugar, the <u>further</u> the colour change goes — you can use this to <u>compare</u> the amount of reducing sugar in different solutions.

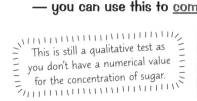
This is still a qualitative test as you don't have a numerical value for the concentration of sugar.

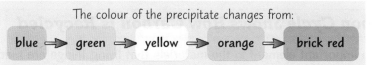
The colour of the precipitate changes from:
blue ⇒ green ⇒ yellow ⇒ orange ⇒ brick red

Starch is Tested for with Iodine

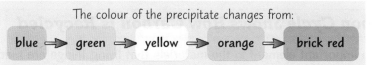
Iodine solution is iodine dissolved in potassium iodide solution.

Just add <u>iodine solution</u> to the test sample.

1) If starch <u>is present</u>, the sample changes from <u>browny-orange</u> to a dark, <u>blue-black</u> colour.

2) If there's <u>no starch</u>, it stays browny-orange.

Use the Emulsion Test for Lipids

An emulsion is when one liquid doesn't dissolve in another — it just forms little droplets.

To find out if there are any <u>lipids</u> in a sample:

1) <u>Shake</u> the test substance with <u>ethanol</u> for about a minute until it <u>dissolves</u>, then pour the solution into <u>water</u>.

2) If there <u>are</u> any <u>lipids present</u>, they will show up as a <u>milky emulsion</u>.

3) The <u>more lipid</u> there is, the <u>more noticeable</u> the milky colour will be.

Test substance and ethanol   Shake   Add to water   Milky colour indicates lipid

The Biuret Test is Used for Proteins

If you needed to find out if a sample contains <u>protein</u> you'd use the <u>biuret test</u>:

1) First, add a few drops of <u>sodium hydroxide</u> solution to make the solution <u>alkaline</u>.

2) Then add some <u>copper(II) sulfate</u> solution (which is <u>bright blue</u>).

- If there's <u>no protein</u>, the solution will stay <u>blue</u>.
- If protein <u>is present</u>, the solution will turn <u>purple</u>.

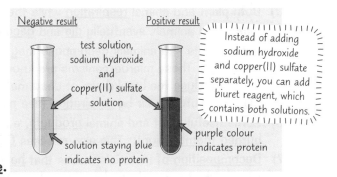
Negative result

Positive result

test solution, sodium hydroxide and copper(II) sulfate solution

solution staying blue indicates no protein

Instead of adding sodium hydroxide and copper(II) sulfate separately, you can add biuret reagent, which contains both solutions.

purple colour indicates protein

The Anger Test — annoy test subject. Red face = anger present...

OK, so this stuff isn't thrilling but learning it is better than being dissolved in a giant vat of vinegar. Yowch.

Q1   A solution that has been mixed with sodium hydroxide and copper(II) sulfate solution turns purple. What conclusion would you draw from this test?   [1 mark]

Cycles in Ecosystems

Substances like carbon and water are essential to life on Earth. Luckily for us, they flow through the Earth's ecosystems in cycles, meaning that we (and other organisms) can reuse them over and over again — splendid.

Materials are Constantly Recycled in an Ecosystem

1) Remember, an ecosystem is a community of organisms living in an area, as well as all the non-living (abiotic) conditions, e.g. soil quality, availability of water, temperature. There's more on these on p.37.

2) Materials organisms need to survive, such as carbon and water (see next page) are recycled through both the biotic and abiotic components of ecosystems.

3) This means they pass through both living organisms (the biotic components of an ecosystem) and things like the air, rocks and soil (abiotic components of an ecosystem) in a continuous cycle.

The Carbon Cycle Shows How Carbon is Recycled

Carbon is an important element in the materials that living things are made from. But there's only a fixed amount of carbon in the world. This means it's constantly recycled:

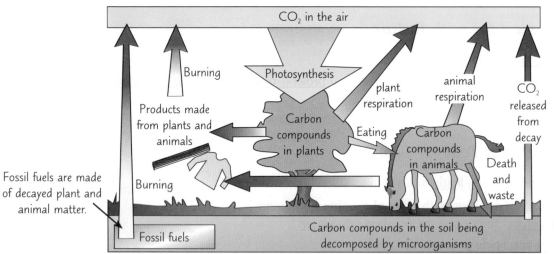

This diagram isn't half as bad as it looks. Learn these important points:

1) There's only one arrow going down from CO_2 in the air. The whole thing is 'powered' by photosynthesis. Green plants use the carbon from CO_2 to make carbohydrates, lipids and proteins.

2) Eating passes the carbon compounds in the plant along to animals in a food chain or web (see p.41).

3) Both plant and animal respiration while the organisms are alive releases CO_2 back into the air.

4) Plants and animals eventually die and decompose, or are killed and turned into useful products.

5) When plants and animals decompose they're broken down by microorganisms, such as bacteria and fungi. These microorganisms are known as decomposers and they release enzymes, which catalyse the breakdown of dead material into smaller molecules. Decomposers release CO_2 back into the air by respiration (see page 47) as they break down the material.

6) Some useful plant and animal products, e.g. wood and fossil fuels, are burned (combustion). This also releases CO_2 back into the air.

7) Decomposition of materials means that habitats can be maintained for the organisms that live there, e.g. nutrients are returned to the soil and waste material, such as dead leaves, doesn't just pile up.

The Carbon Cycle — a great gift for any bike enthusiast...

Carbon atoms are very important — they're found in plants, animals, your petrol tank and on your burnt toast.

Q1   Suggest two reasons why chopping down trees can increase the concentration of CO_2 in the air.   [2 marks]

More on Cycles in Ecosystems

Like carbon, water on planet Earth is constantly recycled. This is lucky for us because without water, we wouldn't survive. And I don't just mean there'd be no paddling pools, ice lollies or bubble baths...

The Water Cycle Means Water is Endlessly Recycled

As with carbon, there has only ever been a fixed amount of water on the Earth.

1) Energy from the Sun makes water evaporate from the land and sea, turning it into water vapour.

2) Water also evaporates from plants — this is known as transpiration (see p.33).

3) The warm water vapour is carried upwards (as warm air rises). When it gets higher up it cools and condenses to form clouds.

4) Water falls from the clouds as precipitation (usually rain, but sometimes snow or hail) onto land.

5) Some of this water is absorbed by the soil and is taken up by plant roots. This provides plants with fresh water for things like photosynthesis. Some of the water taken up by plants becomes part of the plants' tissues and is passed along to animals in food chains.

Animals also get fresh water by drinking from streams and rivers.

6) Like plants, animals need water for the chemical reactions that happen in their bodies. Animals return water to the soil and atmosphere through excretion (processes that get rid of the waste products of chemical reactions, e.g. sweating, urination and breathing out).

7) Water that doesn't get absorbed by the soil will runoff into streams and rivers.

8) From here, the water then drains back into the sea, before it evaporates all over again.

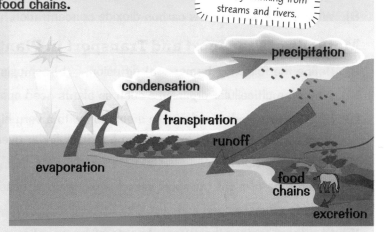

You Can Estimate the Percentage of Mass Transferred in a Cycle

1) In the exams, you might be asked to calculate percentage masses in the context of cycles.

2) For example, you might be asked to calculate the mass of carbon released in an animal's waste as a percentage of the mass of carbon the animal takes in from its food. Or you might be asked to calculate the mass of water a tree transfers to the environment through transpiration as a percentage of the mass of water it takes in through its roots.

> **EXAMPLE:** A tree takes in 4000 kg of water in a day through its roots. It loses 3960 kg of water in a day through transpiration. Calculate the percentage mass of water transferred from the plant roots to the atmosphere through transpiration.
>
> percentage mass of water transferred $= \dfrac{3960}{4000} \times 100 = 99\%$

Come on out, it's only a little water cycle, it won't hurt you...

The most important thing to remember is that it's a cycle — a continuous process with no beginning or end. Water that falls to the ground as rain (or any other kind of precipitation) will eventually end up back in the clouds again.

Q1   a) In the water cycle, how does water move from the land into the air?   [1 mark]
        b) How does the water cycle benefit plants and animals?   [1 mark]

Revision Questions for Chapter B3

It's time to say goodbye to Chapter B3 — but not before a healthy dose of questions to test yourself with...
- Try these questions and tick off each one when you get it right.
- When you've done all the questions for a topic and are completely happy with it, tick off the topic.

Enzymes (p.25-26) ☑

1) What part of an enzyme makes it specific to a particular substrate?
2) Explain how temperature affects enzyme activity.
3) State two ways in which you could measure the rate of an enzyme-controlled reaction.

Photosynthesis (p.27-29) ☑

4) Where in a plant cell does photosynthesis take place?
5) What is the equation for photosynthesis?
6) Describe an investigation you could do to measure the effect of light intensity on photosynthesis.
7) In the inverse square law, how are light intensity and distance linked?
8) What effect would a low carbon dioxide concentration have on the rate of photosynthesis?

Methods of Transport and Transport in Plants (p.30-36) ☑

9) Define the following terms: a) diffusion,   b) osmosis,   c) active transport.
10) Why do multicellular organisms such as plants need specialised exchange surfaces?
11) If a potato cylinder is placed in a solution with a very high sucrose concentration, what will happen to the mass of the potato cylinder over time? Explain why.
12) What is translocation?
13) Which type of plant transport vessel is made up of dead cells?
14) How do stomata open and close?
15) Give three factors that affect the rate of transpiration.
16) What can a potometer be used to measure?

Ecosystems and Interactions Between Organisms (p.37-41) ☐

17) Give two resources that plants compete for in ecosystems.
18) What is bioaccumulation?
19) Briefly describe how you could use quadrats to investigate the population size of a species.
20) Why might you need to use a key when investigating organisms?
21) What is an indicator species and why might you sample one?
22) How do food webs show interdependence?

Biological Molecules (p.42-43) ☑

23) Name a big molecule that's formed from simple sugars.
24) Which two molecules are produced when lipids are broken down?
25) How would you test for the presence of lipids in a sample?

Cycles in Ecosystems (p.44-45) ☐

26) Name two processes that put carbon back into the air in the carbon cycle.
27) What is the role of microorganisms in the carbon cycle?
28) Explain how evaporation, condensation and precipitation are involved in the water cycle.

Respiration

You need _energy_ to keep your body going. Energy comes from _food_, and it's _transferred_ by _respiration_.

Respiration is NOT "Breathing In and Out"

1) _Respiration_ is the process of _transferring energy_ from the _breakdown of glucose_ (a sugar).

2) _Plants_ make their own glucose for respiration through _photosynthesis_ (see p.27). _Animals_ (consumers) produce glucose by _breaking down_ the _biomass_ they get when they _eat_ other organisms (see p.42).

3) Organisms need the energy transferred by respiration to _survive_ — so respiration happens _continuously_ in _every cell_ in _all living organisms_.

4) The energy transferred by respiration _can't be used directly_ by cells — so it's used to make a substance called _ATP_. ATP _stores_ the energy, which is then used for essential processes, such as _breaking_ and _making molecules_, _active transport_ (see p.30) and _contracting muscles_ (in animals only).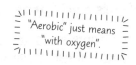

5) Cellular respiration actually involves _several different_ chemical _reactions_. These are all _controlled_ by _enzymes_, so the overall _rate_ of respiration is affected by both _temperature_ and _pH_ (see p.25). Cellular respiration is also _exothermic_ — it transfers _energy_ to the _environment_ (by _heat_).

6) Cells can respire using _glucose_ as a substrate, but organisms can also break down _other organic molecules_ (such as other _carbohydrates_, _proteins_ and _lipids_) to use as _substrates_ for respiration.

7) There are _two types_ of respiration, _aerobic_ and _anaerobic_.

Aerobic Respiration Needs Plenty of Oxygen

1) _Aerobic respiration_ is what happens when there's _plenty of oxygen_ available. It breaks down _glucose_ and combines the products with _oxygen_ to make _carbon dioxide_ (a waste product) and _water_.

2) Aerobic respiration is the most efficient way to transfer _energy_ from _glucose_. It produces _lots_ of _ATP_ — _32_ molecules per molecule of glucose.

3) Here is the overall _equation_ for aerobic respiration:

$$\text{glucose} + \text{oxygen} \longrightarrow \text{carbon dioxide} + \text{water}$$
$$C_6H_{12}O_6 + 6O_2 \longrightarrow 6CO_2 + 6H_2O$$

"Aerobic" just means "with oxygen".

4) In _eukaryotic_ (e.g. plant and animal) _cells_, aerobic respiration mostly takes place in subcellular structures called _mitochondria_ (see p.1). The mitochondria contain most of the _enzymes_ needed to control aerobic respiration reactions.

mitochondria

5) In _prokaryotic cells_ (microorganisms such as bacteria) all aerobic respiration reactions take place in the _cytoplasm_.

You Can Investigate the Effect of Different Substrates on Respiration Rate

You can investigate how the rate of respiration in _yeast_ is affected by _different substrates_, e.g. _glucose_ or _sucrose_. Here's one way to do it:

1) Put a _set volume_ and _concentration_ of _substrate solution_ in a _test tube_.

2) Put the test tube in a _water bath_ set to _25 °C_.

3) Add a _set mass_ of _yeast_ to the test tube and stir for _2 minutes_.

4) Attach the test tube to a _gas syringe_ (as shown in the diagram) and measure the _volume of CO_2 produced_ in a _set amount of time_ (e.g. 10 minutes).

5) If you _divide_ the _volume_ of CO_2 produced by the _time_ taken to produce it, you can _calculate_ the overall _rate of respiration_. You can then _repeat_ the experiment with a _different substrate_ and _compare_ the two rates.

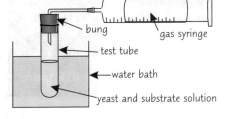

bung — gas syringe — test tube — water bath — yeast and substrate solution

---

Respiration transfers energy — but this page has worn me out...

Thank goodness for respiration — transferring the energy stored in my tea and biscuits to my brain cells. Great.

Q1   Give the word equation for aerobic respiration.   [2 marks]

48

More on Respiration

Now on to the second type of respiration — anaerobic respiration. As you're about to find out, different organisms have different ways of going about it. Makes life a tad more interesting I suppose...

Anaerobic Respiration Doesn't Use Oxygen At All

1) "Anaerobic" just means "without oxygen". It's not the best way to transfer energy from glucose because it transfers much less energy per glucose molecule than aerobic respiration — just 2 molecules of ATP are produced.

2) Anaerobic respiration takes place in the cytoplasm of animal and plant cells (and some microorganisms) when there's very little or no oxygen. For example:

> 1) Human cells — When you do really vigorous exercise your body can't supply enough oxygen to your muscle cells for aerobic respiration — they have to start respiring anaerobically as well.
>
> 2) Plant root cells — If the soil a plant's growing in becomes waterlogged there'll be no oxygen available for the roots, so the root cells will have to respire anaerobically.
>
> 3) Bacterial cells — Bacteria can get under your skin through puncture wounds caused by things like nails. There's very little oxygen under your skin, so only bacteria that can respire anaerobically can survive there.

3) The process of anaerobic respiration is slightly different in different organisms:

Animals and Some Bacteria Produce Lactic Acid

In animals and some bacteria, glucose is only partially broken down during anaerobic respiration and lactic acid is formed as a waste product. Here's the word equation:

glucose ⟶ lactic acid

Plants and Some Microorganisms Produce Ethanol and Carbon Dioxide

When plants and some microorganisms (including yeast) respire anaerobically, they produce ethanol and carbon dioxide instead of lactic acid. This is the word equation:

glucose ⟶ ethanol + carbon dioxide

Anaerobic respiration in yeast is known as fermentation.

You Need to Compare Aerobic and Anaerobic Respiration

This handy table shows the differences and similarities between aerobic and anaerobic respiration.

	Aerobic	Anaerobic
Conditions	Oxygen present	Not enough oxygen present, e.g. during vigorous exercise, in waterlogged soils
Inputs	Glucose (or another organic molecule) and oxygen	Glucose (or another organic molecule)
Outputs	Carbon dioxide and water	In animals and some bacteria — lactic acid. In plants and some microorganisms (e.g. yeast) — ethanol and carbon dioxide
ATP yield	High — 32 ATP made per molecule of glucose	Much lower — 2 ATP made per molecule of glucose

My friend Anna O'Bic is rather odd — I only see her at the gym...

Make sure you know those word equations and can compare the processes of aerobic and anaerobic respiration.

Q1 Name the product(s) of anaerobic respiration in plants. [1 mark]

Q2 Why is it advantageous for organisms to respire aerobically rather than anaerobically? [1 mark]

Chapter B4 — Using Food and Controlling Growth

The Cell Cycle and Mitosis

In order to survive and grow, our cells have got to be able to <u>divide</u>. And that means our DNA as well.

The Cell Cycle Makes New Cells for Growth and Repair

1) <u>Body cells</u> in <u>multicellular</u> organisms <u>divide</u> to produce <u>new cells</u> as part of a series of stages called the <u>cell cycle</u>. The stage of the cell cycle when the cell divides is called <u>mitosis</u>.

2) Multicellular organisms use <u>mitosis</u> to <u>grow</u> (which involves increasing the number of body cells) or to <u>replace cells</u> that have been <u>damaged</u>.

3) The end of the cell cycle results in two new cells <u>identical</u> to the <u>original</u> cell, with the <u>same number</u> of chromosomes.

4) You need to know about these two main stages of the <u>cell cycle</u>:

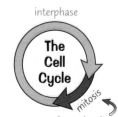

interphase

The Cell Cycle

mitosis

As you can see from the diagram, a cell spends most of its time in interphase — mitosis is a relatively small chunk of the cell cycle.

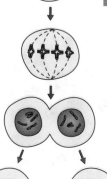

Interphase

1) In a cell that's not dividing, the DNA is all spread out in <u>long strings</u>.
2) Before it divides, the cell has to <u>grow</u> and <u>increase</u> the amount of <u>subcellular structures</u> such as <u>mitochondria</u> and <u>ribosomes</u>.
3) It then <u>duplicates</u> its DNA — so there's one copy for each new cell. The DNA is copied and forms <u>X-shaped</u> chromosomes. Each 'arm' of the chromosome is an <u>exact copy</u> of the other.

The left arm has the same DNA as the right arm of the chromosome.

Mitosis

Once its contents and DNA have been copied, the cell is ready for <u>mitosis</u>...

4) The chromosomes <u>line up</u> at the centre of the cell and <u>cell fibres</u> pull them apart. The <u>two arms</u> of each chromosome go to <u>opposite ends</u> of the cell.
5) <u>Membranes</u> form around each of the sets of chromosomes. These become the <u>nuclei</u> of the two new cells — the <u>nucleus</u> has <u>divided</u>.
6) Lastly, the <u>cytoplasm</u> and <u>cell membrane</u> divide.

The cell has now produced <u>two new daughter cells</u>. The daughter cells contain exactly the <u>same chromosomes</u> (DNA) — they're <u>genetically identical</u>. They're also <u>genetically identical</u> to the <u>parent cell</u>.

5) You can <u>estimate</u> the <u>number of cells</u> there'll be after <u>multiple divisions</u> of a cell by mitosis. The formula you need is: <u>number of cells = 2^n</u>, where '<u>n</u>' is the <u>number of divisions</u> by mitosis.

E.g. a scientist sees that a cell divides by mitosis <u>once every 30 minutes</u>. After <u>4 hours</u> (approx. <u>8 divisions</u>) he estimates that there'll be $\underline{2^8} = 2 \times 2 \times 2 \times 2 \times 2 \times 2 \times 2 \times 2 = \underline{256\ cells}$.

6) This is only an <u>estimate</u> though. In the example above, you can't be sure that the cells will <u>keep dividing</u> at the <u>same rate</u> for four hours (so you can't be sure that there were 8 divisions). That's because the <u>rate of cell division</u> depends on the <u>environmental conditions</u>, e.g. a <u>lack</u> of <u>food</u> could cause the rate to <u>decrease</u>. Also, some of the cells might <u>die</u>, affecting the total number left at the end.

Cancer is a Case of Uncontrolled Cell Division

A random change in a gene is called a mutation.

1) The <u>rate</u> at which <u>cells divide</u> by <u>mitosis</u> is controlled by the cells' <u>genes</u>.
2) If there's a <u>change</u> in one of the genes that controls cell division, a cell may start dividing <u>uncontrollably</u>. This can result in a <u>mass of abnormal cells</u> called a <u>tumour</u>.
3) If the tumour <u>invades and destroys</u> surrounding tissue it is called <u>cancer</u>. Cancer is a <u>non-communicable disease</u> (see page 17).

A cell's favourite computer game — divide and conquer...

Mitosis can seem tricky at first. But don't worry — just go through it slowly, one step at a time.

Q1 Describe what happens during the interphase stage of the cell cycle. [3 marks]

Microscopy

Biologists <u>love microscopes</u>, which is why they're making a <u>second appearance</u> in this book...

Cells are Studied Using Microscopes

1) You might remember from page 2 that microscopes use lenses to <u>magnify</u> images (make them look bigger). They also <u>increase</u> the <u>resolution</u> of an image (the detail in which it can be seen).

2) Microscope technology has <u>developed</u> over time, allowing <u>new observations</u> to be made.

3) <u>Light microscopes</u> were invented in the 1590s. They work by passing <u>light</u> through the specimen. They let us see things like <u>nuclei</u> and <u>chloroplasts</u> and we can also use them to study <u>living cells</u>.

4) <u>Electron microscopes</u> were invented in the 1930s. They use <u>electrons</u> rather than <u>light</u>. Electron microscopes have a higher <u>magnification</u> and <u>resolution</u> than light microscopes, so they let us see much <u>smaller things</u> in <u>more detail</u> like the <u>internal structure</u> of mitochondria and chloroplasts.

5) This has given us a much <u>greater understanding</u> of <u>how cells work</u>. E.g. it's allowed scientists to develop explanations about how the internal structures of mitochondria and chloroplasts relate to their <u>functions</u> in <u>respiration</u> and <u>photosynthesis</u>. However, electron microscopes can't be used to view living cells.

You can Observe Stages of Mitosis Using a Light Microscope

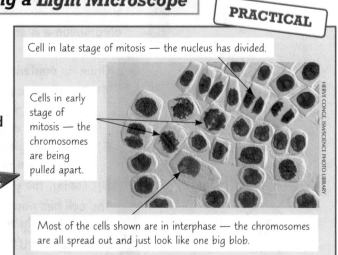

PRACTICAL

1) You might remember how to use a <u>light microscope</u> to <u>observe cells</u> from <u>Chapter B1</u> — if not, have a flick back to page 2.

2) <u>Chromosomes</u> can be <u>stained</u> so you can see them under a microscope. This means you can watch what happens to them <u>during mitosis</u> — and it makes high-adrenaline viewing, I can tell you.

3) These are some <u>cells</u> from a <u>plant root tip</u> shown under a light microscope at different stages of the <u>cell cycle</u> and <u>mitosis</u>.

4) The cells are being viewed on a '<u>squash</u>' <u>microscope slide</u>. In other words, they've been deliberately squashed beneath the cover slip.

5) This makes it easier to see the chromosomes.

6) Cells are taken from the root <u>tip</u> as that's where <u>most cell division happens</u> in the root.

Cell in late stage of mitosis — the nucleus has divided.

Cells in early stage of mitosis — the chromosomes are being pulled apart.

Most of the cells shown are in interphase — the chromosomes are all spread out and just look like one big blob.

HERVÉ CONGE, ISM/SCIENCE PHOTO LIBRARY

You Can Estimate the Size of Cells Under a Microscope

There are some clever <u>calculations</u> you can do to work out the <u>exact size</u> of cells under the microscope — in fact, you can find out how to do them on the next page. But sometimes, to make life easier, you might just want to <u>estimate</u> the <u>relative sizes</u> of two cells.

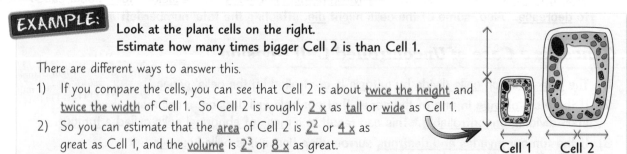

EXAMPLE:

Look at the plant cells on the right.
Estimate how many times bigger Cell 2 is than Cell 1.

There are different ways to answer this.

1) If you compare the cells, you can see that Cell 2 is about <u>twice the height</u> and <u>twice the width</u> of Cell 1. So Cell 2 is roughly $2 \times$ as <u>tall</u> or <u>wide</u> as Cell 1.

2) So you can estimate that the <u>area</u> of Cell 2 is 2^2 or $4 \times$ as great as Cell 1, and the <u>volume</u> is 2^3 or $8 \times$ as great.

Cell 1   Cell 2

I take my microscope everywhere — good job it's a light one...

We're not done with microscopy yet I'm afraid. Do this question, then move on to the next page.

Q1   Explain how electron microscopes have given us a greater understanding of how cells work. [2 marks]

More Microscopy

Sometimes you need to do a bit of <u>maths</u> with microscope images. It's time to get your <u>numbers head on</u>...

What are you looking at?

Magnification is *How Many Times Bigger* the Image is

1) If you know the <u>power</u> of the lenses used by a microscope to view an image, you can work out the <u>total magnification</u> of the image using this simple formula:

> total magnification = eyepiece lens magnification × objective lens magnification

2) For example, the <u>total magnification</u> of an image viewed with an <u>eyepiece lens</u> magnification of <u>× 10</u> and an <u>objective lens</u> magnification of <u>× 40</u> would be 10 × 40 = <u>× 400</u>.

3) If you don't know which lenses were used, you can still work out the magnification of an image as long as you can <u>measure the image</u> and know the <u>actual size of the specimen</u>. This is the <u>formula</u> you need:

$$\text{magnification} = \frac{\text{measured size}}{\text{actual size}}$$

Both measurements should have the same units. If they don't, you'll need to convert them first (see below).

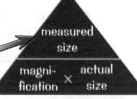

measured size / magnification × actual size

4) If you're working out the <u>measured size</u> or the <u>actual size</u> of the object, you can rearrange the equation using the <u>formula triangle</u>. <u>Cover up</u> the thing you're trying to find. The parts you can <u>still see</u> are the formula you need to use.

You Might Need to Work With Numbers in *Standard Form* and *Convert Units*

1) Because microscopes can see such <u>tiny objects</u>, sometimes it's useful to write figures in <u>standard form</u>.

2) This is where you write a number in the form $A \times 10^n$ — where '<u>A</u>' is a number <u>between 1 and 10</u>, and '<u>n</u>' is the <u>number of places</u> the <u>decimal point</u> moves. 'n' is <u>positive</u> for numbers <u>greater than 1</u> and <u>negative</u> for numbers <u>less than 1</u>. E.g. 0.017 is written 1.7×10^{-2} in standard form.

3) Standard form is useful for writing <u>very big</u> or <u>very small numbers</u> in a more <u>manageable way</u>.

4) You can also use <u>different units</u> to express very big or very small numbers. E.g. <u>0.0007 m</u> could be written as <u>0.7 mm</u>. The <u>table</u> below shows you how to <u>convert between different units</u>. The right hand column of the table shows you how each unit can be expressed as a <u>metre</u> in <u>standard form</u> — the more negative the power of 10, the smaller the value. So, for example, 1 mm = 0.001 m and 1 pm = 0.000000000001 m. (That's tiny!)

5) Here's an example of a <u>calculation</u> in standard form:

	Unit		In standard form:
To convert		To convert	
×1000	Millimetre (mm)	÷1000	$\times 10^{-3}$ m
×1000	Micrometre (μm)	÷1000	$\times 10^{-6}$ m
×1000	Nanometre (nm)	÷1000	$\times 10^{-9}$ m
	Picometre (pm)		$\times 10^{-12}$ m

EXAMPLE: A specimen is 5×10^{-6} m wide. Calculate the width of the image of the specimen under a magnification of × 100. Give your answer in standard form.

1) <u>Rearrange</u> the magnification formula — the width of the image is the <u>measured size</u>, so cover up measured size on the <u>formula triangle</u>.

2) Fill in the <u>values</u> you know.

3) Write out the values <u>in full</u> (i.e. don't use standard form).

4) Carry out the calculation and then <u>convert back</u> into standard form.

measured size = magnification × actual size
measured size = 100 × (5×10^{-6} m)
= 100 × 0.000005 m
= 0.0005 m
= 5×10^{-4} m

Note: 0.0005 m could also be written as 0.5 mm or 500 μm.

Mi-cros-copy — when my twin gets annoyed...

If you've got a scientific calculator, you can put standard form numbers into your calculator using the 'EXP' or '×10^x' button. For example, enter 2.67×10^{15} by pressing 2.67 then 'EXP' or '10^x', then 15. Easy.

Q1 Calculate the actual length of a cell which has a measured size of 7×10^{-1} mm under a magnification of × 400. Write your answer in μm.

[3 marks]

Sexual Reproduction and Meiosis

Ever wondered why you look <u>like</u> your <u>family members</u>, but <u>not exactly the same</u>? Well today's your lucky day.

Sexual Reproduction Produces Genetically Different Cells

1) <u>Sexual reproduction</u> is where genetic information from <u>two</u> organisms (a <u>father</u> and a <u>mother</u>) is combined to produce offspring which are <u>genetically different</u> to either parent.

2) In <u>sexual reproduction</u>, the father and mother produce <u>gametes</u> — in animals these are <u>sperm</u> and <u>egg cells</u>.

3) Gametes only contain <u>half the number</u> of <u>chromosomes</u> of normal cells (see page 4).

4) At <u>fertilisation</u>, a male gamete <u>fuses</u> with a female gamete to produce a <u>fertilised egg</u>, known as a <u>zygote</u>. Chromosomes from the mother <u>pair up</u> with chromosomes from the father, so the zygote ends up with the <u>full set</u> of chromosomes.

5) The zygote then undergoes <u>cell division</u> (by mitosis — see p.49) and develops into an <u>embryo</u>.

6) The embryo <u>inherits characteristics</u> from <u>both parents</u> as it's received a <u>mixture of chromosomes</u> (and therefore <u>genes</u>) from its mum and its dad.

A human body cell nucleus contains 46 chromosomes — a human gamete has 23 chromosomes.

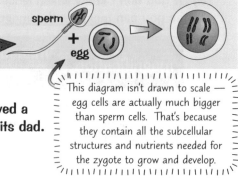

| Gametes | Zygote |

sperm

+

egg

This diagram isn't drawn to scale — egg cells are actually much bigger than sperm cells. That's because they contain all the subcellular structures and nutrients needed for the zygote to grow and develop.

Gametes are Produced by Meiosis

Meiosis is a type of <u>cell division</u>. It produces <u>genetically different</u> cells with <u>half the chromosomes</u> of the original cell. In humans, meiosis <u>only</u> happens in the <u>reproductive organs</u> (ovaries and testes).

Division 1

1) Before meiosis can begin, the cell goes through <u>interphase</u>. During this period it <u>duplicates</u> its <u>DNA</u> (so there's enough for each new cell). One arm of each X-shaped chromosome is an <u>exact copy</u> of the other arm.

2) In the <u>first division</u> in meiosis (there are two divisions) the chromosomes <u>line up</u> in pairs in the centre of the cell. One chromosome in each pair came from the organism's mother and one came from its father.

3) The <u>pairs</u> are then <u>pulled apart</u>, so each new cell ends up with <u>one chromosome</u> from each pair. <u>Some</u> of the father's chromosomes and <u>some</u> of the mother's chromosomes go into each new cell.

4) This means the <u>chromosome number</u> of <u>each new cell</u> will be <u>half</u> that of the original cell. Each new cell will also have a <u>mixture</u> of the mother's and father's chromosomes. Mixing up the genes like this is <u>really important</u> — it creates <u>genetic variation</u> in the offspring (i.e. each offspring will have a different mixture of alleles.

Division 2

5) In the <u>second division</u> the chromosomes <u>line up</u> again in the centre of the cell. It's a lot like mitosis. The <u>arms</u> of the chromosomes are <u>pulled apart</u>.

6) You get <u>four gametes</u> — each only has a <u>single set</u> of chromosomes. The gametes are all <u>genetically different</u>.

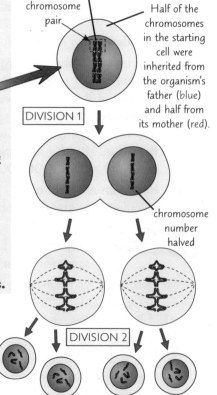

This cell has duplicated each chromosome — each arm of the X-shape is identical.

chromosome pair

Half of the chromosomes in the starting cell were inherited from the organism's father (blue) and half from its mother (red).

DIVISION 1

chromosome number halved

DIVISION 2

Identical twins are genetically identical because they come from a single zygote that splits in two, then develops into two separate embryos.

Now that I have your undivided attention...

Remember — in humans, meiosis only occurs in the reproductive organs, when gametes are made.

Q1   Explain why gametes need to have half the number of chromosomes of a normal body cell.   [2 marks]

Stem Cells

Your body is made up of all sorts of weird and wonderful cells. This page tells you where they all came from...

Stem Cells can Differentiate into Different Types of Cells

1) To start with, the cells in an embryo are all the same. They're called embryonic stem cells.

2) Embryonic stem cells are unspecialised. This means they're able to divide to produce any type of specialised cell (e.g. blood cells, nerve cells). In humans, all the cells in the embryo are unspecialised up to the eight cell stage.

3) The process of stem cells becoming specialised is called differentiation. After the eight cell stage, most of the stem cells in a human embryo start to differentiate. This allows the embryo to grow and develop tissues — these are groups of specialised cells working together with a particular function.

4) Adult humans only have stem cells in certain places like the bone marrow. Adult stem cells can become specialised, but they can only differentiate into certain types of cell. They are important in replacing dead cells, e.g. in making new red blood cells.

5) All body cells contain the same genes, but in specialised cells most of the genes are not active — so the cells only produce the specific proteins they need. Stem cells can switch any gene on or off during their development — the genes that are active (on) produce the proteins that determine the type of specialised cell a stem cell will become.

Meristems Contain Plant Stem Cells

1) In plants, the only cells that divide by mitosis (see p.49) are found in plant tissues called meristems.

2) Meristem tissue is found in the areas of a plant that are growing, e.g. the tips of the roots and shoots.

3) Meristems produce unspecialised cells that are able to divide and form any cell type in the plant — they act like embryonic stem cells. But unlike human stem cells, these cells can differentiate to generate any type of cell for as long as the plant lives.

4) The unspecialised cells go on to form specialised tissues like xylem and phloem (see p.33).

A merry stem.

Stem Cells Can be Used in Medicine

1) Scientists have experimented with extracting stem cells from very early human embryos and growing them. Under certain conditions the stem cells can be stimulated to differentiate into specialised cells.

2) It might be possible to use stem cells to create specialised cells to replace those which have been damaged by disease or injury, e.g. new cardiac muscle cells could be transplanted into someone with heart disease. This potential for new cures is the reason for the huge scientific interest in stem cells.

3) Before this can happen, a lot of research needs to be done. There are many potential risks which scientists need to learn more about. For example:

- Tumour development — stem cells divide very quickly. If scientists are unable to control the rate at which the transplanted cells divide inside a patient, a tumour may develop (see page 49).
- Disease transmission — viruses live inside cells. If donor stem cells are infected with a virus and this isn't picked up, the virus could be passed on to the recipient and so make them sicker.

4) The use of embryonic stem cells in this way also raises ethical issues. For example, some people argue that human embryos shouldn't be used to provide stem cells because the embryo gets destroyed and each one is a potential human life. But others think that the aim of curing patients who are suffering should be more important than the potential life of the embryos.

5) It's such a tricky issue that the use of human embryonic stem cells in scientific research and medicine is regulated by the government in most countries, including the UK.

Cheery cells, those merry-stems...

Turns out stem cells are pretty nifty. Now, let's see if you're specialised to answer this question...

Q1   If the tip is cut off a plant shoot, the tip can be used to grow a whole new plant. Suggest why.   [3 marks]

Revision Questions for Chapter B4

Hurrah. It's the <u>end</u> of <u>Chapter B4</u>. Better get this one last page over with.

- Try these questions and <u>tick off each one</u> when you <u>get it right</u>.
- When you've done <u>all the questions</u> for a topic and are <u>completely happy</u> with it, tick off the topic.

<u>Respiration (p.47-48)</u> ☐

1) What is respiration? ☑
2) Is respiration an exothermic or an endothermic reaction? ☑
3) Name the type of respiration that requires oxygen. ☑
4) Briefly describe an experiment to investigate the effect of different
   substrates on the rate of respiration in yeast. ☑
5) Describe a situation when:
   a) a plant root would have to respire anaerobically.
   b) a bacterium would have to respire anaerobically. ☑
6) Give an example of when lactic acid would be produced as a product of respiration. ☑
7) Which form of respiration has a greater ATP yield per glucose molecule? ☑

<u>The Cell Cycle, Mitosis and Microscopy (p.49-51)</u> ☑

8) What is the cell cycle? ☑
9) What is mitosis used for by multicellular organisms? ☑
10) What major illness can result from uncontrolled cell division? ☑
11) Give an advantage of electron microscopes over light microscopes. ☑
12) Why is it necessary to squash a plant root tip if you want to view the cells
    dividing by mitosis under a light microscope? ☑
13) Write the formula you would use to find the actual size of a specimen using
    the magnification used and the measured size of the image seen through a microscope lens. ☑
14) Describe how you would convert a measurement from mm to μm. ☑
15) Which unit can be expressed in standard form as $\times 10^{-12}$ m? ☑

<u>Sexual Reproduction, Meiosis and Stem Cells (p.52-53)</u> ☑

16) Name the gametes in humans. ☑
17) Describe how gametes are formed by meiosis. ☑
18) What is a stem cell? ☑
19) How are embryonic stem cells different to adult stem cells? ☑
20) Which parts of a plant contain stem cells? ☑
21) What are the potential benefits of stem cells being used in medicine? ☑

Exchange of Materials

As you might remember from Chapter B3, all organisms need to exchange things with their environment...

Humans Exchange Substances with their Environment

Like all organisms, humans and other animals must take in the substances they need from the environment and get rid of any waste products. For example:

There's more on diffusion and osmosis on p.30.

- Cells need oxygen for aerobic respiration (see p.47), which produces carbon dioxide as a waste product. These two gases move between cells and the environment by diffusion.

- Water is needed for many chemical reactions. It's taken up by cells by osmosis. Dissolved food molecules (the products of digestion, e.g. glucose and amino acids) diffuse along with it. These are then used in synthesis reactions (see p.42).

CO_2 and urea need to be removed before they reach toxic levels.

- Urea (a waste product from the breakdown of proteins in the liver) diffuses from cells into the blood plasma. It is then filtered out of the blood by the kidneys and excreted as urine.

You Can Compare Surface Area to Volume Ratios

How easy it is for an organism to exchange substances with its environment depends on the organism's surface area to volume ratio (SA : V). A ratio shows how big one value is compared to another. The larger an organism is, the smaller its surface area is compared to its volume:

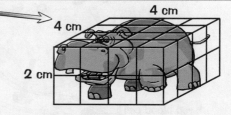

A hippo can be represented by a 2 cm × 4 cm × 4 cm block.

The area of a surface is found by the equation: LENGTH × WIDTH
So the hippo's total surface area is:

$\quad$ (4 × 4) × 2 (top and bottom surfaces of block)
$\quad$ + (4 × 2) × 4 (four sides of the block)
$\quad$ = 64 cm².

The volume of a block is found by the equation: LENGTH × WIDTH × HEIGHT
So the hippo's volume is 4 × 4 × 2 = 32 cm³.

The surface area to volume ratio of the hippo can be written as 64 : 32.
To get the ratio in the form n : 1, divide both sides of the ratio by the volume.
So the surface area to volume ratio of the hippo is 2 : 1.

A mouse can be represented by a 1 cm × 1 cm × 1 cm block.

Its surface area is (1 × 1) × 6 = 6 cm².
Its volume is 1 × 1 × 1 = 1 cm³.
So the surface area to volume ratio of the mouse is 6 : 1.

The cube mouse's surface area is six times its volume, but the cube hippo's surface area is only twice its volume. So the mouse has a larger surface area compared to its volume.

Multicellular Organisms Need Exchange Surfaces

1) Multicellular organisms have relatively small surface area to volume ratios, which makes diffusion to and from cells deep within their bodies slow. This makes it difficult to exchange enough substances to supply their entire volume across their outside surface alone.

2) To get around this, multicellular organisms usually have specialised exchange surfaces to increase their SA : V and therefore the rate at which substances are able to diffuse (see next page for more). Organisms also tend to have a mass transport system (e.g. a circulatory system) to move substances around the body — this shortens the distance these substances have to diffuse to and from cells.

Some small multicellular organisms, e.g. earthworms, have a big enough SA : V that they don't need specialised exchange surfaces.

3) All of the movement into, out of and around the human body is dependent on the gaseous exchange, circulatory, digestive and excretory systems all working together.

Not that I'm endorsing putting animals in boxes...

Have a go at this question to make sure you understand how to calculate surface area to volume ratios.

Q1   A bacterial cell can be represented by a 1 μm × 1 μm × 4 μm block. Calculate the cell's surface area to volume ratio. Give your ratio in its simplest whole number form.   [3 marks]

Human Exchange Surfaces

This page is about how exchange surfaces in humans are <u>adapted</u> so that substances can move through them by <u>diffusion</u>, <u>osmosis</u> and <u>active transport</u>. If you need to look over these processes, flick back to page 30.

O_2 and CO_2 Diffuse Between Alveoli and Capillaries

Remember, human cells are animal cells.

1) The job of the <u>lungs</u> is to transfer <u>oxygen</u> to the <u>blood</u> and to remove <u>waste carbon dioxide</u> from it.

2) To do this, the lungs contain millions of little air sacs called <u>alveoli</u> where <u>gas exchange</u> takes place.

3) The alveoli are surrounded by a network of tiny blood vessels called <u>capillaries</u>.

4) <u>Oxygen</u> (O_2) diffuses from the <u>air</u> in the <u>alveoli</u> into the <u>blood</u> in the <u>capillaries</u>. Carbon dioxide (CO_2) diffuses in the <u>opposite direction</u>.

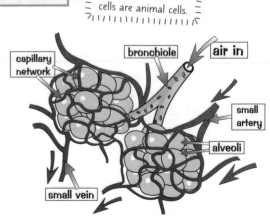

Blue = blood with carbon dioxide.
Red = blood with oxygen.

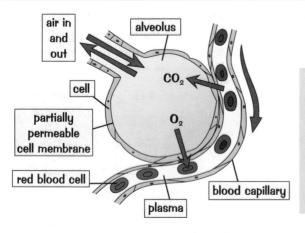

5) The alveoli are specialised to maximise the <u>rate of diffusion</u> of O_2 and CO_2. They have:

- An <u>enormous surface area</u> (about 75 m^2 in humans).
- A <u>moist lining</u> for dissolving gases.
- Very <u>thin walls</u> (consisting of cells with <u>partially permeable</u> cell membranes).
- A <u>good blood supply</u>.

Dissolved Food and Water are Absorbed in the Digestive System

1) <u>Digested food</u> is absorbed in the <u>small intestine</u>. The inside of the small intestine is covered in millions and millions of tiny little projections called <u>villi</u>.

2) Villi <u>increase</u> the <u>surface area</u> in a big way so that digested food is quickly <u>absorbed</u> into the <u>blood</u> by <u>active transport</u> and <u>diffusion</u>. For example:

- When there's a <u>higher concentration</u> of <u>glucose</u> in the intestine, it <u>diffuses</u> naturally <u>into the blood</u>.
- When there's a <u>lower concentration</u> of glucose in the intestine, it is <u>actively transported</u> into the blood. This allows glucose to be taken into the blood, despite the fact that the concentration gradient is the wrong way.

3) Villi have a <u>single</u> layer of surface cells to assist quick absorption. Like all cells, they have <u>partially permeable cell membranes</u>, which regulate the movement of substances across them. Villi also have a very good <u>blood supply</u> to assist <u>quick absorption</u>.

4) <u>Water</u> is <u>absorbed</u> into the blood from the <u>large intestine</u> by <u>osmosis</u>.

Al Veoli — the Italian gas man...

Here's a little fact that needs wedging firmly into your brain — a big surface area means a faster rate of diffusion.

Q1   Give one way in which alveoli are adapted for gas exchange.   [1 mark]

The Circulatory System

As you saw on page 55, multicellular organisms need transport systems to move substances around effectively. In humans, it's the job of the circulatory system. My heart's all of a flutter just thinking about it...

The DOUBLE Circulatory System, Actually

The circulatory system is made up of the heart, blood vessels and blood. Humans and other mammals have a double circulatory system — two circuits joined together:

1) In the first one, the heart pumps deoxygenated blood to the alveoli in the lungs to take in oxygen. The oxygenated blood then returns to the heart.

2) In the second one, the heart pumps oxygenated blood around all the other organs of the body (see right). Here, the blood gives up its oxygen at the body cells. The deoxygenated blood then returns to the heart to be pumped out to the lungs again.

3) As it is pumped around the body, the blood also travels through blood vessels near exchange surfaces — including the villi (where it picks up food molecules and water) and the kidneys (where it is filtered and urea is removed).

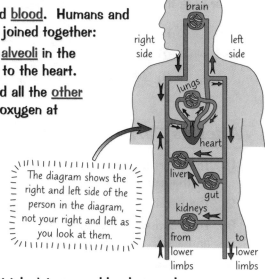

The diagram shows the right and left side of the person in the diagram, not your right and left as you look at them.

The Heart Pumps Blood Around The Body

1) The heart uses its four chambers (right and left atria and ventricles) to pump blood around.

2) The heart has valves to make sure that blood flows in the right direction. When the ventricles contract, the valves to the atria close and the valves to the blood vessels open. This prevents backflow (when the blood flows backwards).

Atria is plural. Atrium is when there is just one.

1) Blood flows into the two atria from the vena cava and the pulmonary vein.

2) The atria contract, pushing the blood into the ventricles.

3) The ventricles contract, forcing the blood into the pulmonary artery and the aorta, and out of the heart.

4) The blood then flows to the organs, including the lungs, through arteries, and returns through veins (see next page).

5) The atria fill again and the whole cycle starts over.

blue = deoxygenated blood
red = oxygenated blood

Internal structure of the heart

- The left ventricle has a much thicker wall than the right ventricle. It needs the greater pressure generated by the thicker muscle because it has to pump blood around the whole body, whereas the right ventricle only has to pump it to the lungs.

- The heart is made up of cardiac muscle. Cardiac muscle cells contain loads of mitochondria to provide them with ATP. This releases the energy needed for the muscle to contract.

- Blood is supplied to the cardiac muscle by two coronary arteries, which branch from the base of the aorta. They allow the oxygen and glucose needed for the heart cells to respire to diffuse through the thick walls of the heart.

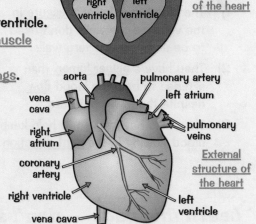

External structure of the heart

Okay — let's get to the heart of the matter...

Make sure you learn the names of the different parts of the heart and all the blood vessels that are attached to it.

Q1   Which chamber of the heart pumps deoxygenated blood to the lungs?   [1 mark]

Blood Vessels

If you want to know more about the circulatory system you're in luck. Because here's a whole extra page.

Blood Vessels are Designed for Their Function

There are three main types of blood vessel:

1) ARTERIES — these carry the blood away from the heart.
2) CAPILLARIES — these are involved in the exchange of materials at the tissues.
3) VEINS — these carry the blood to the heart.

Arteries Carry Blood Under Pressure

1) The heart pumps the blood out at high pressure so the artery walls are strong and elastic.
2) The walls are thick compared to the size of the lumen.
3) They contain thick layers of muscle to make them strong, and elastic fibres to allow them to stretch and spring back.

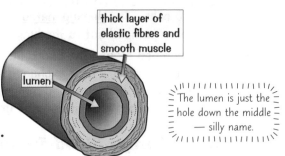

thick layer of elastic fibres and smooth muscle

lumen

The lumen is just the hole down the middle — silly name.

Capillaries are Really Small

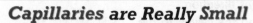

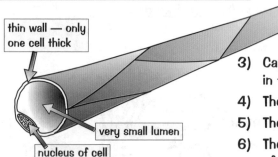

thin wall — only one cell thick

very small lumen

nucleus of cell

1) Capillaries are really tiny — too small to see.
2) Networks of capillaries in tissue are called capillary beds.
3) Capillaries carry the blood really close to every cell in the body to exchange substances with them.
4) They have permeable walls, so substances can diffuse in and out.
5) They supply food and oxygen, and take away waste like CO_2.
6) Their walls are usually only one cell thick. This increases the rate of diffusion by decreasing the distance over which it occurs.

Veins Take Blood Back to the Heart

1) The blood is at lower pressure in the veins so the walls don't need to be as thick as artery walls.
2) They have a bigger lumen than arteries to help the blood flow despite the lower pressure.
3) They also have valves to help keep the blood flowing in the right direction.

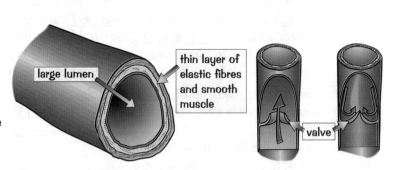

large lumen

thin layer of elastic fibres and smooth muscle

valve

Learn this page — don't struggle in vein...

Here's an interesting fact for you — your body contains about 60 000 miles of blood vessels. That's about six times the distance from London to Sydney in Australia. Of course, capillaries are really tiny, which is how such a massive amount of them can fit in your body — they can only be seen with a microscope.

Q1 Describe how veins are adapted to carry blood back to the heart. [2 marks]

Q2 Explain how capillaries are adapted to their function. [3 marks]

Blood

Now that we've looked at blood vessels, it's time to look at the wonders of <u>blood</u> itself.
(Hmmm — is it me, or is this starting to sound a tiny bit like a lecture for <u>vampires</u>...)

Blood Acts as a Transport System

1) Blood is a <u>tissue</u>, consisting of many similar cells working together.
2) These cells are <u>red blood cells</u>, <u>white blood cells</u> and <u>platelets</u>, and they're suspended in a liquid called <u>plasma</u>.
3) This page is all about <u>plasma</u> and <u>red blood cells</u> — the bits of the blood responsible for <u>transporting substances</u> around the body.

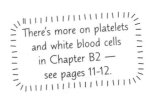
There's more on platelets and white blood cells in Chapter B2 — see pages 11-12.

Plasma is the Liquid Bit of Blood

It's basically blood minus the blood cells. Plasma is a pale yellow liquid which <u>carries just about everything</u> that needs transporting around your body:

1) <u>Red blood cells</u> (see below), <u>white blood cells</u>, and <u>platelets</u>.
2) <u>Water</u>.
3) Digested <u>food products</u> like <u>glucose</u> and <u>amino acids</u> from the small intestine to all the body cells.
4) <u>Carbon dioxide</u> from the body cells to the lungs.
5) <u>Urea</u> from the liver to the kidneys (where it's removed in the urine).
6) <u>Hormones</u> — these act like chemical messengers (see p.62).
7) <u>Antibodies</u> — these are proteins involved in the body's immune response (see p.12).

Red Blood Cells Have the Job of Carrying Oxygen

Red blood cells transport <u>oxygen</u> from the <u>lungs</u> to <u>all</u> the cells in the body.
The <u>structure</u> of a red blood cell is adapted to its <u>function</u>:

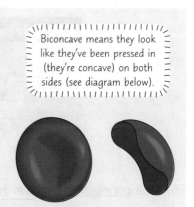
Biconcave means they look like they've been pressed in (they're concave) on both sides (see diagram below).

1) Red blood cells are <u>small</u> and have a <u>biconcave disc shape</u> to give a <u>large surface area to volume ratio</u>. This <u>increases</u> the <u>rate</u> at which <u>oxygen</u> can <u>diffuse</u> into and out of the cell.
2) They are packed with <u>haemoglobin</u>, which is what gives the cells a red <u>colour</u> — it contains a lot of <u>iron</u>. In the lungs, haemoglobin <u>combines with oxygen</u> to become <u>oxyhaemoglobin</u>. In body tissues, the reverse happens to <u>release oxygen to the cells</u>.
3) Red blood cells <u>don't</u> have a <u>nucleus</u> — this frees up <u>space</u> for more haemoglobin, so they can carry more oxygen.
4) As they are <u>small</u> and very <u>flexible</u> they can easily pass through the <u>tiny capillaries</u> close to the body cells.

A <u>low number</u> of red blood cells can make you feel <u>tired</u>. This is because <u>less oxygen</u> can be transported around the body, and so there is <u>less aerobic respiration</u> taking place to produce <u>ATP</u> (see p.47).

Blood's other function is to let you know you're bleeding...

Every single drop contains millions of red blood cells — all of them perfectly designed for carrying plenty of oxygen to where it's needed. Which right now is your brain, so you can get cracking with learning this page.

Q1 Name the substance that combines with oxygen and gives red blood cells their colour. [1 mark]

Q2 Describe three ways in which red blood cells are adapted to carry oxygen. [3 marks]

The Nervous System

In order to <u>survive</u>, organisms need to <u>detect changes</u> in their external and internal environments and <u>respond</u> to them. The <u>nervous system</u> lets you <u>react</u> to what goes on around you, so you'd find life tough without it.

The Central Nervous System Coordinates a Response

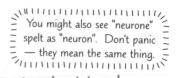

You might also see "neurone" spelt as "neuron". Don't panic — they mean the same thing.

1) The nervous system is made up of <u>neurones</u> (nerve cells), which go to <u>all parts</u> of the body.

2) The body has lots of <u>sensory receptors</u>, which can detect a <u>change in your external or internal environment</u> (a <u>stimulus</u>). Different sensory receptors detect different stimuli. For example, receptors in your <u>eyes</u> detect <u>light</u>, and receptors in your <u>skin</u> detect <u>touch</u> (pressure) and <u>temperature change</u>.

3) When a <u>stimulus</u> is detected by <u>receptors</u>, the information is sent as <u>nervous (electrical) impulses</u> along <u>sensory neurones</u> to the <u>central nervous system</u> (<u>CNS</u>).

4) The CNS consists of the <u>brain</u> and <u>spinal cord</u>.

5) The CNS is a processing centre. It <u>coordinates</u> the response (in other words, it <u>decides what to do</u> about the stimulus and tells something to do it).

Light receptors

6) The CNS sends information to an <u>effector</u> (<u>muscle</u> or <u>gland</u>) along a <u>motor neurone</u>. The effector then <u>responds</u> accordingly — e.g. a <u>muscle</u> may <u>contract</u> or a <u>gland</u> may <u>secrete a hormone</u>.

7) Nervous communication is very <u>fast</u>, but the responses are <u>short-lived</u> (they don't last long).

Neurones Transmit Information Rapidly as Electrical Impulses

1) <u>Electrical impulses</u> are passed along the <u>axon</u> of a neurone.

2) Neurones have <u>branched endings</u> (<u>dendrites</u>) so they can <u>connect</u> with lots of other neurones.

3) Some axons are also surrounded by a <u>fatty (myelin) sheath</u>. This acts as an <u>electrical insulator</u>, <u>speeding up</u> the impulse.

4) Neurones are <u>long</u>, which also <u>speeds up</u> the impulse (<u>connecting</u> with <u>another neurone</u> slows the impulse down, so one long neurone is much <u>quicker</u> than lots of short ones joined together).

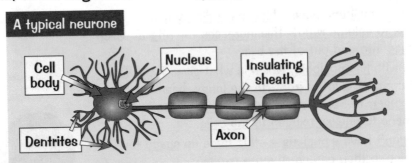

A typical neurone

Cell body

Nucleus

Insulating sheath

Dentrites

Axon

5) The <u>connection</u> between <u>two neurones</u> is a very tiny gap called a <u>synapse</u>:

- The electrical impulse triggers the release of <u>transmitter chemicals</u>, which <u>diffuse</u> across the gap.

- These chemicals bind to <u>receptor molecules</u> in the membrane of the <u>next neurone</u>. This <u>stimulates</u> the neurone, setting off a <u>new electrical impulse</u>.

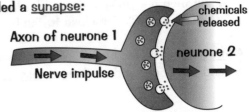

Axon of neurone 1

Nerve impulse

chemicals released

neurone 2

Don't let the thought of exams play on your nerves...

Make sure you understand how the different parts of the nervous system (including receptors and effectors) work together to coordinate a response. There's more of the same coming up on the next page...

Q1   Name the two main parts of the central nervous system.

[2 marks]

Reflexes

Information is passed between neurones really <u>quickly</u>, especially when there's a <u>reflex</u> involved.

Reflex Actions Stop You Injuring Yourself

1) <u>Reflex actions</u> are <u>involuntary</u> (done without thinking) so they're <u>even quicker</u> than normal responses. The passage of information in a reflex (from receptor to effector) is called a <u>reflex arc</u>.

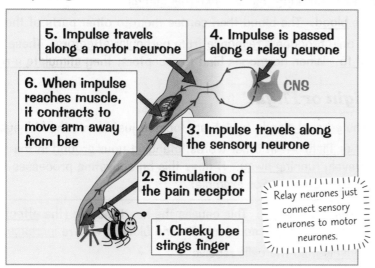

5. Impulse travels along a motor neurone

4. Impulse is passed along a relay neurone

6. When impulse reaches muscle, it contracts to move arm away from bee

CNS

3. Impulse travels along the sensory neurone

2. Stimulation of the pain receptor

1. Cheeky bee stings finger

Relay neurones just connect sensory neurones to motor neurones.

2) The <u>conscious brain</u> isn't involved in a <u>reflex arc</u>. The <u>sensory neurone</u> connects to a <u>relay neurone</u> in the <u>spinal cord</u> or in an <u>unconscious part of the brain</u> — which links <u>directly</u> to the <u>right motor neurone</u>, so no time's <u>wasted</u> thinking about the response.

3) Reflex actions often have a <u>protective role</u>, e.g. snatching back your hand when you touch a <u>burning hot</u> plate.

4) The conscious brain can sometimes <u>override</u> a reflex response, e.g. to stop us dropping a hot plate we don't want to break. This involves a neurone that connects to the <u>motor neurone</u> in the reflex arc.

The Iris Reflex — Adjusting for Bright Light

1) <u>Very bright</u> light can <u>damage</u> the retina — so you have a reflex to protect it:

The retina is the bit at the back of the eye that contains receptor cells sensitive to light.

- <u>Light receptors</u> in the eye detect very bright light and send a message along a <u>sensory neurone</u> to the <u>brain</u>.

- The message then travels along a <u>relay neurone</u> to a <u>motor neurone</u>, which tells <u>circular muscles</u> in the <u>iris</u> (the coloured part of the eye) to <u>contract</u>.

- This reflex makes the <u>pupil</u> (the hole in the centre of the iris) <u>smaller</u>, <u>reducing</u> the amount of <u>light</u> that can enter the eye.

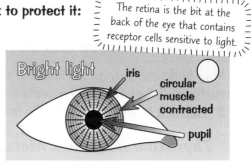

Bright light — iris, circular muscle contracted, pupil

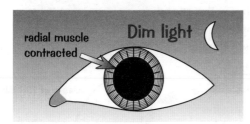

Dim light — radial muscle contracted

The opposite process happens in dim light. This time, the <u>radial muscles contract</u> and the pupils gets <u>wider</u>.

2) You can <u>investigate</u> these reflex actions by <u>dimming the lights</u> and timing how long it takes for your pupils (or a friend's) to <u>widen</u>.

3) When you turn up the lights, you can see the pupils <u>return</u> to <u>normal</u> as the <u>circular muscles</u> in the iris <u>contract</u>.

The iris reflex — watch out, flowers are getting their own back...

Reflexes allow organisms to respond rapidly to a stimulus — they're often essential for survival.

Q1   When food is tasted, the salivary glands automatically start to produce saliva. This is a reflex action. Describe the pathway of the reflex arc from receptors to effectors.   [5 marks]

Hormones and Negative Feedback

The other way to <u>send information</u> around the body (apart from along neurones) is by using <u>hormones</u>.

Hormones are *Chemical Messengers Sent in the Blood*

1) Hormones are chemicals produced in various <u>glands</u> called <u>endocrine glands</u>. These glands make up your <u>endocrine system</u>. Like the nervous system, the endocrine system allows you to respond to both <u>internal</u> and <u>external stimuli</u>.

Hormones are slow compared to nervous impulses but they have longer-lasting effects.

2) Hormones are released directly into the <u>blood</u>. The blood then carries them to other parts of the body.

3) Hormones travel all over the body, but only produce a <u>response</u> from <u>particular effectors</u>. These effectors have <u>receptors</u> that the hormones <u>bind to</u>. When hormones bind to receptors, they <u>stimulate a response</u>.

Adrenaline Prepares You for 'Fight or Flight'

1) <u>Adrenaline</u> is a hormone released by the <u>adrenal glands</u> (which are located just above the kidneys).

2) Adrenaline prepares the body for '<u>fight or flight</u>' — in other words, <u>standing</u> your <u>ground</u> in the face of a <u>threat</u> (e.g. a predator) or bravely <u>running away</u>. It does this by activating processes that increase the supply of <u>oxygen and glucose</u> to cells. For example:

- Adrenaline <u>binds</u> to specific <u>receptors</u> in the <u>heart</u>. This causes the heart muscle (the <u>effector</u>) to <u>contract</u> more frequently and with <u>more force</u>, so heart rate and blood pressure <u>increase</u>.

- This increases <u>blood flow</u> to the <u>muscles</u>, so the cells receive more <u>oxygen</u> and <u>glucose</u> for increased <u>respiration</u>.

- Adrenaline also binds to receptors in the <u>liver</u>. This causes the liver to <u>break down</u> its <u>glycogen</u> stores (see p.66) to release <u>glucose</u>.

- This increases the <u>blood glucose level</u>, so there's more glucose in the blood to be transported to the cells.

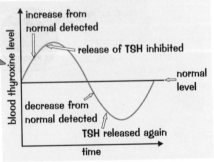

Other animals have hormones too, not just humans.

3) When your brain detects a <u>stressful situation</u>, it sends <u>nervous impulses</u> to the <u>adrenal glands</u>, which respond by secreting <u>adrenaline</u>. This gets the body ready for <u>action</u>.

Hormone Release can be Affected by Negative Feedback

Your body can <u>control</u> the levels of hormones (and other substances) in the blood using <u>negative feedback</u> <u>systems</u>. When the body detects that the level of a substance has gone <u>above or below</u> the <u>normal level</u>, it <u>triggers a response</u> to bring the level <u>back to normal</u> again. Here's an example of just that:

Thyroxine Regulates Metabolism

1) <u>Thyroxine</u> is a hormone released by the <u>thyroid gland</u> (found in the <u>neck</u>).

2) It plays an important role in regulating <u>metabolic rate</u> — the speed at which chemical reactions in the body occur. It's important for loads of processes in the body, such as <u>growth</u> and <u>protein synthesis</u>.

3) Thyroxine is released in response to <u>thyroid stimulating hormone</u> (<u>TSH</u>), which is released from the <u>pituitary gland</u>.

Thyroxine is made in the thyroid gland from iodine and amino acids.

4) A <u>negative feedback system</u> keeps the amount of thyroxine in the blood at the right level — when the level of thyroxine in the blood is <u>higher than normal</u>, the secretion of <u>TSH</u> from the pituitary gland is <u>inhibited</u>. This reduces the amount of thyroxine released from the thyroid gland so the level in the blood <u>falls</u> back towards normal.

Graph: blood thyroxine level vs time — increase from normal detected → release of TSH inhibited → normal level; decrease from normal detected → TSH released again.

Negative feedback sucks, especially from your science teacher...

Hormones and negative feedback both crop up again in this book — best learn this page good 'n' proper.

Q1   Explain how the endocrine system allows communication within the body.   [5 marks]

Hormones in Reproduction

You need to know about <u>sex hormones</u> and how some of them <u>interact</u> to control the <u>menstrual cycle</u>.

Hormones are Needed for Sexual Reproduction

Human <u>sexual reproduction</u> would be <u>impossible without hormones</u>. Hormones regulate the female <u>menstrual cycle</u> — this is the <u>monthly sequence of events</u> in which the female body releases an <u>egg</u> (ovulation) and prepares the <u>uterus</u> (womb) in case the egg is <u>fertilised</u>. The cycle has <u>four stages</u>:

<u>Stage 1</u> <u>Day 1 is when menstruation starts</u>.
The lining of the uterus breaks down and is released.

> The fancy name for the lining of the uterus is the 'endometrium'.

<u>Stage 2</u> <u>The uterus lining is repaired</u>, from day 4 to day 14, until it becomes a thick spongy layer full of blood vessels ready for a fertilised egg to implant there.

<u>Stage 3</u> <u>An egg develops and is released</u> from the ovary (<u>ovulation</u>) at about day 14.

<u>Stage 4</u> <u>The lining is then maintained</u> for about 14 days, until day 28. If no fertilised egg has landed on the uterus wall by day 28, the spongy lining starts to break down again and the whole cycle starts over.

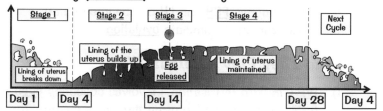

The Menstrual Cycle is Controlled by Four Hormones

① FSH (follicle-stimulating hormone)

1) Released by the <u>pituitary gland</u>.
2) Causes a <u>follicle</u> (an <u>egg</u> and its surrounding cells) to <u>mature</u> in one of the ovaries.
3) Stimulates <u>oestrogen</u> production.

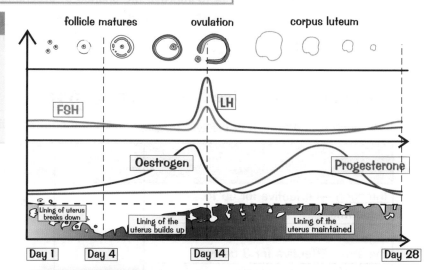

② Oestrogen

1) Released by the <u>ovaries</u>.
2) Causes the lining of the uterus to <u>thicken</u> and <u>grow</u>.

③ LH (luteinising hormone)

1) Released by the <u>pituitary gland</u>.
2) An LH <u>surge</u> (rapid increase) stimulates <u>ovulation</u> at day 14 — the follicle ruptures and the <u>egg is released</u>.
3) Stimulates the <u>remains</u> of the <u>follicle</u> to develop into a structure called a <u>corpus luteum</u> — which secretes <u>progesterone</u>.

④ Progesterone

1) Released by the <u>ovaries</u>.
2) <u>Maintains</u> the lining of the uterus for the <u>implantation</u> of a fertilised egg.
3) Along with <u>oestrogen</u>, progesterone <u>inhibits</u> the release of <u>FSH</u> and <u>LH</u>.
4) When the level of progesterone <u>falls</u>, and there's a low oestrogen level, the uterus lining <u>breaks down</u>.
5) A <u>low</u> progesterone level allows <u>FSH</u> to <u>increase</u> (and then the whole cycle starts again).

If a fertilised egg implants in the uterus (i.e. the woman becomes <u>pregnant</u>) then the level of <u>progesterone</u> will <u>stay high</u> to maintain the lining of the uterus during pregnancy.

What do you call a fish with no eye — FSH...

OK, this stuff is pretty tricky. Try scribbling down everything on the page until you can get it all without peeking.

Q1   Explain the role of LH in the menstrual cycle.   [2 marks]

Hormones for Fertility and Contraception

Hormones play a big role in reproduction. No surprise then that hormones are used to help infertile women have babies and to help fertile women not have babies. What a topsy-turvy world we live in.

Hormones can be Used to Treat Infertility

If a person is infertile, it means they can't reproduce naturally. Infertility can now be treated due to developments in modern reproductive technologies, many of which involve hormones.

Hormones are Used to Promote Natural Pregnancy...

1) Some women have levels of FSH (see previous page) that are too low to cause the follicle to develop and their eggs to mature. This means that no ovulation takes place (no eggs are released) and the women can't get pregnant.

2) The hormones FSH and LH can be injected by these women to stimulate ovulation.

The use of hormones to treat infertility has helped many people — it's a good example of a positive application of scientific technology.

...and They Play a Role in IVF

1) IVF ("in vitro fertilisation") involves collecting eggs from the woman's ovaries and fertilising them in a lab using the man's sperm. These are then grown into embryos.

2) Once the embryos are tiny balls of cells, one or two of them are transferred to the woman's uterus to improve the chance of pregnancy.

3) FSH and LH are given before egg collection to stimulate egg production and ovulation so more than one egg can be collected (improving the chance of successful fertilisation).

See the next page for contraceptive methods that don't involve hormones.

Hormones can be Used as Contraceptives

Contraceptives are used to prevent pregnancy. Some contraceptive methods involve hormones:

Contraceptive method	Hormone(s) involved	How it works
Injection — effective for up to 3 months.	Progesterone	• Stimulates the production of thick cervical mucus (at the entrance to the uterus) making it less likely that any sperm will get through and reach an egg. • Thins the lining of the uterus to reduce the chance of a fertilised egg implanting. • Prevents ovulation* by inhibiting the production of FSH and LH (see previous page). *not true for all types of mini-pill
Implant — inserted beneath the skin of the arm. Effective for 3 years.		
Intrauterine system (IUS) — a T-shaped piece of plastic inserted into the uterus. Effective for 3-5 years.		
Mini-pill (aka progesterone-only pill) — has to be taken every day.		
Combined pill — taken in a '21 day pill, 7 days no pill' cycle.	Progesterone and oestrogen	All of the effects of progesterone listed above, plus oestrogen also prevents ovulation by inhibiting FSH. *The mini-pill and the combined pill are 'oral contraceptives'.*
Patch — worn on the skin in a 4-week cycle (replaced once a week for 3 weeks, then no patch worn for a week).		

If used correctly (e.g. pills taken on time) all of these contraceptive methods are more than 99% effective.

IVF... FSH... IUS... LH... — I feel like I'm at the opticians...

Hormones can be used to manipulate the menstrual cycle so that the reproductive system does what we want it to do, when we want it to do it. Great for both increasing and decreasing the chance of pregnancy.

Q1   Explain how hormones may be used to promote a natural pregnancy in an infertile woman.   [3 marks]

More on Contraception

There are ways to prevent pregnancy that <u>don't</u> include the use of hormones. Now, as a warning, this page does include themes of a <u>sexual nature</u> from the outset. You might not want to read it aloud to your parents.

There are Plenty of Non-Hormonal Contraceptive Methods

1) <u>Barrier methods</u> — these try to stop the egg and sperm meeting. For example:

The figures given here for effectiveness assume that the methods are used properly.

- <u>Condom</u> (<u>98% effective</u>) — worn over the <u>penis</u> during intercourse to prevent sperm entering the vagina.
- <u>Female condom</u> (<u>95% effective</u>) — worn inside the <u>vagina</u> during intercourse.
- <u>Diaphragm</u> (<u>92-96% effective</u>) — fits over the <u>cervix</u> (opening of the uterus) to stop sperm from meeting the egg. Has to be fitted by a GP/nurse the first time it's used and has to be used with a <u>spermicide</u> (a chemical that kills sperm).

2) <u>Intrauterine devices</u> (<u>IUDs</u>) — T-shaped devices that contain <u>copper</u>. They're <u>inserted</u> into the <u>uterus</u> and prevent sperm from surviving. They also alter the lining of the womb so that fertilised eggs can't implant. They're more than <u>99% effective</u> and can be kept in for up to <u>ten years</u>.

3) <u>'Natural' methods</u> — these don't use any bits and bobs like all the other methods. They refer to basically just <u>not having sexual intercourse</u> when the woman is <u>most fertile</u> (the period around ovulation) or <u>'withdrawal'</u> (the man pulling the penis out before ejaculation). These methods are the <u>least effective</u> at preventing pregnancy as they rely on getting the timing exactly right.

4) <u>Sterilisation</u> — involves a <u>surgical procedure</u> to cut or tie tubes in the reproductive system. In women, the procedure means eggs are prevented from travelling from the ovaries to the uterus. In men, it prevents sperm from being ejaculated. The methods are <u>over 99% effective</u>.

There are Pros and Cons to All Forms of Contraception

In the exam you may have to <u>evaluate hormonal</u> (see previous page) and <u>non-hormonal</u> methods of contraception. Here are some things to think about:

I've got this barrier thing sorted...

1) <u>Side-effects</u> — <u>hormonal methods</u> can have unpleasant side-effects, e.g. heavy or irregular periods, acne, headaches, mood changes.

2) <u>Possibility of 'doing it wrong'</u> — <u>barrier methods</u> and <u>'natural'</u> methods have to be done <u>properly</u> each time a couple have intercourse. If, for example, a condom splits or a man doesn't withdraw soon enough, then the methods <u>won't work</u>. The same is true with some <u>hormonal</u> methods, e.g. if a woman doesn't take her pills correctly or replace her patch at the right time, the methods won't work properly.

3) <u>Medical input</u> — many methods involve at least one trip to a <u>nurse</u> or <u>doctor</u> (e.g. to get a prescription for pills or to have a device inserted). Although these methods tend to be more effective than barrier or 'natural' methods, people may feel <u>uncomfortable</u> about the procedures involved.

4) <u>Length of action</u> — <u>long-lasting methods</u> (i.e. those that last several months or years) may be <u>preferable</u> over having to think about contraception every day or every time intercourse is on the cards.

5) <u>Sexually transmitted infections</u> (<u>STIs</u>) — these are infections that are passed from person to person during sexual intercourse. The <u>only method</u> of contraception that can protect against them is <u>condoms</u> (male or female types).

The winner of best contraceptive ever — just not doing it...

By now you should be pretty clued up on the different methods of contraception. Whether hormonal or non-hormonal, no method is guaranteed to be 100% effective and each method has its own pros and cons.

Q1 Give one reason why a woman may prefer to use a diaphragm rather than an oral contraceptive. [1 mark]

Q2 Give two advantages of using an intrauterine device (IUD) as a contraceptive method rather than male condoms. [2 marks]

Homeostasis and Blood Sugar Level

Homeostasis involves balancing body functions to maintain a 'constant internal environment'. Smashing.

Homeostasis is Maintaining a Constant Internal Environment

1) Conditions in your body need to be kept within a narrow range — this is really important so that all the enzyme-controlled metabolic reactions that take place in your cells continue at an appropriate rate. It also allows the cells themselves to continue to function normally. It can be dangerous for your health if conditions vary too much from normal levels.

2) To maintain a constant internal environment, your body needs to respond to both internal and external changes whilst balancing inputs (stuff going into your body) with outputs (stuff leaving).

3) It does this using receptors, nerves, hormones and effectors (muscles and glands). Some effectors involved in homeostasis are antagonistic — this means they work in opposition to one another (e.g. one increases a level and another decreases it).

4) Things that you need to keep steady include:

   • Blood glucose (sugar) concentration — you need to make sure the amount of glucose in your blood doesn't get too high or too low (see below).

   • Water content — you need to keep a balance between the water you gain (in drink, food and from respiration) and the water you urinate, sweat and breathe out.

   • Body temperature — you need to make sure it doesn't get too high or too low.

Insulin and Glucagon Control Blood Sugar Level

1) Eating foods containing carbohydrate puts glucose into the blood from the small intestine.

2) The normal metabolism of cells removes glucose from the blood.

3) Vigorous exercise removes much more glucose from the blood.

4) Excess glucose can be stored as glycogen in the liver and in the muscles.

5) When these stores are full then the excess glucose is stored as lipid (fat) in the tissues.

6) The level of glucose in the blood must be kept steady. Changes in blood glucose are monitored and controlled by the pancreas, using the hormones insulin and glucagon. These hormones work antagonistically — they have opposite effects to return the body to normal conditions:

Blood Glucose Level Too High — Insulin is Added

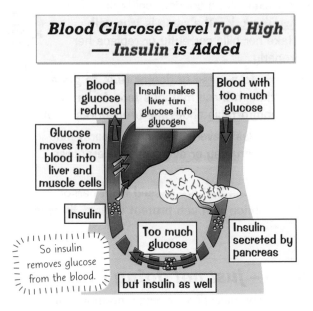

Blood Glucose Level Too Low — Glucagon is Added

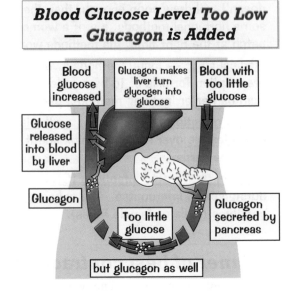

My sister never goes out — she's got homeostasis...

Make sure you learn the definition of homeostasis and can explain how your body responds to blood sugar changes.

Q1 Describe how the body responds to increase the blood glucose level when it gets too low. [3 marks]

Diabetes

When things go wrong with homeostasis, the problems can be pretty serious.
One example of homeostasis not working as it should is diabetes — which is what this page is all about.

Having Diabetes Means You Can't Control Your Blood Sugar Level

Diabetes is a condition that affects your ability to control your blood sugar level.
There are two types of diabetes:

Type 1 Diabetes — No Insulin Made

> Remember, insulin removes glucose from the blood.

1) Type 1 diabetes is where the pancreas stops producing insulin.
2) The result is that a person's blood glucose level can rise to a level that can kill them.
3) People with type 1 diabetes need insulin therapy. This usually involves injecting insulin into the blood several times a day (often at mealtimes).
4) This makes sure that glucose is removed from the blood quickly once food has been digested. This stops the level of glucose in the blood from getting too high and is a very effective treatment.
5) The amount of insulin needed depends on the person's diet and how active they are.
6) As well as insulin therapy, people with type 1 diabetes need to think about:

- limiting their intake of food rich in simple carbohydrates, e.g. sugars (which cause the blood glucose to rise rapidly),
- taking regular exercise (which helps to remove excess glucose from the blood).

Type 2 Diabetes — Insulin Resistance or Not Enough Insulin

1) Type 2 diabetes is where a person becomes resistant to insulin (their body's cells don't respond properly to the hormone) or the pancreas doesn't produce enough insulin.
2) This can also cause blood sugar level to rise to a dangerous level.
3) Being overweight can increase your chance of developing type 2 diabetes, as obesity is a major risk factor in the development of the disease (see page 17).
4) Type 2 diabetes can be controlled by:

- eating a healthy diet (this includes replacing simple carbohydrates with complex carbohydrates, e.g. wholegrains)
- exercising regularly,
- losing weight if necessary.

5) Some people with type 2 diabetes also have medication or insulin injections.

And people used to think the pancreas was just a cushion...

Don't forget that there are two types of diabetes. Make sure you know the differences between each one and what the different treatments are, so you don't get them mixed up in your exam. Remember as well that obesity is a big risk factor for developing type 2 diabetes. There's more on this in Chapter B2.

Q1   Describe how the level of insulin production differs in type 1 and type 2 diabetes.   [3 marks]

Revision Questions for Chapter B5

That was intense — luckily it's the end of <u>Chapter B5</u>. Take a break, then test yourself with these questions.
- Try these questions and <u>tick off each one</u> when you <u>get it right</u>.
- When you've done <u>all the questions</u> for a topic and are <u>completely happy</u> with it, tick off the topic.

Exchange of Materials (p.55-56) ☑

1) Name three substances that humans have to exchange with their environment. ☑
2) How does having a large surface area to volume ratio help organisms exchange materials? ☑
3) Give an example of a specialised exchange surface found in a human and
   explain how it is adapted to maximise the exchange of substances. ☑

The Circulatory System (p.57-59) ☑

4) Name the blood vessel that transports blood from the heart to the rest of the body. ☑
5) Name the four chambers of the heart and the major blood vessel connected to each one. ☑
6) Describe the role of capillaries. ☑
7) Which type of blood vessel carries blood at high pressure? ☑
8) Name ten substances that are found in blood plasma. ☑

The Nervous System and Reflexes (p.60-61) ☑

9) Draw a diagram of a typical neurone and label all the parts. ☑
10) State the purpose of: a) a sensory neurone, b) a motor neurone. ☑
11) What is the purpose of a reflex action? ☑
12) Describe a reflex you could investigate in class. ☑

Hormones, The Menstrual Cycle and Controlling Fertility (p.62-65) ☑

13) What is a hormone? ☑
14) Explain how adrenaline prepares the body for the 'fight or flight' response. ☑
15) Describe how a negative feedback system works in the body. ☑
16) Draw a timeline of the 28 day menstrual cycle.
    Label the four stages of the cycle and label when the egg is released. ☑
17) Describe how one non-hormonal method of contraception works and list its pros and cons. ☑
18) Briefly describe how IVF is carried out. ☑

Homeostasis (p.66-67) ☑

19) What is homeostasis? ☑
20) Why is homeostasis so important? ☑
21) What effect does the hormone glucagon have on blood glucose level? ☑
22) Explain how type 1 and type 2 diabetes can be treated. ☑

Natural Selection and Evolution

The <u>theory of evolution</u> states that one of your (probably very distant) ancestors was a <u>blob</u> in a swamp somewhere. Something like that, anyway. It's probably best to <u>read on</u> for more details...

Natural Selection Increases Advantageous Phenotypes

1) Populations of species usually show a lot of <u>genetic variation</u> — this means that there's a big <u>mix</u> of <u>genetic variants</u> present in the population.

2) Genetic variants arise when DNA <u>randomly mutates</u> (changes).

3) Occasionally, a genetic variant can have a <u>big</u> effect on an organism's <u>phenotype</u> (the characteristics it displays). However, most genetic variants have <u>no effect</u> on <u>phenotype</u> and <u>some</u> of them only have a <u>small influence</u> on a phenotype.

> A genetic variant is an alternative version of a gene. See page 3.

4) Those genetic variants that <u>do</u> affect phenotype can give rise to <u>characteristics</u> that make an organism <u>better suited</u> to a particular environment (e.g. being able to run away from predators faster). This means that the organisms that <u>inherit</u> these variants will have an <u>advantageous phenotype</u>.

5) The <u>resources</u> living things need to survive are <u>limited</u>. Individuals in a community must <u>compete</u> for these resources to <u>survive</u>. Individuals with genetic variants that give <u>advantageous phenotypes</u> will have a <u>better chance</u> of successfully <u>competing</u> for resources, and so have an increased chance of <u>surviving</u>, <u>reproducing</u> and passing on their <u>genes</u>.

6) This means that a <u>greater</u> proportion of individuals in the next generation will <u>inherit</u> the <u>advantageous variants</u> and so they'll also have the <u>phenotypes</u> that help <u>survival</u>.

7) Over many generations, the advantageous phenotype becomes <u>more common</u> in the population. The 'best' characteristics are <u>naturally selected</u> and the species becomes more and more <u>adapted</u> to its environment. Here's an example:

> Once upon a time maybe all rabbits had <u>short ears</u> and managed OK. Then one day a <u>mutated gene</u> meant that one rabbit popped out with <u>big ears</u>. This rabbit could hear better and was always the first to dive for cover at the sound of a predator. Pretty soon he's fathered a whole family of rabbits with <u>big ears</u>, all diving for cover before the other rabbits, and before you know it, there are only <u>big-eared</u> rabbits left — because the rest just didn't hear trouble coming quick enough.
>
> FOX!

Natural Selection Leads to the Evolution of Species

1) <u>Evolution</u> is the change in <u>inherited characteristics</u> of a population over <u>several generations</u>, through the process of <u>natural selection</u>.

2) Evolution by natural selection may mean that a species' <u>phenotype</u> changes so much that a completely <u>new species</u> is formed (i.e. the <u>old</u> and <u>new</u> version of the species wouldn't be able to <u>breed</u> together to produce <u>fertile offspring</u>). When a new species is formed it's called <u>speciation</u>.

3) Speciation can happen when a physical barrier <u>isolates two populations</u> of a species — conditions on each side of the barrier will be slightly <u>different</u> so the <u>phenotypes</u> that are <u>beneficial</u> will be <u>different</u> for each population. <u>Natural selection</u> acts on each population to increase the <u>proportion</u> of the <u>advantageous phenotype</u> in that population, until they are so <u>different</u> that they can no longer <u>breed together</u>.

4) The <u>speed</u> at which a species <u>evolves</u> depends partly on how quickly it <u>reproduces</u> — some species reproduce very <u>quickly</u> (e.g. <u>bacteria</u> can be ready to start dividing in just 20 minutes), whereas others reproduce much more <u>slowly</u> (e.g. usually <u>humans</u> only start reproducing after around 20-30 years).

'Natural selection' — sounds like vegan chocolates...

In terms of evolution, it's no good an organism being great at surviving if it doesn't breed and pass on its genes. And it'll only be good at surviving if it inherits great genetic variants or has awesome mutations in its DNA.

Q1 Musk oxen have thick fur, which is advantageous in the cold climate in which they live. Explain how the musk oxen may have developed this characteristic over many years. [4 marks]

Evidence for Evolution

If you're sitting there thinking evolution is a load of <u>old codswallop</u>, here's a bit of <u>evidence</u> to help sway you...

There is Good Evidence for Evolution

Scientists believe that all <u>complex organisms</u> on Earth have evolved from <u>simple organisms</u> that existed about <u>3500 million years ago</u>. Of course, they wouldn't think this without good evidence to back it up. <u>Fossil records</u> and <u>antibiotic resistance in bacteria</u> both provide <u>evidence</u> for evolution:

Observations of Fossils Can Provide Evidence for Evolution

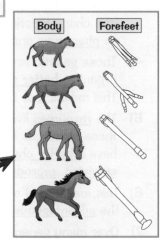

1) A fossil is <u>any trace</u> of an animal or plant that lived <u>long</u> ago. They are most commonly found in <u>rocks</u>.

2) They can tell us a lot about what the organisms <u>looked like</u> and <u>how long ago</u> they existed. Generally, the <u>deeper</u> the rock, the <u>older</u> the fossil.

3) By arranging fossils in <u>chronological</u> (date) order, <u>gradual changes</u> in organisms can be observed. This provides <u>evidence</u> for <u>evolution</u>, because it shows how species have <u>changed</u> and <u>developed</u> over many years. For example, if you look at the <u>fossilised bones</u> of a <u>horse</u>, you can put together a family tree to suggest how the modern horse might have <u>evolved</u>.

Bacteria Can Show Evolution As it Happens

1) Like all organisms, bacteria sometimes develop <u>random mutations</u> in their DNA, which introduces new <u>variants</u> into the population. These can lead to <u>changes</u> in the bacteria's <u>phenotype</u> — for example, a bacterium could become <u>less affected</u> by a particular <u>antibiotic</u> (a substance designed to kill bacteria or prevent them from reproducing).

2) For the bacterium, this ability to resist antibiotics is a big <u>advantage</u>. The bacterium is better able to <u>survive</u>, even in a host who's being treated with antibiotics, and so it <u>lives for longer</u> and <u>reproduces</u> many more times.

One way that bacteria might be resistant to an antibiotic is if they have an enzyme that can break the antibiotic down.

3) This leads to the <u>resistant variant</u> being <u>passed on</u> to offspring and becoming more and more common over time — it's just <u>natural selection</u>.

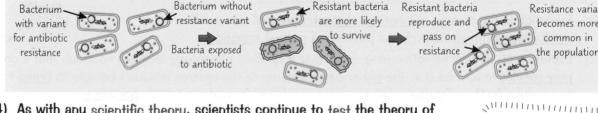

| Variation in the population | Survival | Reproduction |

Bacterium with variant for antibiotic resistance — Bacterium without resistance variant — Bacteria exposed to antibiotic — Resistant bacteria are more likely to survive — Resistant bacteria reproduce and pass on resistance — Resistance variant becomes more common in the population

4) As with any <u>scientific theory</u>, scientists continue to <u>test</u> the theory of evolution by natural selection by making <u>new observations</u> and <u>collecting new evidence</u>. The emergence of antibiotic-resistant bacteria can be <u>explained</u> by the theory of evolution by natural selection (as there is change in the inherited characteristics of a population over time). What's more, because bacteria reproduce <u>very quickly</u>, scientists can observe evolution <u>as it's occurring</u>, so it provides great <u>support</u> for the theory.

The theory of evolution by natural selection was developed to explain observations by Charles Darwin, Alfred Russel Wallace and other scientists.

5) It's due to strong evidence like this that the theory of evolution by natural selection is now widely <u>accepted</u> by the <u>scientific community</u>.

The different characteristics shown by isolated populations of the same species in different environments also provide evidence for evolution.

The fossil record — it rocks...

Life on Earth is still evolving — the evidence is right under our feet and under our microscopes.

Q1   How do genetic variants for antibiotic resistance arise in a population of bacteria?   [1 mark]

Q2   Describe how fossils provide evidence for evolution.   [2 marks]

ValiderMontrent

Selective Breeding

So, you know that organisms change through evolution by natural selection, but humans can also cause organisms to change, through the process of selective breeding.

Selective Breeding is Mating the Best Organisms to Get Good Offspring

Humans use selective breeding to develop new varieties of organisms with beneficial characteristics for human use. For example, organisms can be bred to have:

- A maximum yield of meat, milk, grain, etc. — this means that food production is as high as possible. Most of what we eat nowadays comes from organisms which have been selectively bred.
- Good health and disease resistance.
- In animals, other qualities like temperament, speed, fertility, good mothering skills, etc.

This is the basic process involved in selective breeding:

1) The parent organisms with the best characteristics are selected, e.g. the largest sheep and rams — those with the highest meat yield.
2) They're bred with each other.
3) The best of the offspring are selected and bred.
4) This process is repeated over several generations to develop the desired traits, e.g. to produce sheep with very large meat yields.

Selective breeding is also known as artificial selection.

Selective Breeding Causes a Reduction in the Gene Pool

1) Although selective breeding can be very useful for humans, the main problem with it is that it reduces the gene pool — the number of different genetic variants (alleles) in a population. This is because the farmer keeps breeding from the "best" animals or plants — which are all closely related. This is known as inbreeding.
2) Inbreeding can cause health problems because there's more chance of the organisms developing harmful genetic disorders when the gene pool is limited.
3) There can also be serious problems if a new disease appears, because there's not much variation in the population. All the stock are closely related to each other, so if one of them is going to be killed by a new disease, the others are also likely to succumb to it.

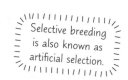
Oh Eck!

Darwin Used Selective Breeding to Help Form His Theory of Evolution

1) Selective breeding's not a new thing. People have been doing it for hundreds of years. In fact, it helped Charles Darwin come up with his theory of evolution by natural selection.
2) He noticed that the selective breeding of plants and animals had created different varieties of species, and that these new varieties were sometimes very different from the original 'wild' version of the species they had descended from.
3) He started to question whether natural processes (rather than humans) somehow selected individuals with traits that made them more likely to survive in a particular environment, and whether this could be the reason for the variety of different organisms, and the creation of new species, on Earth.

I use the same genes all the time too — they flatter my hips...

The basic process of selective breeding has stayed the same over many years — select the best individuals, let them reproduce, repeat over many generations, and voilà...

Q1 A farmer who grows green beans lives in an area that experiences a lot of drought. Explain how he could use selective breeding to improve the chances of his bean plants surviving the droughts. [3 marks]

Chapter B6 — Life on Earth — Past, Present and Future

Classification

It seems to be a basic human urge to want to classify things — that's the case in biology anyway...

Classification is Organising Living Organisms into Groups

1) Traditionally, organisms were classified according to similarities and differences in their observable characteristics, i.e. things you can see (like how many legs something has). As technology improved, this included things you can see with a microscope, e.g. cell structure.

2) These characteristics were used to classify organisms in the five kingdom classification system. In this system, living things are first divided into five groups called kingdoms (e.g. the plant kingdom, the animal kingdom).

3) The kingdoms are then subdivided into smaller and smaller groups that have common features — phylum, class, order, family, genus, species.

Developments in Biology Lead to Improvements in Classification

1) The five kingdom classification system is still used, but it's now a bit out of date.

2) Over time, technology has developed further and our understanding of things like biochemical processes and genetics has increased. This has resulted in new discoveries being made and the relationships between organisms being clarified.

3) For example, DNA analysis allows scientists to find out the differences between organisms, even if the organisms are physically very similar to each other.

An organism's genome is all of its genetic material.

- Scientists can use DNA sequencing to compare particular genes or entire genomes of different organisms, using only small samples of tissue.
- They look for similarities, e.g. if the different species share the same number of genes, or a similar number of genetic variants for a particular gene.
- If different organisms share the same number of genes or genetic variants for a gene, then they are likely to have inherited these similarities from a common ancestor.
- The more similar the DNA sequences between species, the more closely related they are and the more likely it is that they'll be classified in the same group. E.g. the base sequence for human and chimpanzee DNA is about 94% the same, so humans and chimpanzees are closely related to each other.

4) Scientists can also use DNA sequences to estimate how long ago two species separated from each other.

5) This is because genetic variants arise by mutations and scientists have estimates for how frequently these mutations can happen.

6) By finding the number of different genetic variants between two species, scientists can estimate when speciation (the emergence of new species) occurred.

Evolutionary Trees Show How Species are Related to Each Other

1) Scientists can use classification data to join species together in evolutionary trees.

2) In an evolutionary tree, species are connected to each other by lines via their most recent common ancestor. This helps to show their relationship to each other.

3) The more closely related two species are to each other, the fewer the number of steps between them on the tree.

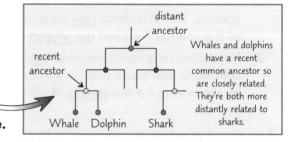
distant ancestor
recent ancestor
Whales and dolphins have a recent common ancestor so are closely related. They're both more distantly related to sharks.
Whale   Dolphin   Shark

My brother's been reclassified — he's back with the apes...

As new techniques enable us to study organisms at the level of their genes, our classification systems get better.

Q1   Suggest one limitation of classifying organisms based only on their physical characteristics.   [1 mark]

Chapter B6 — Life on Earth — Past, Present and Future

Biodiversity

Time for something less joyous. We <u>humans</u> can have some <u>really damaging negative impacts</u> on ecosystems...

Biodiversity is all About the Variety of Life in an Area

<u>Biodiversity</u> is a combination of <u>three different factors</u>. These are:

- the diversity (variety) of <u>living organisms</u> in a particular area.
- the diversity of different <u>genes</u> and <u>alleles</u> in a particular area (also known as <u>genetic diversity</u>).
- the diversity of different <u>ecosystems</u> in a particular area.

A <u>high level</u> of biodiversity (whether globally or just in a small area) is a good thing — it means that if the environment <u>changes</u> in some way, there's a good chance that at least <u>some species and ecosystems</u> will be able to <u>survive</u>. It also means that we <u>humans</u> can get the most out of the <u>world's resources</u> (see p.75).

Human Interactions Can Reduce Biodiversity

1) Like all organisms, we humans have an <u>impact</u> on the <u>ecosystems around us</u>. The impact humans have on ecosystems has <u>changed a lot</u> in the last couple of centuries. This is largely due to:

   1) An <u>increasing human population</u> — the human population on Earth has grown <u>hugely</u> over the last 200 years and is <u>continuing</u> to rise. Many more people on the planet means we need to take up <u>more land</u> and use <u>more resources</u> in order to <u>survive</u>.

   2) <u>Industrialisation</u> — due to improvements in <u>technology</u> and the need for more <u>goods</u> and <u>services</u>, there is now much more <u>industry</u> on the planet than there was a couple of centuries ago. This means we are using <u>more raw materials</u> (e.g. oil, wood) and <u>more energy</u> to <u>manufacture goods</u>. It also means we're creating <u>more waste products</u>, which can lead to <u>more pollution</u>.

   3) <u>Globalisation</u> — as <u>communication</u> and <u>transport</u> have improved, different countries have become more <u>connected</u> with each other. This means that countries are able to <u>buy</u> and <u>sell</u> products from each other more easily and the <u>same companies</u> are able to operate in <u>several different countries</u>.

2) These changes can <u>damage</u> or <u>destroy</u> ecosystems and can <u>reduce</u> biodiversity. Here are a few reasons why:

   1) <u>Habitat destruction</u> — <u>human activities</u> (e.g. farming, building, quarrying) reduce the amount of <u>land</u> and <u>resources</u> available to <u>other</u> animals and plants, which can reduce <u>biodiversity</u> in an area. For example, <u>woodland</u> may be <u>cleared</u> for farmland and can result in a <u>reduction</u> in the number of <u>tree species</u>, so reducing <u>biodiversity</u>. It also destroys the <u>habitats</u> of other organisms — species will <u>die</u> or be forced to <u>migrate</u> elsewhere, further reducing biodiversity.

   2) <u>Waste</u> — the <u>increasing population</u> and <u>industrialisation</u> means we're producing more waste, which can <u>damage ecosystems</u> in many ways. For example, <u>sewage</u> and <u>toxic chemicals</u> from <u>industry</u> and <u>agriculture</u> can pollute lakes, rivers and oceans, affecting the plants and animals that rely on them for <u>survival</u> (including humans).

   3) <u>Sharing resources</u> — increasing <u>globalisation</u> (see above) means that resources can be <u>shared</u> between many countries. Unfortunately, this can lead to a loss of <u>biodiversity</u>. For example, large companies can sell the 'best' varieties of seeds to farmers in many different countries, reducing the <u>number</u> of seed varieties used for crops <u>globally</u> and therefore reducing <u>global biodiversity</u>.

3) Populations can often <u>adapt</u> to changes in the environment through <u>evolution</u> by <u>natural selection</u>.

4) However, many <u>human impacts</u> on ecosystems take place so <u>quickly</u> that there is not <u>enough time</u> for organisms to adapt. This could lead to the <u>loss of populations</u> of species from an area or even the complete <u>extinction</u> of species.

5) When a species is lost from an ecosystem it can have <u>knock-on effects</u> for other organisms. For example, it can negatively impact <u>food chains</u>, which could cause a <u>further decrease</u> in biodiversity.

I'm sorry but I'd prefer it if biodiversity was low inside my house...

Industrialisation and globalisation may be useful for us, but unfortunately it tends to be bad news for biodiversity.

Q1   Explain one way in which chemicals used in agriculture may lead to a loss in biodiversity.   [2 marks]

More on Biodiversity

You've seen on the last page how humans can have a negative effect on biodiversity, so now for some positivity. Here's how humans can help to prevent the loss of biodiversity and preserve it for future generations.

Humans Can Use Resources Sustainably

1) Sustainability means meeting the needs of today's population without harming the environment or using up resources, so that future generations can still meet their own needs. Using resources sustainably means that the rate at which we use resources is not greater than the rate at which they are replaced.

> For example, sustainable harvesting of timber may involve the replanting of trees after harvesting so that new trees replace the ones that are cut.

2) Sustainability means humans will have less of a negative impact on ecosystems and biodiversity.

Conservation Schemes Can Protect Biodiversity

Conservation schemes can help to protect biodiversity by conserving species or their habitats. This can be done on several different levels. For example:

Protecting specific species

1) Specific species can be protected in their natural habitat, e.g. by banning the hunting of some species.

2) Species can also be protected by being kept in safe areas, away from harmful activities such as hunting or habitat destruction. For animals, safe areas include zoos and for plants they include botanical gardens and seed banks (large collections of seeds from many different plant species). Breeding programmes in captivity can also increase the number of a species before releasing them back into the wild.

Protecting habitats and ecosystems

1) Setting aside specific protected areas helps to conserve entire habitats and ecosystems by restricting the development of the land — e.g. for building houses and farming.

2) Protected areas include places like national parks and nature reserves. They can also be found in the sea where human activities like fishing are controlled to protect marine ecosystems.

Preventing ecosystem damage on a global scale

1) Some human activities, such as burning fossil fuels, are increasing the level of greenhouse gases in the atmosphere, which is contributing to global warming (the gradual warming up of the planet).

2) Global warming is a type of climate change and causes other types of climate change, e.g. changing rainfall patterns.

3) Climate change could reduce biodiversity on Earth — e.g. some species may be unable to survive a change in the climate, so become extinct.

4) So, in order to protect global biodiversity, it may be necessary to control human activities in order to reduce greenhouse gas emissions.

My room is a protected area from the species Brother horribilis...

So, there you go — it's not all doom and gloom. There are lots of things that we can do to help biodiversity — we just have to hurry up if we want as many species as possible to survive in the future.

Q1 The Siberian tiger is an endangered species. Explain how zoos could help to increase the number of Siberian tigers in the wild. [2 marks]

Maintaining Biodiversity

Trying to preserve biodiversity can be tricky but there are benefits for doing it, so it's pretty worthwhile...

Maintaining Biodiversity Benefits Wildlife and Humans

Humans, like all other organisms, depend on other organisms for their survival, e.g. for things such as food and shelter. So, as well as benefitting endangered species, maintaining biodiversity often helps humans too:

1) Protecting the human food supply — over-fishing has greatly reduced fish stocks in the world's oceans. Conservation programmes can ensure that future generations will have fish to eat.

2) Ensuring minimal damage to food chains — if one species becomes extinct it will affect all the organisms that feed on and are eaten by that species, so the whole food chain is affected. This means conserving one species may help others to survive.

3) Providing future medicines — many of the medicines we use today come from plants. Undiscovered plant species may contain new medicinal chemicals. If these plants are allowed to become extinct, perhaps through rainforest destruction, we could miss out on valuable medicines.

4) Providing industrial materials and fuels — plant and animal species are involved in the production of industrial materials (e.g. wood, paper, adhesives and oils) and some fuels. If these species become extinct these important resources may become more difficult to produce.

Maintaining Biodiversity can be Challenging

Ways of maintaining biodiversity are great in theory but they can be difficult to do in the real world, whether at a local or global level. Many factors have to be considered before deciding to go ahead with conservation schemes. Here are a few examples of why:

Economic issues

1) It can be expensive to conserve species or habitats. The cost of a conservation scheme has to be weighed against the potential benefits of maintaining biodiversity.

2) Many developing countries are rich in natural resources, e.g. Ecuador is a developing country with many biodiverse areas, however it also has large reserves of petroleum. Accessing these natural resources and selling them may help to boost the country's economy, but this could also have a negative effect on the country's ecosystems.

Moral issues

1) The conservation of some endangered species may have no obvious benefit for humans (e.g. the Giant Panda), but many people think we should still help to prevent species from becoming extinct.

2) Some people think it's morally wrong to stop humans in developing countries from using natural resources that could boost their economy (see above) in favour of protecting plants and animals.

3) Protecting one species may mean killing individuals of another species, which some people think is wrong, e.g. possums in New Zealand have reduced the numbers of organisms of native species, so there are widespread schemes to kill possums in order to protect native wildlife.

Ecological issues

Ecosystems are very complex — conservation schemes that try to protect one species or habitat could have knock-on effects in other parts of the ecosystem. This means that people have to think very carefully about what future effects conservation schemes could have before they are set up.

Political issues

1) Some conservation schemes require several different countries to work together. This can be difficult if some countries aren't willing to sign up to an agreement. E.g. many countries have signed up to agreements to restrict whaling but there are still some that haven't (e.g. Norway, Japan).

2) On a smaller scale, conservation schemes can be objected to by local communities. E.g. people might not be keen if a local scheme reduces their income (e.g. fishing restrictions in a fishing village).

It's a shame exams aren't an endangered species...

Hmmm, I guess the maintenance of biodiversity can be a bit tricky but if it keeps food on the table I'm keen...

Q1   Explain why maintaining biodiversity could be important for providing medicines in the future.   [2 marks]

Revision Questions for Chapter B6

Good work — now you should know all about how life evolved and how we should protect it in the future.
- Try these questions and tick off each one when you get it right.
- When you've done all the questions for a topic and are completely happy with it, tick off the topic.

Natural Selection, Evolution and Selective Breeding (p.69-71) ☑

1) How likely is it that a genetic variant will have a really big effect on an organism's phenotype? ☑
2) Describe how organisms evolve by the process of natural selection. ☑
3) Define 'evolution'. ☑
4) Explain how speciation can occur when two populations of a species are isolated. ☑
5) What is a fossil? ☑
6) Other than fossils, give one other example of evidence which shows that species evolve over time. ☑
7) What is selective breeding? ☑
8) Give one disadvantage of selective breeding. ☑

Classification (p.72) ☑

9) Complete the sentence: "Traditionally, organisms were classified according to similarities and differences in their _____". ☑
10) Explain how DNA analysis helps scientists to classify organisms. ☑

Biodiversity (p.73-75) ☑

11) What is meant by biodiversity? ☑
12) Explain one way in which industrialisation can reduce biodiversity. ☑
13) What is meant by globalisation? ☑
14) What does using resources sustainably mean? Give an example. ☑
15) Describe one way in which humans can conserve a specific species. ☑
16) Explain why conservation schemes to protect global biodiversity might aim to reduce the amount of fossil fuels we burn. ☑
17) Give one advantage to humans of maintaining biodiversity. ☑
18) Describe one moral issue which may be discussed when deciding on schemes to protect biodiversity. ☑
19) Give an example of a political issue that could challenge the success of a conservation scheme. ☑

States of Matter

Better get your thinking hat on, as states of matter really... err... matter. You'll need to imagine the particles in a substance as little snooker balls. Sounds strange, but it's useful for explaining lots of stuff in chemistry.

The Three States of Matter — Solid, Liquid and Gas

1) Materials come in three different forms — solid, liquid and gas. These are the three states of matter.

2) Which state something is at a certain temperature (solid, liquid or gas) depends on how strong the forces of attraction are between the particles of the material.

The particles could be atoms, ions or molecules.

3) You can use a model called particle theory to explain how the particles in a material behave in each state of matter by considering each particle as a small, solid, inelastic sphere.

Solids
- In solids, there are strong forces of attraction between particles, which holds them close together in fixed positions to form a very regular lattice arrangement.
- The particles don't move from their positions, so all solids keep a definite shape and volume, and don't flow like liquids.
- The particles vibrate about their positions — the hotter the solid becomes, the more they vibrate (causing solids to expand slightly when heated).

Liquids
- In liquids, the forces of attraction between particles are weaker than in solids. They're randomly arranged and free to move past each other, but they tend to stick closely together.
- Liquids have a definite volume but don't keep a definite shape, and will flow to fill the bottom of a container.
- The particles are constantly moving with random motion. The hotter the liquid gets, the faster they move. This causes liquids to expand slightly when heated.

Gases
- In gases, the particles are well separated so there's no attraction between them — they're free to move and are far apart. The particles in gases travel in straight lines.
- Gases don't keep a definite shape or volume and will always fill any container.
- The particles move constantly with random motion. The hotter the gas gets, the faster they move. Gases either expand when heated, or their pressure increases.

4) Particle theory is a great model for explaining the three states of matter, but it isn't perfect. In reality, the particles aren't solid or inelastic and they aren't spheres — they're atoms, ions or molecules. The model shows all the particles in a substance as the same size, but if you've got several different types of atoms, ions or molecules present, chances are there'll be some variation in size. Also, the model doesn't show the forces between the particles, so there's no way of knowing how strong they are.

Substances in different states of matter are all around us — in the earth, the oceans and the atmosphere.

Atoms are Rearranged During Chemical Reactions

1) Substances can change from one state of matter to another (see next page). When that happens, the change is a physical change. No new substances are made — the original chemicals just change state.

2) Physical changes are pretty easy to undo, e.g. by heating or cooling. Chemical reactions are different...

3) During a chemical reaction, bonds between atoms break and the atoms change places — the atoms from the substances you start off with (the reactants) rearrange themselves to form different chemicals. These new chemicals are called the products.

4) Compared to physical changes, chemical changes are often hard to reverse.

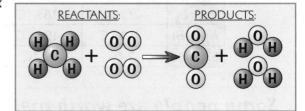

I felt like changing state, so I moved from Texas to Michigan...

After all this stuff about particle theory, let's have a go at putting theory into practice...

Q1   Describe the forces, arrangement and movement of particles in: a) solids, b) gases, c) liquids. [9 marks]

Changing State

This page is like a game show. To start, everyone seems nice and solid, but turn up the <u>heat</u> and it all changes.

Substances Can Change from One State to Another

<u>Physical changes</u> don't change the particles — just their <u>arrangement</u> or their <u>energy</u>.

1) When a solid is <u>heated</u>, its particles gain more <u>energy</u>.

2) This makes the particles vibrate <u>more</u>, which <u>weakens</u> the <u>forces</u> that hold the solid together.

3) At a <u>certain temperature</u>, called the <u>melting point</u>, the particles have enough energy to <u>break free</u> from their positions. This is called <u>MELTING</u> and the <u>solid</u> turns into a <u>liquid</u>.

4) When a liquid is <u>heated</u>, the particles get even <u>more</u> energy.

5) This energy makes the particles move <u>faster</u>, which <u>weakens</u> and <u>breaks</u> the bonds holding the particles together.

6) At a <u>certain temperature</u>, called the <u>boiling point</u>, the particles have <u>enough</u> energy to <u>break</u> all of their bonds. This is <u>BOILING</u>. The <u>liquid</u> becomes a <u>gas</u>.

Solid

melting | freezing

Liquid

boiling | condensing

Gas

12) At the <u>melting point</u>, so many bonds have formed between the particles that they're <u>held in place</u>. The <u>liquid</u> becomes a <u>solid</u>. This is <u>FREEZING</u>.

11) There's not enough energy to overcome the attraction between the particles, so more <u>bonds</u> form between them.

10) When a <u>liquid cools</u>, the particles have <u>less energy</u>, so move around less.

9) At the <u>boiling point</u>, so many bonds have formed between the gas particles that the <u>gas</u> becomes a <u>liquid</u>. This is called <u>CONDENSING</u>.

8) <u>Bonds form</u> between the particles.

7) As a gas <u>cools</u>, the particles no longer have <u>enough energy</u> to overcome the forces of attraction between them.

So, the amount of energy needed for a substance to change state depends on <u>how strong</u> the forces between particles are. The <u>stronger</u> the forces, the <u>more energy</u> is needed to break them, and so the <u>higher</u> the melting and boiling points of the substance.

The changes of state that occur in the water cycle or that happened when the atmosphere and oceans formed, can be described using the particle model.

You Have to be Able to Predict the State of a Substance

You might be asked to predict <u>what state</u> a substance is in at a <u>certain temperature</u>. If the temperature's <u>below</u> the <u>melting point</u> of substance, it'll be a <u>solid</u>. If it's <u>above</u> the <u>boiling point</u>, it'll be a <u>gas</u>. If it's <u>in between</u> the two points, then it's a <u>liquid</u>.

The bulk properties such as the melting point of a material depend on how lots of particles interact together. A particle on its own doesn't have these properties.

EXAMPLE: Which of the molecular substances in the table is a liquid at room temperature (25 °C)?

	melting point	boiling point
oxygen	−219 °C	−183 °C
nitrogen	−210 °C	−196 °C
bromine	−7 °C	59 °C

Oxygen and nitrogen have boiling points below 25 °C, so will both be gases at room temperature.

So the answer's **bromine**. It melts at −7 °C and boils at 59 °C. So, it'll be a liquid at room temperature.

Some people are worth melting for...

In exam questions, you might need to know roughly what the value of room temperature is. Be prepared to use some common sense and know that, for example, something that boils at −100 °C is a gas at room temperature.

Q1 Ethanol melts at −114 °C and boils at 78 °C. Predict the state that ethanol is in at:
   a) −150 °C   b) 0 °C   c) 25 °C   d) 100 °C   [4 marks]

Chemical Formulas

If the thing that annoys you most about chemistry is having to <u>write out</u> the names of <u>elements</u> and <u>compounds</u> in full every single time you mention them, then you are going to <u>love</u> this page.

Atoms Can be Represented by Symbols

Atoms of each element can be represented by a <u>one or two letter symbol</u> — it's a type of <u>shorthand</u> that saves you the bother of having to write the full name of the element.

Some make <u>perfect sense</u>, e.g. | C = carbon   O = oxygen   Mg = magnesium |

Others less so, e.g. | Na = sodium   Fe = iron   Pb = lead |

Most of these odd symbols actually come from the Latin names of the elements.

You'll see these symbols on the periodic table (see page 92).

The Formula of a Molecule Shows the Numbers of Atoms

You can work out <u>how many atoms</u> of each type there are in a substance when you're given its <u>formula</u>.

This is called a <u>molecular formula</u>. It shows the <u>number</u> and <u>type</u> of atoms in a molecule.

 CH_4

Methane contains 1 carbon atom and 4 hydrogen atoms.

This is called a <u>displayed formula</u>. It shows the <u>atoms</u> and the <u>covalent bonds</u> in a molecule as a picture.

Don't panic if a formula has <u>brackets</u> in it — they're easy to deal with.

$$CH_3(CH_2)_2CH_3$$

For example, the 2 after the bracket here means that there are 2 lots of CH_2. So altogether there are 4 carbon atoms and 10 hydrogen atoms.

If you have the <u>displayed formula</u> of a molecule, you can use it to write the <u>molecular formula</u> — just count up and write down how many atoms of each element there are in the displayed formula.

Here, each carbon in the formula matches up with one carbon in the displayed formula.

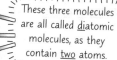

C_4H_{10} or $CH_3(CH_2)_2CH_3$

You Need to Learn the Formulas of Some Molecules

1) <u>Prefixes</u> can tell you how many of a certain atom are in a molecule. The main ones you'll need to know are <u>mono-</u> = one, <u>di-</u> = two and <u>tri-</u> = three. E.g. each molecule of carbon <u>mono</u>xide contains <u>one</u> oxygen atom and each molecule of carbon <u>di</u>oxide contains <u>two</u> oxygen atoms.

2) It's a good idea to <u>learn</u> the chemical formulas of these common molecules. They crop up all the time.

• Water — H_2O	• Hydrogen — H_2
• Ammonia — NH_3	• Chlorine — Cl_2
• Carbon dioxide — CO_2	• Oxygen — O_2

These three molecules are all called <u>diatomic</u> molecules, as they contain <u>two</u> atoms.

tricycle   dicycle   monocycle

Formulas of Ionic Compounds Are More Like Ratios

See p.101 for more about ionic compounds.

1) <u>Ionic compounds</u> form giant <u>lattices</u> instead of individual molecules, so you can't say exactly how many atoms there are in a particular lattice.

2) Instead, the formula of an ionic compound tells you the <u>ratio</u> of the elements in the compound. E.g. sodium chloride, NaCl, has <u>one</u> chlorine atom for every <u>one</u> sodium atom, while magnesium chloride, $MgCl_2$, has <u>two</u> chlorines for every <u>one</u> magnesium.

3) The <u>names</u> of ionic compounds don't include <u>prefixes</u> to help you work out the numbers in the formula — you have to figure them out from the <u>charges</u> on the ions (see p.100).

I can't tell you what's in compound X — it's a secret formula...

I expect a lot of this is pretty familiar, but that's no reason to just skip this page — make sure you know it all.

Q1 The formula of the compound pentanol can be written $CH_3(CH_2)_4OH$.
How many hydrogen atoms are there in one molecule of pentanol?   [1 mark]

Chemical Equations

If you're going to get anywhere in chemistry you need to know about <u>chemical equations</u>...

Chemical Changes are Shown Using Chemical Equations

One way to show a chemical reaction is to write a <u>word equation</u>. It's not as <u>useful</u> as using chemical symbols because you can't tell straight away <u>what's happened</u> to each of the <u>atoms</u>, but it's <u>dead easy</u>.

> **Here's an example** — <u>methane</u> burns in <u>oxygen</u> giving <u>carbon dioxide</u> and <u>water</u>:
>
> The molecules on the <u>left-hand side</u> of the equation are called the <u>reactants</u> (because they react with each other).
>
> methane + oxygen → carbon dioxide + water
>
> The molecules on the <u>right-hand side</u> are called the <u>products</u> (because they've been produced from the reactants).

Symbol Equations Show the Atoms on Both Sides

Chemical <u>changes</u> can be shown in a kind of <u>shorthand</u> using symbol equations. Symbol equations just show the <u>symbols or formulas</u> of the <u>reactants</u> and <u>products</u>...

> magnesium + oxygen → magnesium oxide
> $$2Mg + O_2 \rightarrow 2MgO$$
>
> You can use the numbers in front of the formulas to work out the ratio between the number of moles of each substance (see pages 132-134 for more on moles and equations).

Symbol Equations Need to be Balanced

1) There must always be the <u>same</u> number of atoms of each element on <u>both sides</u> of the equation — they can't just <u>disappear</u>. This is called <u>conservation of mass</u> — there's more about it on page 131.

2) You <u>balance</u> the equation by putting numbers <u>in front</u> of the formulas where needed. Take this equation for reacting sulfuric acid with sodium hydroxide:

$$H_2SO_4 + NaOH \rightarrow Na_2SO_4 + H_2O$$

3) The <u>formulas</u> are all correct but the numbers of some atoms <u>don't match up</u> on both sides.

4) You <u>can't change formulas</u> like H_2SO_4 to H_2SO_5. You can only put numbers <u>in front of them</u>.

5) The more you <u>practise</u>, the <u>quicker</u> you get, but all you do is this:

- Find an element that <u>doesn't balance</u> and <u>pencil in a number</u> to try and sort it out.
- <u>See where it gets you</u>. It may create <u>another imbalance</u>, but if so, pencil in <u>another number</u> and see where that gets you.
- Carry on chasing <u>unbalanced</u> elements and the equation will <u>sort itself out</u> pretty quickly.

$E=mc^2$

> **EXAMPLE:** In the equation above you'll notice we're short of <u>H atoms</u> on the RHS (Right-Hand Side).
>
> 1) The only thing you can do about that is make it <u>2H$_2$O</u> instead of just H$_2$O:
> $$H_2SO_4 + NaOH \rightarrow Na_2SO_4 + 2H_2O$$
> 2) But that now gives <u>too many</u> H atoms and O atoms on the RHS, so to balance that up you could try putting <u>2NaOH</u> on the LHS (Left-Hand Side):
> $$H_2SO_4 + 2NaOH \rightarrow Na_2SO_4 + 2H_2O$$
> 3) And suddenly there it is! <u>Everything balances</u>. And you'll notice the Na just sorted itself out.

Revision is all about getting the balance right...

Balancing equations is all about practice. Once you have a few goes you'll see it's much less scary than it seemed before you took on, challenged and defeated this page. Go grab some chemistry glory.

Q1 Balance the equation: $Fe + Cl_2 \rightarrow FeCl_3$ [1 mark]

Q2 Hydrogen and oxygen molecules are formed in a reaction where water splits apart.
For this reaction: a) State the word equation. b) Give a balanced symbol equation. [3 marks]

Endothermic and Exothermic Reactions

Whenever chemical reactions occur, there are changes in <u>energy</u>. This is kind of interesting if you think of the number of chemical reactions that are involved in everyday life.

Reactions are Exothermic or Endothermic

An <u>EXOTHERMIC</u> <u>reaction</u> is one which <u>gives out energy</u> to the surroundings. This is usually shown by a <u>rise in temperature</u> of the surroundings.

An <u>ENDOTHERMIC</u> <u>reaction</u> is one which <u>takes in energy</u> from the surroundings. This is usually shown by a <u>fall in temperature</u> of the surroundings.

Combustion reactions (where something burns in oxygen — see page 84) are always exothermic.

Reaction Profiles Show if a Reaction's Exo- or Endothermic

<u>Reaction profiles</u> show the energy levels of the <u>reactants</u> and the <u>products</u> in a reaction. You can use them to work out if energy is <u>released</u> (exothermic) or <u>taken in</u> (endothermic).

1) This shows an <u>exothermic reaction</u> — the products are at a <u>lower energy</u> than the reactants.

2) The <u>difference in height</u> represents the <u>energy given out</u> in the reaction.

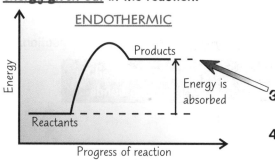

3) This shows an <u>endothermic reaction</u> because the products are at a <u>higher energy</u> than the reactants.

4) The <u>difference in height</u> represents the <u>energy taken in</u> during the reaction.

Activation Energy is the Energy Needed to Start a Reaction

1) The <u>activation energy</u> is the <u>minimum</u> amount of energy needed for <u>bonds to break</u> (see page 82) and a reaction to start. For example, you need to provide energy before a <u>fuel</u> will <u>burn</u>.

2) On a reaction profile, the activation energy is the difference between the reactants and the highest point on the curve.

3) It's a bit like having to <u>climb up</u> one side of a hill before you can ski/snowboard/sledge/fall down the <u>other side</u>.

4) If the <u>energy</u> input is <u>less than</u> the activation energy there <u>won't</u> be enough energy to <u>start</u> the reaction — so nothing will happen.

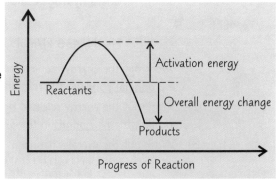

So if you <u>compare</u> two reaction profiles drawn on the <u>same set of axes</u> (or using the same scale):
- The one with the greater <u>energy change</u> will have a bigger difference between the <u>energy of the reactants</u> and the <u>energy of the products</u>.
- The one with the greater <u>activation energy</u> will have a bigger difference between the <u>energy of the reactants</u> and the <u>top of the curve</u>.

Exothermic reactions are a hot topic right now...

Remember, "exo-" = external, "-thermic" = heat, so an exothermic reaction is one that gives out heat to the exterior — and endothermic means just the opposite. To make sure you really understand these terms, try this question.

Q1 The temperature of a reaction mixture increases from 21 °C to 28.5 °C over the course of the reaction.
a) Is the reaction exothermic or endothermic? [1 mark]
b) Sketch a reaction profile to show the reaction. Label the energy of the reactants, the energy of the products and the activation energy. [3 marks]

Bond Energies

Energy transfer in chemical reactions is all to do with <u>making and breaking bonds</u>.

There's more on energy transfer on page 81.

Energy Must Always be Supplied to Break Bonds

1) During a chemical reaction, <u>existing bonds are broken</u> and <u>new bonds are formed</u>.

2) Energy must be <u>supplied</u> to break <u>existing bonds</u> — so bond breaking is an <u>endothermic</u> process.

3) Energy is <u>released</u> when new bonds are <u>formed</u> — so bond formation is an <u>exothermic</u> process.

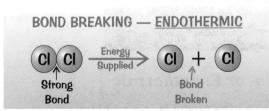
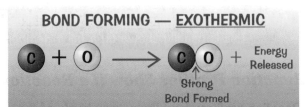

4) In <u>endothermic</u> reactions, the energy <u>used</u> to break bonds is <u>greater</u> than the energy <u>released</u> by forming new bonds.

5) In <u>exothermic</u> reactions, the energy <u>released</u> by forming bonds is <u>greater</u> than the energy used to <u>break</u> 'em.

Bond Energy Calculations — Need to be Practised

1) <u>Every</u> chemical bond has a particular <u>bond energy</u> associated with it.

2) You can use these <u>known bond energies</u> to calculate the <u>overall energy change</u> for a reaction.

> **Overall Energy Change** = Energy required to break bonds − Energy released by forming bonds

3) A <u>positive</u> energy change means an <u>endothermic</u> reaction and a <u>negative</u> energy change means an <u>exothermic</u> reaction.

4) You need to <u>practise</u> a few of these, but the basic idea is really very simple...

EXAMPLE: Using the bond energy values below, calculate the energy change for the following reaction, where hydrogen and chlorine react to produce hydrogen chloride:

$$H—H + Cl—Cl \rightarrow H—Cl + H—Cl$$

H—H: 436 kJ/mol   Cl—Cl: 242 kJ/mol   H—Cl: 431 kJ/mol

1) Work out the energy required to break the <u>original bonds</u> in the reactants.

   (1 × H—H) + (1 × Cl—Cl) = 436 + 242
   = 678 kJ/mol

2) Work out the energy released by forming the <u>new bonds</u> in the products.

   (2 × H—Cl) = 2 × 431
   = 862 kJ/mol

3) Work out the overall change.

   overall energy change = energy required to break bonds − energy released by forming bonds
   = 678 − 862 = −184 kJ/mol

In this reaction, the energy released by forming bonds is greater than the energy used to break them so the reaction is exothermic.

A student and their mobile — a bond that can never be broken...

This stuff might look hard at the moment, but with a bit of practice it's dead easy and it'll win you easy marks if you understand all the theory behind it. See how you get on with this question:

Q1 During the Haber Process, N_2 reacts with H_2 in the following reaction: $N_2 + 3H_2 \rightleftharpoons 2NH_3$
The bond energies for these molecules are:
N≡N: 941 kJ/mol, H–H: 436 kJ/mol,
N–H: 391 kJ/mol.
Calculate the overall energy change
for the forward reaction, shown on the right.

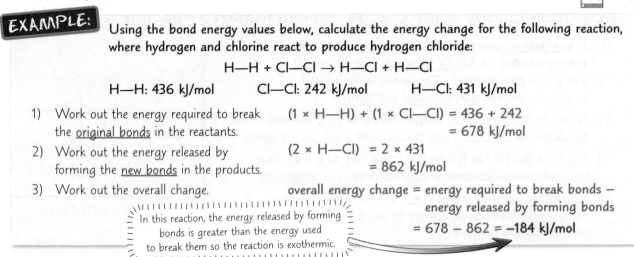

[3 marks]

Chapter C1 — Air and Water

The Evolution of the Atmosphere

Theories for how the Earth's atmosphere <u>evolved</u> have changed a lot over the years — it's hard to gather evidence from such a <u>long time period</u> and from <u>so long ago</u> (4.6 billion years). Here is one idea we've got:

Phase 1 — Volcanoes Gave Out Gases

1) The first <u>billion years</u> of Earth's history were pretty explosive — the surface was covered in <u>volcanoes</u> that erupted and released lots of gases. We think this was how the <u>early atmosphere</u> was formed.

2) The early atmosphere was probably mostly <u>carbon dioxide</u>, with <u>virtually no oxygen</u>. This is quite like the atmospheres of <u>Mars</u> and <u>Venus</u> today.

3) Volcanic activity also released <u>nitrogen</u>, which built up in the atmosphere over time, as well as <u>water vapour</u> and small amounts of <u>methane</u> and <u>ammonia</u>.

Phase 2 — Oceans, Algae and Green Plants Absorbed Carbon Dioxide

1) As the Earth <u>cooled</u>, the water vapour in the atmosphere <u>condensed</u> and formed the <u>oceans</u>.

2) Lots of carbon dioxide was removed from the early atmosphere as it <u>dissolved</u> in the oceans. This dissolved carbon dioxide then went through a series of reactions to form <u>carbonate precipitates</u> that formed <u>sediments</u> on the <u>seabed</u>.

3) The first <u>bacteria</u> (called <u>cyanobacteria</u>), followed by <u>green plants</u> and <u>algae</u>, evolved and absorbed some of the carbon dioxide so that they could carry out <u>photosynthesis</u> (see below) to produce <u>glucose</u>.

4) Later, marine <u>animals</u> evolved. Their <u>shells</u> and <u>skeletons</u> contained <u>carbonates</u> from the oceans.

5) When plants, plankton and marine animals <u>died</u>, they fell to the seabed and got <u>buried</u> by <u>layers of sediment</u>. Over millions of years, they became <u>compressed</u> and formed <u>sedimentary rocks</u>, <u>oil</u> and <u>gas</u> — trapping the carbon within them and keeping the carbon dioxide levels in the atmosphere <u>reduced</u>.

Phase 3 — Green Plants and Algae Produced Oxygen

1) As well as absorbing the carbon dioxide in the atmosphere, cyanobacteria, green plants and algae produced oxygen by <u>photosynthesis</u> — this is when organisms use light to convert carbon dioxide and water into <u>glucose</u>:

$$\text{carbon dioxide} + \text{water} \rightarrow \text{glucose} + \text{oxygen}$$
$$6CO_2 + 6H_2O \rightarrow C_6H_{12}O_6 + 6O_2$$

2) Cyanobacteria evolved <u>first</u> — about <u>2.7 billion</u> years ago. Then algae and green plants evolved later.

3) As oxygen levels built up in the atmosphere over time, more <u>complex life</u> (like animals) could evolve.

4) Eventually, the atmosphere reached a composition similar to what it is <u>today</u>: approximately 78% nitrogen, 21% oxygen and small amounts of other gases (each only makes up less than 1% of the atmosphere), mainly carbon dioxide, noble gases and water vapour.

There's Evidence to Support This Explanation

1) Scientists have gathered <u>evidence</u> to back up this view of how the atmosphere evolved.

2) For example, some <u>rock formations</u> that contain iron compounds only form when there's <u>hardly any oxygen</u> about. These rock formations are all very <u>ancient</u>, which suggests there was little oxygen in the early atmosphere.

3) The <u>fossil record</u> also supports this — the earliest fossils are of <u>tiny organisms</u> that could survive without much oxygen in the <u>atmosphere</u>. Fossils suggest more complex organisms such as <u>animals</u> which need oxygen to survive, only appeared later, after the atmosphere had changed.

The atmosphere's evolving — shut the window will you...

So all you need for a habitable planet is a few volcanoes, water, some algae and a few billion years. Easy-peasy.

Q1   Explain how the Earth's atmosphere was changed by the evolution of green plants and algae.   [3 marks]

Combustion and Air Pollution

We burn lots of <u>fossil fuels</u> to supply the <u>energy</u> to sustain our <u>modern lifestyles</u> — but this comes at a <u>cost</u>...

Combustion Reactions are an Example of Oxidation

1) The term <u>oxidation</u> is used to describe the <u>addition of oxygen</u> to a substance in a reaction.

2) <u>Combustion reactions</u>, which happen when you burn substances in <u>oxygen</u>, are oxidation reactions.

3) For example, when you burn <u>hydrocarbons</u> (compounds made of hydrogen and carbon only) in oxygen, the hydrogen and carbon in the hydrocarbons are <u>oxidised</u>.

4) When you burn hydrocarbons in plenty of oxygen, the only products are <u>carbon dioxide</u> and <u>water</u> — this is called <u>complete combustion</u>.

> hydrocarbon + oxygen → carbon dioxide + water
> E.g. C_3H_8 + $5O_2$ → $3CO_2$ + $4H_2O$

5) If there's <u>not enough oxygen</u> around for complete combustion, you get <u>incomplete combustion</u>. This can happen when <u>fossil fuels</u> are burned in power stations or in the engines of vehicles.

6) As well as carbon dioxide, other carbon-based products can form that contain <u>less oxygen</u>.

7) Incomplete combustion produces a mixture of <u>carbon monoxide</u> (CO), which is a <u>toxic gas</u>, and <u>carbon</u> in the form of soot, as well as carbon dioxide and water.

The bits of carbon that form soot are called particulates.

- <u>Carbon monoxide</u> can combine with haemoglobin in red blood cells and stop your blood from doing its proper job of <u>carrying oxygen</u> around the body.
- A lack of oxygen in the blood supply to the brain can lead to <u>fainting</u>, a <u>coma</u> or even <u>death</u>.

- During incomplete combustion, tiny <u>particles of carbon</u> can be released into the atmosphere. When they fall back to the ground, they deposit themselves as the horrible black dust we call <u>soot</u>.
- Soot makes buildings look <u>dirty</u>, <u>reduces air quality</u> and can cause or worsen <u>respiratory problems</u>.

Sulfur Dioxide and Oxides of Nitrogen Can be Released

1) Some fossil fuels, such as <u>coal</u>, contain <u>sulfur impurities</u>. When these fuels are burnt, the sulfur can be <u>oxidised</u>, which means that <u>sulfur dioxide</u> (SO_2) is released.

2) <u>Nitrogen oxides</u> are created from a reaction between the <u>nitrogen</u> and <u>oxygen</u> in the <u>air</u>, caused by the <u>heat</u> of the burning. (This can happen in the <u>internal combustion engines</u> of cars.)

3) When these gases mix with <u>clouds</u> they form <u>dilute sulfuric acid</u> or <u>dilute nitric acid</u>. This then falls as <u>acid rain</u>, which kills <u>plants</u>, <u>damages</u> buildings and statues, and makes metal <u>corrode</u>.

4) Sulfur dioxide and nitrogen oxides can cause smog to form — ground-level air pollution that can cause <u>respiratory problems</u> if it's breathed in.

<u>Sulfur can be removed from fuels:</u>

1) Most of the sulfur can be <u>removed</u> from fuels <u>before</u> they're burnt, but this can be <u>expensive</u>.

2) Removing sulfur from fuels also takes <u>a lot of energy</u>. This usually comes from burning more fuel, which releases more of the greenhouse gas <u>carbon dioxide</u>.

3) However, in many countries (including the UK) petrol and diesel have now been replaced by <u>low-sulfur</u> versions.

<u>Emissions can be reduced:</u>

1) <u>Power stations</u> now have <u>acid gas scrubbers</u> to take the harmful gases <u>out</u> before they release their fumes into the atmosphere.

2) Most <u>cars</u> are now fitted with <u>catalytic converters</u>, which remove nitrogen oxides from <u>exhaust gases</u>.

3) The other way of reducing harmful emissions is simply to <u>reduce</u> our usage of <u>fossil fuels</u>.

Scientists monitor the levels of these pollutants in the air to make sure air quality standards are maintained.

Do you want to hear a joke about nitrogen monoxide? NO...

Acid rain's bad news for sculptors, fish and trees alike. It's bad news for you too, as you need to know it...

Q1 Name two pollutants formed by incomplete combustion. [2 marks]

Greenhouse Gases and Climate Change

Greenhouse gases keep the Earth cosy and warm. But turns out you can have too much of a good thing...

Carbon Dioxide is a Greenhouse Gas

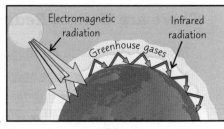

Electromagnetic radiation

Infrared radiation

Greenhouse gases

1) Greenhouse gases like carbon dioxide, methane and water vapour act like an insulating layer in the Earth's atmosphere — this helps to keep the Earth warm enough to support life.

2) The Sun gives out electromagnetic radiation. Some of this passes through the atmosphere and is absorbed by Earth — warming it up. The Earth emits long wavelength radiation which is absorbed by greenhouse gases in the atmosphere and then re-emitted in all directions — including back towards the Earth. The longwave radiation is infrared (thermal) radiation, so it makes Earth warmer than it would otherwise be. This is the greenhouse effect.

3) Some forms of human activity affect the amount of greenhouse gases in the atmosphere. E.g.

- Deforestation: fewer trees means less CO_2 is removed from the atmosphere via photosynthesis.
- Burning fossil fuels: carbon that was 'locked up' in these fuels is released as CO_2.
- Agriculture: farm animals produce methane through their digestive processes.
- Creating waste: more landfill sites and more waste from agriculture means more CO_2 and methane are released by decomposition of waste.

Increasing Carbon Dioxide is Linked to Climate Change

1) Over the last 200 years, the percentage of carbon dioxide in the atmosphere has increased — this correlates with an increased use of fossil fuels by people as well as an increase in global temperature.

2) The Earth's temperature varies naturally, but recently the average temperature of the Earth's surface has been increasing. Most scientists agree that extra CO_2 and other greenhouse gases from human activity are causing this increase and this will lead to further climate change.

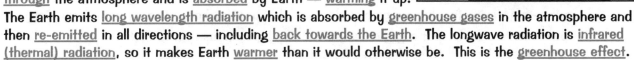

Global Temp. Change Compared to 1951-1980 average (°C)

Atmospheric CO_2 Concentration (ppm)

3) Many studies looking at rising CO_2 levels and climate change have produced similar findings — increasing our confidence in the evidence.

4) However, it's hard to predict how the climate will change in the future. This is because we don't know how greenhouse gas emissions might change, so predictions made by extrapolating existing data may not be realistic. The Earth's climate is also complex, and there are many variables, so it's hard to make a model that isn't oversimplified.

5) More data on climate change is being collected all the time so the uncertainties in data are decreasing. This means the predictions and models that scientists make are more likely to be realistic.

Climate Change Could Have Dangerous Consequences

The Earth's climate is complex, but it's still important to make predictions about the consequences of climate change so that policy-makers can make decisions now. For example:

1) An increase in global temperature could lead to increased melting of the polar ice caps — causing a further rise in sea levels, increased flooding in coastal areas and coastal erosion.

2) Changes in rainfall patterns (the amount, timing and distribution of rain) may cause some regions to get too much or too little water. This, along with changes in temperature, may affect the ability of certain regions to produce food.

3) The frequency and severity of storms may also increase, which can cause flooding on low land.

When scientists and governments assess the impacts of changes to the climate, they need to consider a range of factors, e.g. how many people will be affected by a change or how severely they will be affected.

Yep, we all know what 'digestive processes' means...

Everyone's talking about climate change these days — it's pretty scary stuff, but make sure you get it.

Q1   Give three potential consequences of climate change.   [3 marks]

Reducing Pollution and Tests for Gases

To slow down <u>global warming</u>, we need to <u>reduce</u> the amount of CO_2 and methane we put into the atmosphere.

There are Ways of Reducing Greenhouse Gas Emissions

There are methods to try to <u>reduce</u> the amount of greenhouse gases we produce. For example:

- <u>Renewable energy sources</u> or <u>nuclear energy</u> could be used instead of <u>fossil fuels</u>.
- Using more <u>efficient processes</u> could cut <u>waste</u>, producing less methane and <u>conserving energy</u>.
- Governments could <u>tax</u> companies or individuals based on the amount of greenhouse gases they <u>emit</u> — e.g. taxing <u>fuel-hungry cars</u> could mean that people <u>choose</u> to buy more <u>fuel efficient</u> ones.
- Governments can also put a <u>cap</u> on emissions of <u>all</u> greenhouse gases that companies make — then <u>sell licences</u> for emissions <u>up to</u> that cap.

Greenhouse gas producers can also take steps to <u>deal with</u> the gases they do produce:

- <u>Carbon off-setting</u> can be done by buying <u>carbon credits</u> — this means companies or individuals invest in a scheme that removes CO_2 from the atmosphere. For example, for a <u>certain amount</u> of greenhouse gases emitted, <u>trees can be planted</u> to <u>remove</u> an equivalent amount of CO_2 by <u>photosynthesis</u>.
- If a business off-sets <u>all</u> its greenhouse gas emissions, it's said to be <u>carbon neutral</u>.
- There's also technology that <u>captures</u> the CO_2 produced by burning fossil fuels <u>before</u> it's released into the atmosphere — it can then be <u>stored deep underground</u> in gaps in the rock such as old <u>oil wells</u>.

But Making Reductions is Still Difficult

1) It's easy enough <u>saying</u> that we should cut emissions, but <u>actually doing it</u> — that's a <u>different story</u>.

2) There's still a lot of work to be done on <u>alternative technologies</u> that result in <u>lower</u> CO_2 emissions.

3) New technologies can have <u>unexpected impacts</u> — e.g. <u>carbon capture</u> schemes use a lot of energy, so capturing the CO_2 produced by a power plant can effectively make the plant much <u>less efficient</u>. New technologies could also impact the <u>environment</u> in ways that we haven't predicted.

4) The <u>scale of emissions</u> makes it hard to reduce them — it would be impossible to store all the greenhouse gases we produce underground, or to plant enough trees to cancel them out entirely.

5) A lot of <u>governments</u> are also worried that these changes will impact on <u>economic growth</u> — which could be <u>bad</u> for people's <u>well-being</u>. This is particularly important for countries that are <u>still developing</u>.

6) Because not everyone is on board, it's hard to make <u>international agreements</u> to reduce emissions. Most countries don't want to <u>sacrifice</u> their <u>economic development</u> if they think that others <u>won't do the same</u>.

There are Tests for 4 Common Gases | PRACTICAL

1) Chlorine: Chlorine <u>bleaches</u> damp blue <u>litmus paper</u>, turning it white. (It may turn <u>red</u> for a moment first though — that's because a solution of chlorine is <u>acidic</u>.)

Litmus paper
Chlorine

2) Oxygen: If you put a glowing splint inside a test tube containing <u>oxygen</u>, the oxygen will <u>relight</u> the <u>glowing splint</u>.

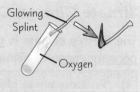

Glowing Splint
Oxygen

3) Hydrogen: If you hold a <u>lit splint</u> at the open end of a test tube containing hydrogen, you get a "<u>squeaky pop</u>". (The noise comes from the hydrogen burning quickly with the oxygen in the air to form H_2O.)

POP!
Lighted Splint
Hydrogen

4) Carbon Dioxide: Bubbling carbon dioxide through (or shaking carbon dioxide with) an aqueous solution of <u>calcium hydroxide</u> (known as <u>limewater</u>) makes the solution turn <u>cloudy</u>.

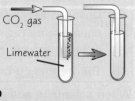

CO_2 gas
Limewater

Cutting greenhouse gas production — emission possible...?

If you're wondering why the gas tests are on this page, it's not just because I had to fit them in *somewhere*. Honest...

Q1   State two things governments can do to try to reduce the greenhouse gas emissions of businesses. [2 marks]

Potable Water

Potable water is not to be confused with portable water, which is water you can fit in your pocket.

There are a Variety of Water Resources

The global population is increasing, so there is a greater need for potable water (water that is fit to drink). There are a number of sources of water, which can be treated to provide potable water. These include:

1) GROUND WATER: from aquifers (rocks that trap water underground).

2) WASTE WATER: from water that's been contaminated by a human process, e.g. waste water from sewage.

3) SALT WATER: from the sea.

Potable water doesn't have to be chemically pure (see p.126) — e.g. it usually contains low levels of dissolved salts.

Water Needs to be Treated to Make it Potable

1) The water that comes out of your taps has been treated to make sure it's safe to drink.

2) The first step to treat ground water is often aeration — the water is mixed with air to increase the levels of dissolved oxygen. This forces other dissolved gases out of the water, and also removes certain ions, which react with the oxygen to form solid oxides.

3) Then the water is filtered to remove any solid impurities.

Waste Water Treatment Happens in Several Stages

1) Waste water usually has to undergo several stages of treatment to make it potable.

2) It has to be filtered, which often involves multiple steps to remove different sizes of solid impurities.

3) Next, air is pumped through the water to encourage aerobic bacteria (bacteria that need oxygen to survive) to grown and break down any organic matter.

4) For waste water containing toxic substances, additional stages of treatment may involve adding chemicals (e.g. to precipitate metals), UV radiation or using membranes.

5) Waste water treatment requires more processes than treating ground water but uses less energy than the desalination of salt water, so could be used as an alternative in areas where ground water is limited.

You Can Get Potable Water by Distilling Sea Water

1) In some dry countries, sea water is distilled to produce drinking water.

2) On a small scale, sea water can be distilled using a solar still — a bowl filled with salt water and covered with a clear, domed lid. If it's left in direct sunlight, the water warms up and evaporates. The water condenses on the lid, and can be collected, leaving the salt behind. On a larger scale, traditional distillation apparatus (p.129) is used, which usually involves burning fossil fuels to heat the water.

3) Sea water can also be treated by processes that use membranes — like reverse osmosis. The salt water is forced through a membrane that only allows water molecules to pass through. Ions and larger molecules are trapped by the membrane and so separated from the water.

4) Both processes involve fewer stages than other purification methods, but on a large scale, both thermal distillation and reverse osmosis need loads of energy — making them expensive and impractical.

The Last Step is Chlorination

1) Whatever the source, the final step in water treatment is usually chlorination.

2) Chlorine gas is bubbled through to kill harmful bacteria and other microbes.

3) In certain conditions, chlorine can react with compounds found in the water to form potentially dangerous chemicals. Levels of these chemicals have to be carefully monitored. But because it kills off some really nasty bacteria, the benefits of chlorination are generally thought to far outweigh any risks.

In many countries, the government makes sure water supplies are chlorinated. In places where this isn't the case, there is a greater risk of water-borne diseases.

If water from the ground is ground water, why isn't rain sky water?

Ahhh... Every glass of tap water I drink tastes all the sweeter for knowing all it had to go through to get to me...

Q1   Give two different reasons why air is added to water during water treatment processes.   [2 marks]

Revision Questions for Chapter C1

Hey, we made it to the end of Chapter C1 — well done us. I'm proud of you, buddy.

- Try these questions and tick off each one when you get it right.
- When you've done all the questions for a topic and are completely happy with it, tick off the topic.

States of Matter (p.77-78) ☑

1) Name the three states of matter. ☑

2) How does the strength of the forces between particles in a substance influence the temperature at which it changes from being a solid to being a liquid? ☑

3) What name is given to the temperature at which a liquid becomes a gas? ☑

Chemical Formulas and Equations (p.79-80) ☑

4) Give the formula for: a) carbon dioxide b) ammonia ☑

5) What are the chemicals on the left-hand side of a chemical equation called? ☑

6) Balance these equations: a) $Mg + O_2 \rightarrow MgO$ b) $H_2SO_4 + NaOH \rightarrow Na_2SO_4 + H_2O$ ☑

Temperature Changes and Bond Energies (p.81-82) ☑

7) What is the difference between an endothermic and an exothermic reaction? ☑

8) Sketch a reaction profile for an exothermic reaction. ☑

9) What is meant by the term 'activation energy'? ☑

10) Is energy released when bonds are broken or when they are made? ☑

11) How would you calculate the overall energy change in a reaction from the bond energies? ☑

The Atmosphere (p.83-86) ☑

12) Name the gases given out by volcanoes billions of years ago. ☑

13) What change in the early atmosphere allowed complex organisms to evolve? ☑

14) Give the word equation for the complete combustion of hydrocarbons. ☑

15) Under what conditions does incomplete combustion occur? ☑

16) Name a gas that contributes to the production of acid rain. ☑

17) Give three problems associated with acid rain. ☑

18) Explain how the greenhouse effect works to keep the Earth warm. ☑

19) State three ways in which human activity is leading to an increase in carbon dioxide in the atmosphere. ☑

20) Explain why reducing carbon dioxide emissions can be a difficult issue. ☑

21) What is the chemical test for oxygen? ☑

Water Treatment (p.87) ☑

22) Name two methods could you use for making salt water potable. ☑

23) Why is chlorine added to drinking water? ☑

The History of the Atom

Atoms are really, really <u>tiny</u> so we can't see what they look like. Over time, <u>scientists</u> have carried out different <u>experiments</u> to figure out <u>atomic structure</u>. Hold on to your hat, you're going on a journey through <u>time</u>...

The Theory of Atomic Structure Has Changed Over Time

1) In <u>Ancient Greece</u>, some people thought that there were four basic '<u>elements</u>' that made up everything — <u>earth</u>, <u>air</u>, <u>fire</u> and <u>water</u>. <u>Leucippus</u> and <u>Democritus</u> believed that there must be something <u>smaller</u> that made up these 'elements' — a solid substance that could not be split into smaller units — the <u>atom</u>.

2) At the start of the 19th century <u>John Dalton</u> described atoms as <u>solid spheres</u>, and said that different spheres made up the different chemical <u>elements</u> we know today.

3) In 1904 <u>J J Thomson</u> concluded from his experiments that atoms <u>weren't</u> solid spheres. His measurements of <u>charge</u> and <u>mass</u> showed that an atom must contain even smaller, negatively charged particles — <u>electrons</u>. The 'solid sphere' idea of atomic structure had to be changed. The new theory was known as the '<u>plum pudding model</u>'.

4) The plum pudding model showed the atom as a <u>ball</u> of <u>positive charge</u> with <u>electrons</u> stuck in it.

positively charged 'pudding'   electrons

delicious pudding

Rutherford Showed that the Plum Pudding Model Was Wrong

1) In 1911 Ernest <u>Rutherford</u> and two of his <u>students</u> published the results of the famous <u>alpha scattering experiments</u>. They fired positively charged <u>alpha particles</u> at an extremely thin sheet of gold.

2) From the plum pudding model, they were <u>expecting</u> the particles to <u>pass straight through</u> the sheet or be <u>slightly deflected</u> at most. This was because the positive charge of each atom was thought to be very <u>spread out</u> through the 'pudding' of the atom. But, whilst most of the particles <u>did</u> go <u>straight through</u> the gold sheet, some were deflected <u>more than expected</u>, and a small number were <u>deflected backwards</u>. So the plum pudding model <u>couldn't</u> be right.

3) So Rutherford came up with an idea that could explain this new evidence — the <u>nuclear model</u> of the atom. In this, there's a tiny, positively charged <u>nucleus</u> at the centre, surrounded by a 'cloud' of negative electrons

A few particles are deflected backwards by the nucleus.

Most of the particles pass through empty space, but a few are deflected.

— most of the atom is <u>empty space</u>. When alpha particles came near the <u>concentrated</u>, <u>positive charge</u> of the <u>nucleus</u>, they were <u>deflected</u>. If they were fired directly at the nucleus, they were deflected <u>backwards</u>. Otherwise, they passed through the empty space.

Bohr's Model Explains a Lot

1) Scientists realised that electrons in a 'cloud' around the nucleus of an atom, as Rutherford described, would be attracted to the nucleus, causing the atom to <u>collapse</u>. Niels Bohr's model of the atom suggested that all the electrons were contained in <u>shells</u>.

2) Bohr proposed that electrons <u>orbit</u> the nucleus in <u>fixed shells</u> and aren't anywhere in between. Each shell is a fixed distance from the nucleus.

3) Bohr's theory of atomic structure was supported by many <u>experiments</u> and it helped to explain lots of other scientists' <u>observations</u> at the time.

nucleus   shells

electron

Scientific Theories Have to be Backed Up by Evidence

1) Scientists have continued to develop Bohr's theory — the current atomic model looks very <u>different</u> to earlier ideas. These ideas were <u>accepted</u> because they fitted the <u>evidence</u> available at the time.

2) As scientists did more <u>experiments</u>, new evidence was found and our theory of the <u>structure</u> of the atom was <u>modified</u> to fit it. This is nearly always the way <u>scientific knowledge</u> develops — new evidence prompts people to come up with new, <u>improved ideas</u>. These ideas can be used to make <u>predictions</u> which, if proved correct, are a pretty good indication that the ideas are <u>right</u>.

I wanted to be a model — but I ate too much plum pudding...

This is a great example of how science works. Scientists working together to find evidence. Lovely.

Q1   Describe the 'plum pudding' model of the atom.   [1 mark]

The Atom

There are quite a few different (and equally useful) modern models of the atom — but chemists tend to like this model best. You can use it to explain loads of chemistry... which is nice. Well, here goes...

The Atom is Made Up of Protons, Neutrons and Electrons

The atom is made up of three subatomic particles — protons, neutrons and electrons.

- Protons are heavy and positively charged.
- Neutrons are heavy and neutral.
- Electrons have hardly any mass and are negatively charged.

Particle	Relative Mass	Relative Charge
Proton	1	+1
Neutron	1	0
Electron	0.0005	−1

Relative mass (measured in atomic mass units) measures mass on a scale where the mass of a proton or neutron is 1.

In reality, protons and neutrons are still teeny tiny. They're just heavy compared to electrons.

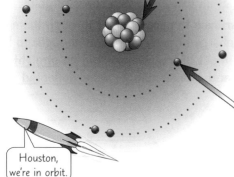

Houston, we're in orbit.

All of the objects that we come across in our day-to-day lives contain millions and millions of atoms. For example, a 50p coin contains 7.74×10^{22} atoms alone.

The Nucleus

1) The nucleus is in the middle of the atom.

2) It contains protons and neutrons.

3) It has a positive charge because of the protons.

4) Almost the whole mass of the atom (between about 10^{-23} g and 10^{-21} g) is concentrated in the nucleus.

5) Compared to the overall size of the atom, the nucleus is tiny — about a hundred-thousandth of the diameter of the atom (the nucleus has a radius of between about 10^{-15} m and 10^{-14} m).

If you magnified a nucleus to the size of a street rubbish bin in London, the electrons would be whizzing around the M25.

The Electrons

1) Electrons move around the nucleus in electron shells (or energy levels).

2) They're negatively charged.

3) They're tiny, but their shells cover a lot of space.

4) The volume of their shells determines the size of the atom — atoms are typically 10^{-10} m across.

5) Electrons have virtually no mass — it's often taken as zero.

Molecules Form When Atoms Bond Together

1) Molecules are made up of two or more atoms held together by covalent bonds.

2) Molecules can be made of the same element (e.g. hydrogen), or different elements (e.g. ammonia).

3) Simple molecules (see page 111) are pretty tiny (like atoms). The bonds that form between these molecules are generally a similar length to the atomic diameter — about 10^{-10} m.

4) Nanoparticles (see page 123) are a bit bigger than simple molecules. They can contain between a few hundred and tens of thousands of atoms and range from 1 nm to 100 nm in size.

ammonia molecule

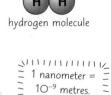
hydrogen molecule

1 nanometer = 10^{-9} metres.

Don't trust atoms — they make up everything...

You need to learn what's in that table with the relative masses and charges of the different parts of the atom. Try remembering Protons are Positive, Neutrons are Neutral and Electrons are E... Never mind.

Q1 Where is most of the mass of an atom to be found? [1 mark]

Q2 Put the following things in order of size, starting with the smallest:
atomic radius, nuclear radius, nanoparticle, simple molecule (e.g. Cl_2). [2 marks]

Atoms, Ions and Isotopes

As if <u>atoms</u> weren't fiddly enough, time to meet those pesky <u>ions</u>. Oh, and don't get me started on <u>isotopes</u>...

Atomic Number and Mass Number Describe an Atom

These two numbers tell you how many of each kind of <u>subatomic particle</u> an atom has.

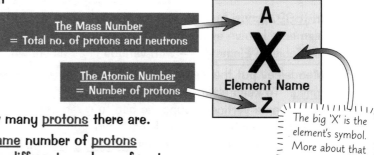

> In some notations and periodic tables (like the one on the data sheet in the exam), these numbers are the other way round. Just remember the bigger one is the mass number.

The Mass Number
= Total no. of protons and neutrons

The Atomic Number
= Number of protons

$$^A_Z X \quad \text{Element Name}$$

> The big 'X' is the element's symbol. More about that on page 79.

1) The <u>atomic (proton) number</u> tells you how many <u>protons</u> there are.

2) Atoms of the <u>same</u> element all have the <u>same</u> number of <u>protons</u> — so atoms of <u>different</u> elements will have <u>different</u> numbers of protons.

3) To get the number of <u>neutrons</u>, just subtract the <u>atomic number</u> from the <u>mass number</u>.

4) The <u>mass (nucleon) number</u> is always the <u>biggest</u> number. On a periodic table the mass number is actually the <u>relative atomic mass</u> (see page 130).

5) Neutral atoms have <u>no charge</u> overall (unlike ions, see below). This is because they have the <u>same number</u> of <u>protons</u> as <u>electrons</u>. The charge on the electrons is the same size as the charge on the protons, but opposite — so the charges cancel out. So, the number of electrons in a neutral atom is also <u>equal</u> to the <u>atomic number</u>.

Ions have Different Numbers of Protons and Electrons

1) Ions form when atoms (or groups of atoms) <u>gain</u> or <u>lose electrons</u> (see page 100 for more).

2) <u>Negative ions</u> form when atoms <u>gain electrons</u> — they have more electrons than protons. <u>Positive ions</u> form when atoms <u>lose electrons</u> — they have more protons than electrons.

- F^- — there's a <u>single negative charge</u>, so there must be one more electron than protons. F has an atomic number of 9, so has 9 protons. So F^- must have $9 + 1 = $ <u>10 electrons</u>.

- Fe^{2+} — there's a <u>2+ charge</u>, so there must be two more protons than electrons. Fe has an atomic number of 26, so has 26 protons. So Fe^{2+} must have $26 - 2 = $ <u>24 electrons</u>.

Isotopes are the Same Except for the Number of Neutrons

> Isotopes are different forms of the same element, which have the same number of protons but a different number of neutrons.

1) Isotopes have the <u>same atomic number</u> but <u>different mass numbers</u>.

2) If they had <u>different</u> atomic numbers, they'd be <u>different</u> elements altogether.

3) A famous example is the two main isotopes of <u>carbon</u>.

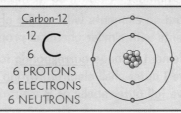

Carbon-12

$$^{12}_6 C$$

6 PROTONS
6 ELECTRONS
6 NEUTRONS

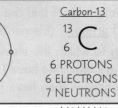

Carbon-13

$$^{13}_6 C$$

6 PROTONS
6 ELECTRONS
7 NEUTRONS

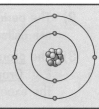

4) Because many <u>elements</u> can exist as a number of different isotopes, <u>relative atomic mass</u> (A_r) is used instead of mass number when referring to the element as a whole. A_r is an average mass taking into account the <u>different</u> masses of <u>isotopes</u> that make up the element.

> If an element only has one stable isotope, the A_r is the same as the mass number and will be a whole number on the periodic table.

Na⁺ was positive that he'd misplaced one of his electrons...

There's a smattering of maths here, but it's just some adding and subtracting, so don't worry too much.

Q1   a)   Bromine has an atomic number of 35. It exists naturally with 2 isotopes, bromine-79 and bromine-81. Work out how many neutrons, protons and electrons are in each isotope. [2 marks]

   b)   Bromine tends to react by forming Br^- ions. How many electrons are in a Br^- ion? [1 mark]

The Periodic Table

We haven't always known as much about chemistry as we do now. No sirree. Take the periodic table.
Early chemists looked to try and understand patterns in the elements' properties to get a bit of understanding.

Dmitri Mendeleev Made the First Proper Periodic Table

1) In 1869, Dmitri Mendeleev took the 50 or so elements known at the time and arranged them into his Table of Elements — with various gaps as shown.

Mendeleev's Table of the Elements

```
H
Li  Be                                              B  C  N  O  F
Na  Mg                                              Al Si P  S  Cl
K   Ca  *  Ti V  Cr  Mn Fe  Co Ni Cu Zn  *  *  As Se Br
Rb  Sr  Y  Zr Nb Mo  *   Ru Rh Pd Ag Cd In Sn Sb Te I
Cs  Ba  *  *  Ta W   *   Os Ir Pt Au Hg Tl Pb Bi
```

2) Mendeleev put the elements in order of atomic mass. To keep elements with similar properties in the same vertical groups, he had to swap one or two elements round and leave a few gaps. He was prepared to leave some very big gaps in the first two rows before the transition metals come in on the third row.

3) The gaps were the really clever bit because they were left for so far undiscovered elements and allowed Mendeleev to predict what their properties would be. When they were found and they fitted the pattern, it helped confirm Mendeleev's ideas. For example, Mendeleev made really good predictions about the chemical and physical properties of an element he called ekasilicon, which we know today as germanium.

This is How the Periodic Table Looks Today

atomic number → chemical symbol
relative atomic mass → name

| | Group 0 |
Key:
- reactive metals
- transition metals
- post-transition metals
- non metals
- noble gases
- separates metals from non-metals

The periodic table represents each element using its chemical symbol.
These can be used to write chemical formulas and equations (see pages 79-80).

1) Once protons and electrons were discovered, the atomic number (see p.91) of each element could be found, based on the number of protons in its nucleus. The modern periodic table shows the elements in order of ascending atomic number — and they fit the same patterns that Mendeleev worked out.

2) The periodic table is laid out so elements with similar chemical properties form columns — these are called groups. (Elements with similar chemical properties react in similar ways.)

3) The group to which the element belongs corresponds to the number of electrons it has in its outer shell. E.g. Group 1 elements have 1 outer shell electron, Group 7 elements have 7, etc. Group 0 elements are the exception — they have full outer shells of 8 electrons (or 2 in the case of helium).

4) The rows are called periods. Each new period represents electrons going into the next highest electron shell (see next page).

5) The period to which the element belongs corresponds to the number of shells which contain electrons.

I'm in a chemistry band — I play the symbols...

Because of how the periodic table is organised in groups and periods, you can see the trends in the reactivity (and other properties) of the elements and therefore make predictions on how reactions will occur. How neat is that?

Q1   Using a periodic table, state how many electrons barium has in its outer shell.   [1 mark]

Q2   Based on its position in the periodic table, would you expect the chemical properties of potassium to be more similar to those of sodium or calcium? Explain your answer.   [2 marks]

Electronic Structure

Like snails, <u>electrons</u> live in <u>shells</u>. Unlike snails, electrons won't nibble on your petunias...

Electron Shell Rules:

1) Electrons occupy <u>shells</u> (sometimes called <u>energy levels</u>).
2) The <u>lowest</u> energy levels are <u>always filled first</u>.
3) Only <u>a certain number</u> of electrons are allowed in each shell:

1st shell	2nd shell	3rd shell
<u>2</u> electrons	<u>8</u> electrons	<u>8</u> electrons

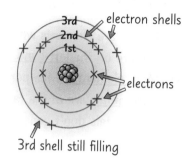

Working Out Electronic Structures

The <u>electronic structures</u> for the first <u>20</u> elements are shown below. You can also <u>work them out</u>.

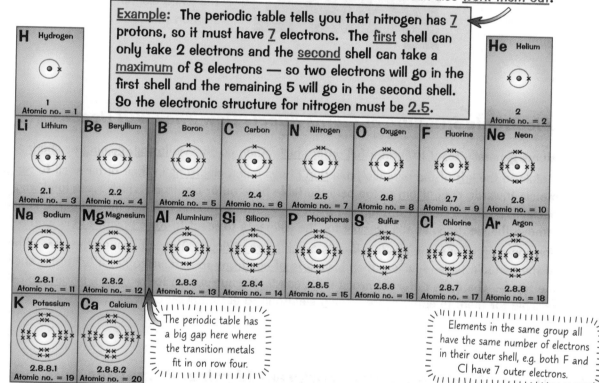

Example: The periodic table tells you that nitrogen has <u>7</u> protons, so it must have <u>7</u> electrons. The <u>first</u> shell can only take 2 electrons and the <u>second</u> shell can take a <u>maximum</u> of 8 electrons — so two electrons will go in the first shell and the remaining 5 will go in the second shell. So the electronic structure for nitrogen must be <u>2.5</u>.

The periodic table has a big gap here where the transition metals fit in on row four.

Elements in the same group all have the same number of electrons in their outer shell, e.g. both F and Cl have 7 outer electrons.

You can also work out the electronic structure of an element from its <u>period</u> and <u>group</u>.
- The <u>number of shells</u> which contain electrons is the same as the <u>period</u> of the element.
- The <u>group number</u> tells you <u>how many electrons</u> occupy the <u>outer shell</u> of the element.

Example: Sodium is in <u>period 3</u>, so it has <u>3</u> shells occupied — so the first two shells must be full (2.8). It's in <u>Group 1</u>, so it has <u>1</u> electron in its outer shell. So its electronic structure is <u>2.8.1</u>.

Position in the Periodic Table can Help You Predict Reactivity of Elements

1) The <u>way</u> that an element reacts depends on the <u>number of electrons</u> in its <u>outer shell</u>.
2) Elements with the <u>same number</u> of electrons in their outer shell (members of the same group) will react in <u>similar ways</u>.
3) The <u>number of shells</u> that an element has affects <u>how reactive</u> it is.

In Group 1, the more shells an element has, the more reactive it will be (see p.95), whereas increasing the number of shells in Group 7 makes the element less reactive (see p.97).

The electronic structure of the fifth element — it's a bit boron...

Electronic structures may seem a bit complicated at first but once you learn the rules, it's a piece of cake.

Q1 Give the electronic structure of potassium (atomic number = 19). [1 mark]

Metals and Non-Metals

I can almost guarantee you'll touch something metallic today, that's how important metals are to modern life.

Most Elements are Metals

1) Metals are elements which can form positive ions when they react.
2) They're on the left-hand side and towards the right and bottom of the periodic table.
3) Most elements in the periodic table are metals.
4) Non-metals are at the far right of the periodic table.
5) Non-metals don't generally form positive ions when they react.

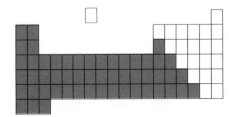

The orange elements are metals

The white elements are non-metals

The Electronic Structure of Atoms Affects How They Will React

1) Atoms generally react to form a full outer shell. They do this via losing, gaining or sharing electrons.
2) Metals to the left of the periodic table don't have many electrons in their outer shell to remove and metals towards the bottom of the periodic table have outer electrons which are a long way from the nucleus, so feel a weaker attraction. Both these effects means that not much energy is needed to remove the electrons so it's feasible for the elements to react to form positive ions with a full outer shell.
3) For non-metals, forming positive ions is much more difficult. This is because they are either to the right of the periodic table — where they have lots of electrons to remove to get a full outer shell, or towards the top — where the outer electrons are close to the nucleus so feel a strong attraction. It's far more feasible for them to either share or gain electrons to get a full outer shell.

Metals and Non-Metals Have Different Physical Properties

All metals have metallic bonding, which causes them to have similar basic physical properties. The non-metals don't have metallic bonding, so they exhibit different properties.

Properties of Metals:
- They generally have a shiny appearance.
- They're great at conducting heat and electricity.
- They tend to have high densities.
- They have high boiling and melting points — so they're generally solids at room temperature.
- Reactivity increases down the periodic table.
- They form compounds with ionic or metallic bonds.

Properties of Non-Metals:
- They tend to be dull looking.
- They're poor conductors of heat and electricity.
- They often have a lower density.
- They're more likely to be gases or liquids at room temperature — they have lower melting and boiling points.
- Reactivity decreases down the periodic table.
- They form compounds with ionic or covalent bonds.

You can 'rock out' to metal, you can sway gently to non-metal...

When it comes to properties, metals and non-metals couldn't be much more opposite. Much like me and my sister...

Q1   State three properties of metals.   [3 marks]

Group 1 Elements

Group 1 elements are known as the <u>alkali metals</u> — these are silvery solids that have to be stored in oil (and handled with forceps) as they react vigorously with water. As elements go, they're pretty demanding...

The Group 1 Elements are Reactive, Soft Metals

1) The alkali metals are lithium, sodium, potassium, rubidium, caesium and francium.

2) They all have <u>one electron</u> in their outer shell which makes them <u>very reactive</u> and gives them <u>similar properties</u>.

3) The alkali metals are all <u>soft</u> and have <u>low density</u>. The <u>first three</u> in the group are <u>less dense than water</u>.

4) The <u>trends</u> for the alkali metals as you go <u>down</u> Group 1 include:

- <u>Increasing reactivity</u>
- <u>Lower melting</u> and <u>boiling</u> points
- <u>Higher relative atomic mass</u>
- <u>Higher density</u>
- <u>Decrease</u> in <u>hardness</u>

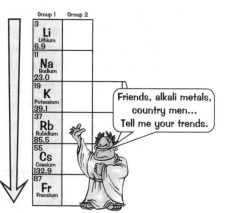

In the exam, you could be given the property of one Group 1 metal and asked to predict the property of a different Group 1 metal. So make sure you know these trends.

Friends, alkali metals, country men... Tell me your trends.

Melting and Boiling Points Decrease Down Group 1

1) <u>Group 1 metals</u> form regular structures held together with <u>metallic bonds</u> (see page 103). In these bonds, the <u>outer electron</u> of each atom is <u>free to move</u> around (<u>delocalised</u>). There are <u>strong attractions</u> between these electrons and positively charged nuclei.

2) As you go <u>down</u> Group 1, the atoms get <u>bigger</u> — the nucleus is <u>further away</u> from the free electrons, so the attractions get <u>weaker</u>.

3) This means that <u>less energy</u> is needed to break the metallic bonds and turn the solid metal into a liquid and then to a gas — so melting and boiling points <u>decrease</u> down the group.

Group 1 Metals are Very Reactive

1) The Group 1 metals readily <u>lose</u> their single <u>outer electron</u> to form a <u>1+ ion</u> with a <u>stable electronic structure</u>.

2) The <u>more readily</u> a metal loses its outer electrons, the <u>more reactive</u> it is — so the Group 1 metals are very reactive.

3) As you go <u>down</u> Group 1, the alkali metals get <u>more reactive</u>. The negatively charged <u>outer electron</u> is <u>less strongly attracted</u> to the positively charged nucleus. This is because it's further away (there are more electron shells) — so it's more easily <u>lost</u>, as <u>less energy</u> is needed to remove it.

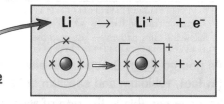

$$Li \rightarrow Li^+ + e^-$$

State Symbols Tell You the State of a Substance in an Equation

Chemical reactions can be shown using <u>symbol equations</u>. Symbol equations can also include <u>state symbols</u> next to each substance — they tell you what <u>physical state</u> the reactants and products are in:

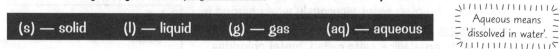

| (s) — solid | (l) — liquid | (g) — gas | (aq) — aqueous |

Aqueous means 'dissolved in water'.

For example, <u>solid</u> potassium reacts with <u>liquid</u> water to form <u>aqueous</u> potassium hydroxide and hydrogen <u>gas</u>:

$$2K_{(s)} + 2H_2O_{(l)} \rightarrow 2KOH_{(aq)} + H_{2(g)}$$

Wanna know more about Group 1 metals? K. Really? Na...

Well, I'm afraid we still have another page to go about Group 1. It's a good one though — I'm not even Li-ing...

Q1 Explain the trend in reactivity as you go down Group 1. [2 marks]

Reactions of Group 1 Elements

So you've just seen how Group 1 elements get <u>more reactive</u> as you go down the group. On this page you'll see that some reactions even cause <u>explosions</u>. Nothing like a bit of pyrotechnics to liven up science revision...

Group 1 Elements React in Similar Ways

1) <u>Group 1</u> elements can take part in different reactions, including with <u>water</u> and <u>chlorine gas</u>.

2) Group 1 elements all have a <u>single outer electron</u>. This means different Group 1 metals will react with a particular reactant to produce the <u>same type of product</u>. E.g. the reactions of Group 1 metals with chlorine gas produce metal chlorides. This means that the <u>balanced symbol equations</u> will follow the <u>same pattern</u> (see below) — make sure you know how to write them.

3) Although the <u>reactions are similar</u>, the reactions become <u>more vigorous</u> as <u>atomic number increases</u>. This is because the elements become <u>more reactive</u> down the group (see previous page).

4) So, if you know how one Group 1 metal reacts, you can use the <u>pattern</u> of reactivity to <u>predict</u> how other Group 1 metals will react and the <u>products</u> that will form.

Group 1 Metals Tarnish in Moist Air

1) The Group 1 metals are <u>shiny</u> when <u>freshly cut</u>, but quickly react with <u>oxygen</u> in <u>moist air</u> and <u>tarnish</u> as a <u>metal oxide</u> is formed. Different types of <u>oxide</u> will form depending on the Group 1 metal.

2) As you go down Group 1, the elements tarnish much more <u>quickly</u>.

3) Lithium, sodium and potassium are <u>stored in oil</u> to prevent the reaction with air.

4) Rubidium and caesium are much more reactive, so are <u>sealed</u> in <u>glass tubes</u> under special conditions.

Reaction with Cold Water Produces a Hydroxide and Hydrogen Gas

1) When the <u>alkali metals</u> are put in <u>water</u>, they react to produce <u>hydrogen gas</u> and a metal <u>hydroxide</u> (an <u>alkali</u>, see page 135). For example, here's the overall equation for the reaction of <u>lithium</u> with <u>water</u>:

$$2Li_{(s)} + 2H_2O_{(l)} \rightarrow 2LiOH_{(aq)} + H_{2(g)}$$
lithium + water → lithium hydroxide + hydrogen

The same reaction happens with all of the alkali metals — the equations all follow the same pattern — just swap the Group 1 metal symbol for another.

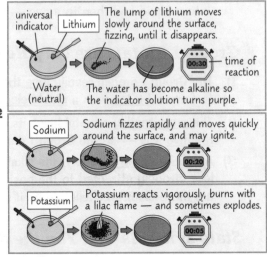

universal indicator | Lithium | The lump of lithium moves slowly around the surface, fizzing, until it disappears.
Water (neutral) — The water has become alkaline so the indicator solution turns purple.

Sodium | Sodium fizzes rapidly and moves quickly around the surface, and may ignite.

Potassium | Potassium reacts vigorously, burns with a lilac flame — and sometimes explodes.

2) As you go <u>down</u> Group 1, the elements become <u>more reactive</u> (in fact, rubidium and caesium actually <u>explode</u>).

3) You can see this in the <u>rate of reaction</u> with water (i.e. the time taken for a lump of the same size of each element to <u>react completely</u> with the water and disappear).

4) <u>Lithium</u> takes longer than sodium or potassium to react, so it's the <u>least reactive</u>. <u>Potassium</u> takes the shortest time to react of these three elements, so it's the <u>most reactive</u>.

Reaction with Chlorine Produces a Salt

Group 1 metals can react with other Group 7 elements too, see p.97.

1) The Group 1 metals react <u>vigorously</u> when heated in <u>chlorine gas</u> (a Group 7 element — see next page) to form <u>white crystalline salts</u> called 'metal chlorides'.

2) As you go down the group, reactivity increases so the reaction with chlorine gets <u>more vigorous</u>.

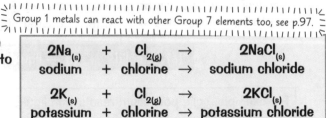

$$2Na_{(s)} + Cl_{2(g)} \rightarrow 2NaCl_{(s)}$$
sodium + chlorine → sodium chloride

$$2K_{(s)} + Cl_{2(g)} \rightarrow 2KCl_{(s)}$$
potassium + chlorine → potassium chloride

Back to the drawing board with my lithium swim shorts design...

Reactions of alkali metals need safety precautions, but they fizz in water and might explode. Cool.

Q1 Which Group 1 element will have the least vigorous reaction with chlorine gas? [1 mark]

Q2 Give the balanced symbol equation for the reaction between rubidium and water. [2 marks]

Group 7 Elements

Here's a page on another periodic table group that you need to be familiar with — the halogens.

Group 7 Elements are Known as the Halogens

Group 7 is made up of the non-metal elements fluorine, chlorine, bromine, iodine and astatine.

1) All Group 7 elements have 7 electrons in their outer shell
— so they all have similar chemical properties.

2) The halogens exist as diatomic molecules (e.g. Cl_2, Br_2, I_2). Sharing one pair of electrons in a covalent bond (see page 110) gives both atoms a full outer shell.

Group 0

Group 6	Group 7
	9 **F** Fluorine 19.0
	17 **Cl** Chlorine 36.5
	35 **Br** Bromine 79.9
	53 **I** Iodine 126.9
	85 **At** Astatine

There are Patterns in the Properties of the Group 7 Elements

1) As you go down Group 7, the melting points and boiling points of the halogens increase.

2) This means that at room temperature and pressure:
- **Fluorine** (F_2) is a highly reactive, toxic, pale yellow gas.
- **Chlorine** (Cl_2) is a fairly reactive, poisonous, green gas.
- **Bromine** (Br_2) is a poisonous, red-brown liquid, which gives off an orange vapour at room temperature.
- **Iodine** (I_2) is a dark grey crystalline solid which gives off a purple vapour when heated.

In the exam you may be given the melting or boiling point of one Group 7 element and asked to estimate the value for another one. So make sure you know the pattern.

3) The increase in melting and boiling point is due to an increase in the number of electrons in each atom as you go down the group. More electrons means there are greater intermolecular forces between the molecules, so more energy is needed to overcome them (see p.111 for more).

Reactivity Decreases Going Down Group 7

1) A halogen atom only needs to gain one electron to form a 1- ion with a stable electronic structure.

2) The easier it is for a halogen atom to attract an electron, the more reactive the halogen will be.

3) As you go DOWN Group 7, the halogens become less reactive — it gets harder to attract the extra electron to fill the outer shell when it's further away from the nucleus (the atomic radius is larger).

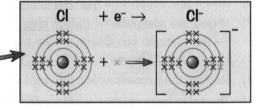

$$Cl + e^- \rightarrow Cl^-$$

The Halogens React With Alkali Metals to Form Salts

1) The halogens will react vigorously with alkali metals (Group 1 elements, see page 95) to form salts called 'metal halides'. For example:

All the reactions between Group 1 and Group 7 elements follow this pattern — make sure you can write equations for any of them.

$$2Na_{(s)} + Cl_{2(g)} \rightarrow 2NaCl_{(s)}$$
sodium + chlorine → sodium chloride

$$2K_{(s)} + Br_{2(l)} \rightarrow 2KBr_{(s)}$$
potassium + bromine → potassium bromide

2) Halogens higher up in Group 7 react more vigorously with the alkali metals because they're more reactive.

3) Since all halogens have the same number of electrons in their outer shells, they all have similar reactions. So you can use the reactions of one halogen to predict how other halogens will react.

To know what type of salt is formed by a halogen, just replace '-ine' with '-ide'. So, fluorine forms fluoride salts and iodine forms iodide salts.

Halogens — one electron short of a full shell...

Another page, another periodic table group to learn the properties and the trends of. When you're pretty confident that you've got all the stuff from this page in your head, have a go at the questions below, just to check.

Q1 The melting point of chlorine (Cl_2) is –101.5 °C. Predict whether bromine (Br_2) would be a solid, a liquid or a gas at –101.5 °C. Explain your answer. [2 marks]

Q2 Write a balanced symbol equation for the reaction between sodium metal (Na) and iodine (I_2). [2 marks]

Displacement Reactions of Group 7

The halogens are a pretty competitive lot really. In fact the <u>more reactive</u> ones will push the <u>less reactive</u> ones out of a compound. How uncivilized — has nobody ever taught them that it's bad manners to push?

A More Reactive Halogen Will Displace a Less Reactive One

1) The elements in Group 7 take part in <u>displacement reactions</u>.

2) A <u>displacement reaction</u> is where a <u>more reactive</u> element '<u>pushes out</u>' (<u>displaces</u>) a <u>less reactive</u> element from a compound.

3) For example, <u>chlorine</u> is more reactive than <u>bromine</u> (it's higher up Group 7). If you add <u>chlorine water</u> (an <u>aqueous solution</u> of <u>Cl$_2$</u>) to <u>potassium bromide</u> solution, the chlorine will <u>displace</u> the <u>bromine</u> from the salt solution.

4) The <u>chlorine</u> is reduced to <u>chloride ions</u>, so the salt solution becomes <u>potassium chloride</u>. The <u>bromide ions</u> are oxidised to <u>bromine</u>, which turns the solution <u>orange</u> (see p.107 for more on oxidation and reduction).

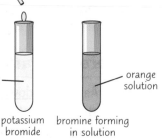

chlorine water

colourless solution — potassium bromide

orange solution — bromine forming in solution

5) The <u>equation</u> for this reaction is shown below:

$$Cl_{2(aq)} + 2KBr_{(aq)} \rightarrow Br_{2(aq)} + 2KCl_{(aq)}$$

chlorine + potassium bromide → bromine + potassium chloride

If you ever need to write an equation for a different halogen displacement reaction, they all follow this pattern.

Displacement Reactions Show Reactivity Trends

You can use <u>displacement reactions</u> to show the reactivity trend of the halogens.

1) Start by measuring out a small amount of a <u>halide salt solution</u> in a test tube.

2) Add a few drops of a <u>halogen solution</u> to it and shake the tube gently.

3) If you see a significant <u>colour change</u>, then a reaction has happened — the halogen has displaced the halide ions from the salt. If no reaction happens, there <u>won't</u> be a colour change.

You should wear a lab coat and goggles when doing this experiment — some of the chemicals are harmful.

4) Repeat the process using different combinations of halide salt and halogen.

5) The table below shows what should happen when you mix different combinations of <u>chlorine</u>, <u>bromine</u> and <u>iodine</u> water with solutions of the salts <u>potassium chloride</u>, <u>potassium bromide</u> and <u>potassium iodide</u>.

Start with:	Potassium chloride solution KCl$_{(aq)}$ — colourless	Potassium bromide solution KBr$_{(aq)}$ — colourless	Potassium iodide solution KI$_{(aq)}$ — colourless
Add chlorine water Cl$_{2(aq)}$ — colourless	no reaction	orange solution (Br$_2$) formed	brown solution (I$_2$) formed
Add bromine water Br$_{2(aq)}$ — orange	no reaction	no reaction	brown solution (I$_2$) formed
Add iodine water I$_{2(aq)}$ — brown	no reaction	no reaction	no reaction

6) <u>Chlorine</u> displaces both bromine and iodine from salt solutions. <u>Bromine</u> can't displace chlorine, but it does displace iodine. <u>Iodine</u> can't displace chlorine or bromine.

7) This shows the <u>reactivity trend</u> — the halogens get <u>less reactive</u> as you go <u>down</u> the group.

This is to do with how easily they gain electrons — see previous page for more.

New information displaces old information from my brain...

If you remember that the halogens get less reactive as you go down the group, you can work out what will happen when you mix any halogen with any halide salt. You need to know the colour changes that go with the reactions too.

Q1   A student added a few drops of a halogen solution to some potassium iodide solution. The solution turned brown. She added a few drops of the same halogen solution to some potassium bromide solution. No reaction occurred. Name the halogen solution that the student used.   [1 mark]

Group 0 Elements

The Group 0 elements are known as <u>noble gases</u> — stuffed full of every honourable virtue.
They don't react with very much and you can't even see them — making them, well, a bit dull really.

Group 0 Elements are All Inert, Colourless Gases

1) Group 0 elements are called the <u>noble gases</u> and include the elements <u>helium</u>, <u>neon</u> and <u>argon</u> (plus a few others).

2) They all have <u>eight electrons</u> in their outer energy level, apart from helium which has two, giving them a <u>full outer shell</u>. As their outer shell is energetically stable they don't need to <u>give up</u> or <u>gain</u> electrons to become more stable. This means they are more or less <u>inert</u> — they <u>don't react</u> with much at all.

Helium only has electrons in the first shell, which only needs 2 to be filled.

		Group 0
		2 **He** Helium 4.0
Group 6	Group 7	10 **Ne** Neon 20.2
		18 **Ar** Argon 39.9
		36 **Kr** Krypton 83.8
		54 **Xe** Xenon 131.3
		86 **Rn** Radon

3) They exist as <u>monatomic gases</u> — single atoms <u>not</u> bonded to each other.

4) All elements in Group 0 are <u>colourless gases</u> at room temperature.

5) As the noble gases are inert they're <u>non-flammable</u> — they won't set on fire.

There are Patterns in the Properties of the Noble Gases

1) The <u>melting points</u> and <u>boiling points</u> of the noble gases <u>increase</u> as you move <u>down</u> the group.

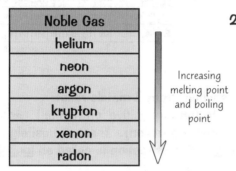

Noble Gas
helium
neon
argon
krypton
xenon
radon

Increasing melting point and boiling point

2) The increase in melting and boiling points is due to an <u>increase</u> in the <u>number of electrons</u> in each <u>atom</u> leading to <u>greater forces</u> between the atoms which need to be overcome. There's more on intermolecular forces on page 111.

Here's another pattern. You don't have to learn this one...

3) In the exam you may be given the melting point or boiling point of one noble gas and asked to <u>estimate</u> the value for <u>another one</u>. So make sure you know the <u>pattern</u>.

EXAMPLE:
Neon is a gas at 25 °C. Predict what state helium is at this temperature.
Helium has a lower boiling point than neon as it is further up the group.
So, helium must also be a gas at 25 °C.

EXAMPLE:
Radon and krypton have boiling points of −62 °C and −153 °C respectively. Predict the boiling point of xenon.
Xenon comes in between radon and krypton in the group so you can predict that its boiling point would be halfway between their boiling points: $(-153) + (-62) = -215$
$$-215 \div 2 = -107.5 \approx -108 \text{ °C}$$
So, xenon should have a boiling point of about −108 °C.

The actual boiling point of xenon is −108 °C — just as predicted. Neat.

...or this one.

Arrrgon — the pirate element...

As noble gases don't really react there isn't too much to learn about them. If you understand why they are unreactive and the trend in melting and boiling points as you go down the group you're sorted.

Q1 Does xenon or neon have the higher boiling point? [1 mark]

Q2 Argon is very unreactive. Using your knowledge of its electronic structure, explain why. [2 marks]

Ionic Bonding

Some atoms are keen on getting rid of some of their <u>electrons</u>. Others want more. That's life. And <u>ions</u>...

Simple Ions Form When Atoms Lose or Gain Electrons

1) <u>Ions</u> are <u>charged</u> particles — they can be <u>single atoms</u> (e.g. Na^+) or <u>groups of atoms</u> (e.g. NO_3^-).

2) When <u>atoms</u> lose or gain electrons to form ions, all they're trying to do is get a <u>full outer shell</u> (also called a "<u>stable electronic structure</u>"). Atoms with full outer shells are very <u>stable</u>.

3) <u>Negative ions</u> (anions) form when atoms <u>gain electrons</u> — they have more electrons than protons. <u>Positive ions</u> (cations) form when atoms <u>lose electrons</u> — they have more protons than electrons.

4) The <u>number</u> of electrons lost or gained is the same as the <u>charge</u> on the ion. E.g. If 2 electrons are <u>lost</u> the charge is 2+. If 3 electrons are <u>gained</u> the charge is 3–.

You calculate the number of protons and neutrons in an ion in the same way as for an atom (see page 91).

You Can Predict the Ions Formed by Elements in Groups 1 & 2 and 6 & 7

1) <u>Group 1 and 2 elements</u> are <u>metals</u>. They <u>lose</u> electrons to form <u>positive ions</u>.

2) <u>Group 6 and 7 elements</u> are <u>non-metals</u>. They <u>gain</u> electrons to form <u>negative ions</u>.

3) Elements in the same <u>group</u> all have the same number of <u>outer electrons</u>. So they have to <u>lose or gain</u> the same number to get a full outer shell. And this means that they form ions with the <u>same charge</u>.

Group 1 elements form 1+ ions.
Group 2 elements form 2+ ions.
Group 6 elements form 2– ions.
Group 7 elements form 1– ions.

Ionic Bonding — Transfer of Electrons

When a <u>metal</u> and a <u>non-metal</u> react together, such as when Group 1 metals react with Group 7 elements, the <u>metal atom loses</u> electrons to form a <u>positive ion</u> (cation) and the <u>non-metal gains these electrons</u> to form a <u>negative ion</u> (anion). These oppositely charged ions are <u>strongly attracted</u> to one another by <u>electrostatic forces</u>. This attraction is called an <u>ionic bond</u>.

E.g. the 1+ charge of a sodium ion is strongly attracted to the 1– charge of a chlorine ion.

You Can Work Out the Formula of an Ionic Compound

1) Ionic compounds are made up of <u>positive</u> and <u>negative</u> ions held together by ionic bonds.

2) The <u>overall charge</u> of <u>any ionic compound</u> is <u>zero</u>. So all the <u>negative charges</u> in the compound must <u>balance</u> all the <u>positive charges</u>.

3) You can use the charges on the <u>individual ions</u> present to work out the formula for the ionic compound.

4) To <u>name</u> the compound you always name the metal <u>cation first</u> (this has the same name as the element). You then name the non-metal <u>anion</u>.

A negative ion's name will end in -ate if the ion contains oxygen and at least one other element (e.g. nitrate). Negative ions will end in -ide (e.g. chloride) if the ion contains only one element (apart from hydroxide ions which are OH^-).

EXAMPLE: What is the chemical formula and the name of the ionic compound that forms from magnesium and bromine?

1) Write out the <u>formulas</u> of the magnesium and bromide ions. Mg^{2+}, Br^-

2) The <u>overall charge</u> on the formula must be <u>zero</u>, so work out the ratio of Mg : Br that gives an overall neutral charge.

To balance the 2+ charge on Mg^{2+}, you need two Br^- ions: $(+2) + (2 \times -1) = 0$. The formula is $MgBr_2$

3) Name the compound formed by identifying the cation and then the anion.

The cation is magnesium. The anion contains one non-metal so the name must end in -ide. The compound's name is **magnesium bromide**.

Magnesium bromide isn't sarcastic, it's just an ironic compound...

Make sure you remember that even though individual ions are charged, ionic compounds are neutral overall.

Q1   What is the formula of the ionic compound, potassium oxide?   [1 mark]

Ionic Compounds

Here's a bit more about how <u>ionic compounds</u> form and the <u>properties</u> that make them special...

You Can Show Ionic Bonding Using Dot and Cross Diagrams

Dot and cross diagrams show the <u>arrangement</u> of electrons in an atom or ion. They can also show what happens to the electrons when atoms <u>react</u> with each other. Each electron is represented by a <u>dot</u> or a <u>cross</u>.

<u>Sodium Chloride</u> (NaCl)
The <u>sodium</u> atom gives up its outer electron, becoming an <u>Na+</u> ion. The <u>chlorine</u> atom picks up the electron, becoming a <u>Cl-</u> (<u>chloride</u>) ion.

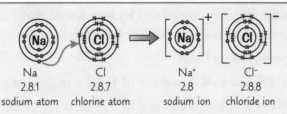

Na
2.8.1
sodium atom

Cl
2.8.7
chlorine atom

Na+
2.8
sodium ion

Cl-
2.8.8
chloride ion

Here, the dots represent the Na electrons and the crosses represent the Cl electrons (all electrons are really identical, but this is a good way of following their movement).

<u>Magnesium Chloride</u> (MgCl$_2$)
The <u>magnesium</u> atom gives up its <u>two</u> outer electrons, becoming an <u>Mg^{2+}</u> ion. The two <u>chlorine</u> atoms pick up <u>one electron each</u>, becoming <u>two Cl-</u> (chloride) ions.

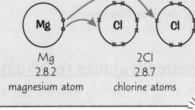

Mg
2.8.2
magnesium atom

2Cl
2.8.7
chlorine atoms

Cl-
2.8.8
chloride ion

Mg^{2+}
2.8
magnesium ion

Cl-
2.8.8
chloride ion

Dot and cross diagrams are really useful for showing how ionic compounds are formed, but they <u>don't</u> show the <u>structure</u> of the compound. For that, you'll need a different type of diagram.

To work out the formula of a compound from a dot and cross diagram, write the chemical symbol for each of the different ions (with the positive ion first) and show how many of each ion there are, e.g. MgCl$_2$.

Ionic Compounds Have a Regular Lattice Structure

<u>Ionic compounds</u> always have <u>giant ionic lattice</u> structures. The ions form a closely packed <u>regular lattice</u>. There are very strong <u>electrostatic forces of attraction</u> between <u>oppositely charged</u> ions, in <u>all directions</u>.

A single crystal of <u>sodium chloride</u> (table salt) is <u>one giant ionic lattice</u>. Lots of <u>Na+</u> and <u>Cl-</u> ions are held together in a regular lattice.

If you know the distance between the ions, you can work out the length of the sides of a cube-shaped section of a crystal and then calculate its volume using the formula: volume = (side length)^3.

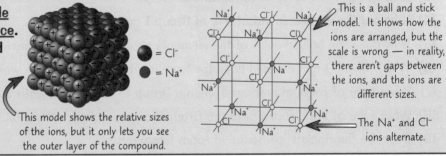

= Cl-
= Na+

This model shows the relative sizes of the ions, but it only lets you see the outer layer of the compound.

This is a ball and stick model. It shows how the ions are arranged, but the scale is wrong — in reality, there aren't gaps between the ions, and the ions are different sizes.

The Na+ and Cl- ions alternate.

Ionic Compounds All Have Similar Properties

1) Ionic compounds have <u>high melting</u> and <u>boiling points</u> due to the <u>strong attraction</u> between the ions. It takes a large amount of <u>energy</u> to overcome this attraction compared to other types of bonding.

2) Solid ionic compounds <u>don't</u> conduct electricity because the ions are fixed in place and can't move. But when an ionic compound <u>melts</u>, the ions are <u>free to move</u> and will <u>carry an electric current</u>.

3) Many also <u>dissolve easily</u> in water because their <u>charges</u> allow them to <u>interact</u> with the <u>water</u> molecules. The ions <u>separate</u> and are all <u>free to move</u> in the solution, so they'll <u>carry an electric current</u>.

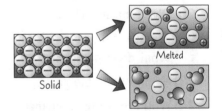

Melted

Solid

Dissolved in Water

Group 1 halides are ionic compounds. E.g. NaCl has a melting point of 801 °C, a boiling point of 1413 °C and can conduct electricity when molten or dissolved in water.

Giant ionic lattices — all over your chips...

When drawing dot and cross diagrams, don't worry about showing the inner shells of electrons — they don't take part in the ionic bond. The important thing to show is the arrangement of electrons in the outer shell.

Q1   Draw a dot and cross diagram to show how potassium (electronic structure 2.8.8.1) and bromine (electronic structure 2.8.8.7) react to form potassium bromide (KBr).   [3 marks]

Revision Questions for Chapter C2

Well, that's <u>Chapter C2</u> almost done and dusted — just a few more questions to go...

- Try these questions and <u>tick off each one</u> when you <u>get it right</u>.
- When you've done <u>all the questions</u> for a topic and are <u>completely happy</u> with it, tick off the topic.

<u>Atoms, Ions and Isotopes (p.89-91)</u> ☑

1) Describe the experiment that was carried out by Rutherford that led to him disproving the plum pudding model of the atom. ☐

2) Describe the model proposed by Bohr. ☐

3) Which subatomic particle has a relative mass of 1 and a relative charge of 0? ☐

4) How big is the nucleus of an atom compared to the diameter of the atom? ☐

5) What does the mass number tell you about an atom? ☐

6) How can you calculate the number of neutrons in an atom? ☐

7) What is an isotope? ☐

<u>The Periodic Table and Electronic Structure (p.92-93)</u> ☑

8) Which scientist's periodic table led directly to the one that we use today? ☐

9) What do the elements in each period have in common? ☐

10) How many electrons can the first electron shell of an atom contain? ☐

11) A magnesium atom contains 12 electrons. What is the electronic structure of magnesium? ☐

<u>Groups of the Periodic Table (p.94-99)</u> ☑

12) Why is it hard for non-metals to form positive ions? ☐

13) Give two properties of non-metals. ☐

14) How are the electronic structures of Group 1 metals similar? ☐

15) How does the boiling point of the elements change as you go down Group 1? ☐

16) Which Group 1 metal would have the least vigorous reaction with water? ☐

17) What type of product is formed when a Group 1 metal reacts with chlorine gas? ☐

18) What type of bond forms between Group 7 atoms in their elemental form? ☐

19) Describe fluorine's appearance at room temperature. ☐

20) Describe and explain the trend in reactivity of the Group 7 elements. ☐

21) Give a balanced symbol equation of the reaction between potassium and bromine. ☐

22) A student mixes a halogen solution with a halide salt solution and observes a colour change. What does this show? ☐

23) Name two noble gases. ☐

24) Why are Group 0 elements extremely unreactive? ☐

25) Which noble gas has the lowest melting point? ☐

<u>Ionic Compounds (p.100-101)</u> ☑

26) Does a positive ion have more protons or more electrons? ☐

27) What is the overall charge of an ionic compound? ☐

28) Draw a dot and cross diagram to show how magnesium (electronic structure 2.8.2) and chlorine (electronic structure 2.8.7) form magnesium chloride ($MgCl_2$). ☐

29) Why can ionic compounds conduct electricity when molten but not when solid? ☐

Metallic Bonding and Reactivity

Ever wondered what makes <u>metals</u> tick? Well, either way, this is the page for you.

Metallic Bonding Involves Delocalised Electrons

1) <u>Metals</u> consist of a <u>giant structure</u>.

2) The <u>bonding</u> in metals can be described by a model. This states that the electrons in the <u>outer shell</u> of the metal atoms are <u>delocalised</u> (they're free to move around). There are strong forces of <u>electrostatic attraction</u> between the <u>positive metal ions</u> and the 'sea' of shared <u>negative electrons</u>.

3) These forces of attraction <u>hold</u> the <u>atoms</u> close together in a <u>regular</u> structure and are known as <u>metallic bonding</u>. Metallic bonding is very <u>strong</u>.

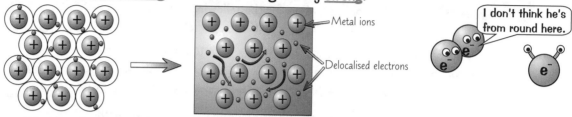

Metal ions
Delocalised electrons

I don't think he's from round here.

4) Substances that are held together by metallic bonding include metallic <u>elements</u>.

Metallic Bonding Determines the Properties of Metals

The properties of metals make them useful (see p.120).

1) Metals have a set of <u>bulk properties</u> which can be explained by their <u>metallic bonding</u>.

2) The electrostatic forces between the metal ions and the sea of delocalised electrons are very <u>strong</u>, so need <u>lots of energy</u> to be broken. This means that most substances with metallic bonds have very <u>high</u> melting and boiling points, so they're generally <u>solid</u> at room temperature.

3) The <u>delocalised electrons</u> are free to move so can carry electrical current and thermal (heat) energy through the material, so metals are good <u>conductors</u> of <u>electricity</u> and <u>heat</u>.

4) The layers of atoms in a metal can <u>slide</u> over each other whilst still being held together by the electrons, making metals <u>malleable</u> and <u>ductile</u> — this means that they can be <u>bent</u>, <u>hammered</u> or <u>rolled</u> into <u>flat sheets</u> and <u>drawn into wires</u>.

The Reactivity Series — How Well a Metal Reacts

1) The <u>reactivity series</u> lists metals in <u>order</u> of their <u>reactivity</u> towards other substances.

2) When <u>metal atoms</u> react, they form <u>positive ions</u> by losing one or more electrons. This means they can form <u>ionic compounds</u>.

3) For metals, their reactivity is determined by how <u>easily</u> they lose electrons. The <u>higher</u> up the reactivity series a metal is, the more easily it loses electrons and forms <u>positive ions</u>. You can use the reactivity series to <u>predict</u> which metal will react <u>fastest</u> with a given reagent.

4) You can deduce the <u>order of reactivity</u> of different metals by looking at their <u>reactions</u> with water, acid or other metal compounds (see pages 104-105).

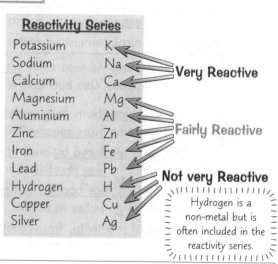

Reactivity Series

Potassium	K	
Sodium	Na	**Very Reactive**
Calcium	Ca	
Magnesium	Mg	
Aluminium	Al	
Zinc	Zn	**Fairly Reactive**
Iron	Fe	
Lead	Pb	
Hydrogen	H	**Not very Reactive**
Copper	Cu	
Silver	Ag	

Hydrogen is a non-metal but is often included in the reactivity series.

I saw a metal on the bus once — he was the conductor...

If your knowledge of metals is still feeling a bit delocalised, the question below will help...

Q1   a)   Copper is a metallic element. Describe and explain a property of copper that makes it suitable for using in electrical circuits.   **[2 marks]**

          b)   Copper can also be shaped into water and gas pipes. Explain why it is possible to shape metals.   **[1 mark]**

Ionic Equations and Reactions of Metals

Ionic equations can be used to show how ions change in a reaction due to the transfer of electrons. You can use ionic equations to show what happens to metal ions during some displacement reactions.

Ionic Equations Show Just the Useful Bits of Reactions

1) You can write an ionic equation for any reaction involving ions that happens in solution.

2) In an ionic equation, only the reacting particles (and the products they form) are included.

3) To write an ionic equation, you've just got to look at the reactants and products. Anything that's exactly the same on both sides of the equation can be left out.

> You should make sure your symbol equation is balanced before you start trying to write the ionic equation (see page 80 for more on how to balance symbol equations).

EXAMPLE: Write the ionic equation for the following reaction:
$$CaCl_{2(aq)} + 2NaOH_{(aq)} \rightarrow Ca(OH)_{2(s)} + 2NaCl_{(aq)}$$

1) Anything that's ionic (i.e. made of ions — see page 100) and aqueous will break up into its ions in solution. So, write out the equation showing all the ions separately.
$$Ca^{2+}_{(aq)} + 2Cl^-_{(aq)} + 2Na^+_{(aq)} + 2OH^-_{(aq)} \rightarrow Ca(OH)_{2\ (s)} + 2Na^+_{(aq)} + 2Cl^-_{(aq)}$$

2) To get to the ionic equation, cross out anything that's the same on both sides of the equation — here, those are the Na^+ and Cl^- ions.
$$Ca^{2+}_{(aq)} + \cancel{2Cl^-_{(aq)}} + \cancel{2Na^+_{(aq)}} + 2OH^-_{(aq)} \rightarrow Ca(OH)_{2\ (s)} + \cancel{2Na^+_{(aq)}} + \cancel{2Cl^-_{(aq)}}$$
$$Ca^{2+}_{(aq)} + 2OH^-_{(aq)} \rightarrow Ca(OH)_{2\ (s)}$$

The overall charge should be the same on both sides of the reaction.

More Reactive Metals Displace Less Reactive Ones

> Ionic equations for displacement reactions in solution let you see the transfer of electrons between the metals.

1) If you put a more reactive metal into a solution of a less reactive metal salt, the reactive metal will replace the less reactive metal in the salt.

Example: If you put an iron nail in a solution of copper sulfate, the more reactive iron will "kick out" the less reactive copper from the salt. You end up with iron sulfate solution and copper metal.

Word equation:	copper sulfate	+	iron	$\rightarrow$ iron sulfate	+ copper
Symbol equation:	$CuSO_{4(aq)}$	+	$Fe_{(s)}$	$\rightarrow$ $FeSO_{4(aq)}$	+ $Cu_{(s)}$
Ionic equation:	$Cu^{2+}_{(aq)}$	+	$Fe_{(s)}$	$\rightarrow$ $Fe^{2+}_{(aq)}$	+ $Cu_{(s)}$

2) If you put a less reactive metal into a solution of a more reactive metal salt, nothing will happen.

3) You can use displacement reactions to work out where in the reactivity series a metal should go.

Example: A student heats some metals with oxides of other metals and records whether any reactions happen. Use her table of results, below, to work out an order of reactivity for the metals.

- Zinc displaces both copper and iron, so it must be more reactive than both.
- Copper is displaced by both iron and zinc, so it must be less reactive than both.
- Iron can displace copper, but not zinc, so it must go between them.

	copper oxide	iron oxide	zinc oxide
copper	no reaction	no reaction	no reaction
iron	iron oxide and copper formed	no reaction	no reaction
zinc	zinc oxide and copper formed	zinc oxide and iron formed	no reaction

The order of reactivity, from most to least, is: zinc, iron, copper.

And that's why Iron Man never goes swimming in copper sulfate...

If you're asked whether you think a particular displacement reaction will take place, remember the reactivity series on the previous page — a metal will only displace another metal if it's higher in the reactivity series.

Q1 Using the reactivity series on the previous page, state whether lead would displace zinc from zinc chloride solution. Explain your answer. [1 mark]

Q2 Write the ionic equation for the reaction between magnesium and iron sulfate solution ($FeSO_4$). [2 marks]

More Reactions of Metals

Reactive metals tend to do exciting, fizzy things when you drop them into acid or water. If you do the same with an unreactive metal, it'll just sit there. How boring. Here's a bit more detail on reactivity experiments...

How Metals React With Acids Tells You About Their Reactivity

1) Some metals react with acids to produce a salt and hydrogen gas.

$$Acid + Metal \rightarrow Salt + Hydrogen$$

2) The easier a metal atom loses its outer electrons and forms a positive ion, the more reactive it will be.

3) Here's a classic experiment that you can do to show that some metals are more reactive than others. All you do is place little pieces of various metals into dilute acid:

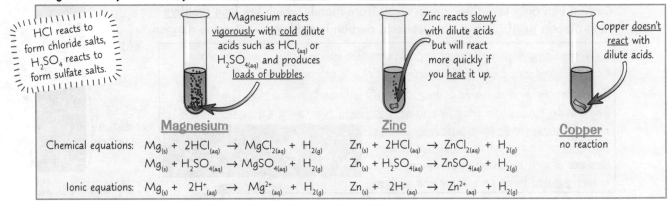

HCl reacts to form chloride salts, H_2SO_4 reacts to form sulfate salts.

Magnesium reacts vigorously with cold dilute acids such as $HCl_{(aq)}$ or $H_2SO_{4(aq)}$ and produces loads of bubbles.

Zinc reacts slowly with dilute acids but will react more quickly if you heat it up.

Copper doesn't react with dilute acids.

Magnesium

Zinc

Copper
no reaction

Chemical equations: $Mg_{(s)} + 2HCl_{(aq)} \rightarrow MgCl_{2(aq)} + H_{2(g)}$ $Zn_{(s)} + 2HCl_{(aq)} \rightarrow ZnCl_{2(aq)} + H_{2(g)}$

$Mg_{(s)} + H_2SO_{4(aq)} \rightarrow MgSO_{4(aq)} + H_{2(g)}$ $Zn_{(s)} + H_2SO_{4(aq)} \rightarrow ZnSO_{4(aq)} + H_{2(g)}$

Ionic equations: $Mg_{(s)} + 2H^+_{(aq)} \rightarrow Mg^{2+}_{(aq)} + H_{2(g)}$ $Zn_{(s)} + 2H^+_{(aq)} \rightarrow Zn^{2+}_{(aq)} + H_{2(g)}$

4) The more reactive the metal is, the faster the reaction will go.

5) Very reactive metals like potassium, sodium and calcium react explosively. Fairly reactive metals (e.g. magnesium and aluminium) will fizz vigorously, less reactive metals (e.g. zinc, iron and lead) will bubble a bit and unreactive metals (e.g. copper and silver) will not react with dilute acids at all.

6) You can show that hydrogen is forming using the burning splint test (see page 86). The louder the squeaky pop, the more hydrogen has been made in the time period and the more reactive the metal is.

7) The speed of reaction is also indicated by the rate at which the bubbles of hydrogen are given off — the faster the bubbles form, the faster the reaction and the more reactive the metal.

You could also follow the rate of the reaction by using a gas syringe to measure the volume of gas given off at regular time intervals or by timing how long it takes for the reaction to produce a certain volume of gas.

Metals Also React With Water

The reactions of metals with water also show the reactivity of metals. This is the basic reaction:

metal + water → metal hydroxide + hydrogen
(Or: less reactive metal + steam → metal oxide + hydrogen)

1) Very reactive metals like potassium, sodium and calcium will all react vigorously with water to form metal hydroxides.

E.g. $2Na_{(s)} + 2H_2O_{(l)} \rightarrow 2NaOH_{(aq)} + H_{2(g)}$

2) Metals further down the reactivity series like magnesium, aluminium, zinc and iron won't react much with cold water, but they will react with steam to form metal oxides. You could show this in the lab using this experiment:

E.g. $2Al_{(s)} + 3H_2O_{(g)} \rightarrow Al_2O_{3(s)} + 3H_{2(g)}$

mineral wool soaked in water

steam   metal

H_2 gas given off. This burns when lit with a burning splint.

heat   heat

3) Lead, copper and silver don't react with either water or steam.

I AM NOT HIGHLY REACTIVE — OK...

This stuff isn't too bad — who knows, you might even get to have a go at these experiments in class...

Q1   A student adds a piece of unknown metal, **X**, to a test tube containing dilute hydrochloric acid. She does not observe any bubble formation. Suggest an identity for metal **X**.   [1 mark]

Extracting Metals

Metals come from the ground, but we can't just dig 'em up to use straight away — they need to be extracted...

Some Metals can be Extracted by Reduction with Carbon

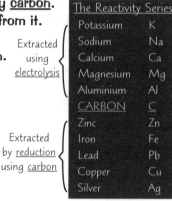

Reduction can mean both loss of oxygen and also the gain of electrons (see next page).

1) Ores are rocks that contain enough metal to make it economically worthwhile extracting the metal from it. They often contain compounds of the metal, e.g. metal oxides. Before we can use the metals, they need to be extracted from their ores.

2) The position of the metal in the reactivity series (see p.103) determines how the metal can be extracted.

3) Metals below carbon in a reactivity series are extracted using displacement by carbon. Carbon (a non-metal) reduces the metal in the ore by removing the oxygen from it. Carbon can only take the oxygen away from metals which are less reactive than carbon itself. During the process, carbon is oxidised — it gains oxygen.

The Reactivity Series	
Potassium	K
Sodium	Na
Calcium	Ca
Magnesium	Mg
Aluminium	Al
CARBON	C
Zinc	Zn
Iron	Fe
Lead	Pb
Copper	Cu
Silver	Ag

Extracted using electrolysis

Extracted by reduction using carbon

Example: Zinc exists in different ores such as zinc sulfide (ZnS), zinc carbonate ($ZnCO_3$) and zinc oxide (ZnO). ZnS and $ZnCO_3$ can be roasted to form ZnO.

To extract the zinc, you need to heat the ZnO with carbon at a high temperature. The carbon reduces the ZnO by removing the oxygen, forming a zinc vapour and either carbon monoxide or carbon dioxide gas. The impure zinc vapour is condensed in the absence of air (to prevent re-oxidation) and is then separated from the mixture and purified.

$$ZnO_{(s)} + C_{(s)} \rightarrow Zn_{(g)} + CO_{(g)}$$
$$2ZnO_{(s)} + C_{(s)} \rightarrow 2Zn_{(g)} + CO_{2(g)}$$

To extract zinc, you can also dissolve ZnO in sulfuric acid and electrolyse (see p.108) the solution of zinc sulfate that forms.

Some Metals have to be Extracted by Electrolysis

1) Metals more reactive than carbon are extracted using electrolysis of molten compounds (see page 108).

2) Once the metal is melted, an electric current is passed through it. The metal is discharged at the cathode and the non-metal at the anode.

3) Electricity is expensive so this process is much more expensive than reduction with carbon.

There are Biological Methods to Extract Metals

Low grade ores contain very little metal.

Scientists are developing biological methods to extract less reactive metals from their ores. These methods can extract metals from low-grade ores and from the waste from other metal extraction processes. Biological methods, such as phytoextraction and bioleaching, use living organisms to extract metals.

Phytoextraction:	Bioleaching:
This involves growing plants in soil that contains metal compounds. The plants can't use or get rid of the metals so they gradually build up in the leaves. The plants can be harvested, dried and burned in a furnace. The ash contains metal compounds from which the metal can be extracted by electrolysis or displacement reactions. Plants will be better suited for phytoextraction if they are large, grow fast and can be grown in large quantities in a given area.	This uses bacteria to convert insoluble metal compounds in the ore into soluble compounds, separating the metal from the ore in the process. The leachate (the solution that is produced) contains a dilute aqueous solution of metal ions, which can be extracted, e.g. by electrolysis or displacement with a more reactive metal.

Phytoextraction and bioleaching have both advantages and disadvantages.

ADVANTAGES — They're less damaging to the environment than traditional methods and take less energy. They can extract metals from waste materials so less 'new' ores need extracting — this makes it a cheaper process. It also means that fewer toxic metals get sent to landfill so it reduces the risk of them contaminating our water supplies.

DISADVANTAGE — They take much more time to produce a large quantity of metal.

[Please insert ore-ful pun here]...

Make sure you've got that reactivity series sorted in your head. If a metal's below carbon in the reactivity series, then it's less reactive than carbon and can be extracted from its ore by reduction using carbon. Phew... got it?

Q1 How would you extract iron from its metal ore? Explain your answer. [2 marks]

Oxidation and Reduction

Oxidation can be to do with something gaining oxygen (makes sense), but it can also be to do with electrons...

If Electrons are Transferred, It's a Redox Reaction

1) Oxidation can mean the reaction with, or addition of oxygen, and reduction can be the removal of oxygen.

$$Fe_2O_3 + 3CO \rightarrow 2Fe + 3CO_2$$

- Iron oxide is reduced to iron (as oxygen is removed).
- Carbon monoxide is oxidised to carbon dioxide (as oxygen is added).

> Combustion reactions involve oxidation. They're always exothermic (see p.81). E.g. $CH_4 + 2O_2 \rightarrow CO_2 + 2H_2O$

2) But on this page, we're looking at oxidation and reduction in terms of electrons. A loss of electrons is called oxidation. A gain of electrons is called reduction.

3) REDuction and OXidation happen at the same time — so this type of reaction is called a redox reaction.

> Remember it as OIL RIG.

> When dealing with electrons:
> Oxidation Is Loss,
> Reduction Is Gain.

Half Equations Show the Movement of Electrons

Half equations show how electrons are transferred during reactions. In half equations, e^- stands for one electron. You can't write half equations for all chemical reactions — only the ones where oxidation and reduction happen (see above).

> Half equations are really useful for showing what happens at each electrode during electrolysis (see pages 108-109).

Examples: In this half equation, sodium is oxidised as it loses one electron to become a sodium ion.

$$Na \rightarrow Na^+ + e^-$$

In this equation, two hydrogen ions are each reduced by gaining one electron to form a hydrogen molecule.

$$2H^+ + 2e^- \rightarrow H_2$$

> The charges on each side of the equation should balance.

You can combine half equations to create full ionic equations (see page 104).
Full equations never contain electrons — the electrons in the reactants and products should cancel out.
So, in the sodium/hydrogen example above, the full ionic equation would be: $2Na + 2H^+ \rightarrow 2Na^+ + H_2$.
(You need to multiply the sodium half equation by 2 so the electrons on each side balance.)

Half Equations Show if Things Have Been Oxidised or Reduced

1) You could be asked to identify whether something's been oxidised or reduced during a chemical reaction. If you are, looking at half equations is a great way of doing this.

2) Remember, if something loses electrons, then it's been oxidised. If something gains electrons, then it's been reduced.

- Iron atoms are oxidised to Fe^{2+} ions when they react with dilute acid: $Fe + 2H^+ \rightarrow Fe^{2+} + H_2$
- The iron atoms lose electrons. They're oxidised by the hydrogen ions: $Fe \rightarrow Fe^{2+} + 2e^-$
- The hydrogen ions gain electrons. They're reduced by the iron atoms: $2H^+ + 2e^- \rightarrow H_2$

EXAMPLE: Work out which element has been reduced in the following equation: $Cu^{2+} + Mg \rightarrow Cu + Mg^{2+}$

1) Work out whether each element has lost or gained electrons by writing out the half equations.

$$Cu^{2+} + 2e^- \rightarrow Cu$$
$$Mg \rightarrow Mg^{2+} + 2e^-$$

Add electrons so the charges on each side of the equation balance.

2) Reduction involves the gain of electrons, so find the element that's gained electrons.

Copper ions have gained two electrons to become copper atoms, so **copper** is reduced.

Half equations — equa, equa, equa, equa, equa, equa...

They may be half equations, but they're double the trouble if you ask me. Better get some practice in...

Q1 Write a half equation to show a chlorine molecule being reduced to become chloride ions (Cl^-). [2 marks]

Electrolysis

Electrolysis uses an <u>electrical current</u> to cause a reaction. It's actually pretty cool. No, really...

Electrolysis Means 'Splitting Up with Electricity'

1) During electrolysis, an electric current is passed through an electrolyte (a <u>molten</u> or <u>dissolved</u> ionic compound). The ions move towards the electrodes, where they react, and the compound <u>decomposes</u>.

2) The <u>positive metal or hydrogen ions</u> in the electrolyte will move towards the <u>cathode</u> (negative electrode) and <u>gain</u> electrons (they are <u>reduced</u>).

3) The <u>negative non-metal ions</u> in the electrolyte will move towards the <u>anode</u> (positive electrode) and <u>lose</u> electrons (they are <u>oxidised</u>).

An electrolyte is a liquid or solution that conducts electricity. An electrode is a solid that conducts electricity.

4) This creates a <u>flow of charge</u> through the <u>electrolyte</u> as ions travel to the electrodes.

5) As ions gain or lose electrons, they form the uncharged element and are <u>discharged</u> from the electrolyte.

Electrolysis of Molten Ionic Solids Forms Elements

1) An <u>ionic solid can't</u> be electrolysed because the ions are in fixed positions and <u>can't move</u>.

2) <u>Molten ionic compounds can</u> be electrolysed because the ions can <u>move freely</u> and conduct electricity.

3) Molten ionic liquids, e.g. lead bromide, are always broken up into their <u>elements</u>.

At the cathode: $Pb^{2+} + 2e^- \rightarrow Pb$
At the anode: $2Br^- \rightarrow Br_2 + 2e^-$

The electrodes should be inert so they don't react with the electrolyte.

Metals can be Extracted From Their Ores Using Electrolysis

If a metal is <u>too reactive</u> to be <u>reduced</u> with <u>carbon</u> (page 106) or reacts with carbon, then electrolysis can be used to extract it. Extracting metals via this method is very <u>expensive</u> as lots of <u>energy</u> is required to melt the ore and produce the required current.

1) Aluminium is extracted from the ore <u>bauxite</u> by <u>electrolysis</u>. Bauxite contains <u>aluminium oxide</u>, Al_2O_3.

2) Aluminium oxide is heated to a <u>very high</u> temperature to form <u>molten</u> aluminium oxide.

3) The <u>molten mixture</u> contains <u>free ions</u> — so it'll <u>conduct electricity</u>.

4) The <u>positive Al^{3+} ions</u> are attracted to the <u>negative electrode</u> where they <u>each pick up three electrons</u> and turn into neutral <u>aluminium atoms</u>. These then <u>sink</u> to the bottom of the electrolysis tank.

5) The <u>negative O^{2-} ions</u> are attracted to the <u>positive electrode</u> where they <u>each lose two electrons</u>. The neutral oxygen atoms <u>combine</u> to form <u>O_2</u> molecules.

At the cathode:

Reduction — a gain of electrons:

$$Al^{3+} + 3e^- \rightarrow Al$$

<u>Aluminium</u> is produced at the <u>cathode</u>.

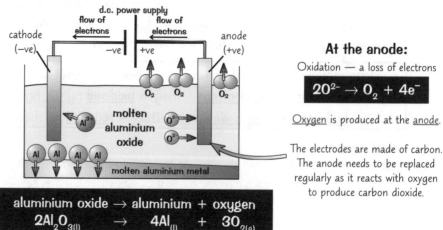

At the anode:

Oxidation — a loss of electrons

$$2O^{2-} \rightarrow O_2 + 4e^-$$

<u>Oxygen</u> is produced at the <u>anode</u>.

The electrodes are made of carbon. The anode needs to be replaced regularly as it reacts with oxygen to produce carbon dioxide.

Overall Equation:

aluminium oxide → aluminium + oxygen
$$2Al_2O_{3(l)} \rightarrow 4Al_{(l)} + 3O_{2(g)}$$

Faster shopping at the supermarket — use Electrolleys...

All this electrolysis stuff is a tad confusing I know — so if you need to, just read this page a few more times.

Q1 A student carries out electrolysis on molten zinc chloride. What is produced at:
a) the anode? b) the cathode? [2 marks]

Electrolysis of Aqueous Solutions

Electrolysis of <u>aqueous solutions</u> splits apart the <u>ionic compound</u> and the <u>water</u> — that means more ions...

Electrolysis of Aqueous Solutions is a Bit More Complicated

1) In <u>aqueous solutions</u>, as well as the <u>ions</u> from the ionic compound, there will be <u>hydrogen ions</u> (H^+) and <u>hydroxide ions</u> (OH^-) from the <u>water</u>: $H_2O \rightleftharpoons H^+ + OH^-$. So <u>water</u> can be <u>electrolysed</u> depending on what other ions are in the solution.

Some reactivity series (see p.103) include hydrogen in the list. You can use these to find out which metals are more or less reactive than hydrogen.

2) At the <u>cathode</u>, if <u>H^+ ions and metal ions</u> are present, <u>hydrogen gas</u> will be produced if the metal is <u>more reactive</u> than hydrogen (e.g. sodium). If the metal is <u>less reactive</u> than hydrogen (e.g. copper or silver), then a solid layer of the <u>pure metal</u> will be produced instead.

3) If there's a <u>concentrated</u> solution of <u>chloride ions</u>, <u>chlorine</u> molecules will be formed at the <u>anode</u>. If <u>no chloride ions</u> (or other halides) are present, then the OH^- ions are discharged and <u>oxygen</u> will be formed.

A solution of <u>copper(II) sulfate</u> ($CuSO_4$) contains <u>four different ions</u>: Cu^{2+}, SO_4^{2-}, H^+ and OH^-.

- <u>Copper</u> metal is less reactive than hydrogen. So at the cathode, <u>copper metal</u> is produced and coats the electrode.
$$Cu^{2+} + 2e^- \rightarrow Cu$$
- There aren't any <u>chloride ions</u> present. So at the anode, <u>oxygen</u> and <u>water</u> are produced. The oxygen can be seen as <u>bubbles</u>.
$$4OH^- \rightarrow O_2 + 2H_2O + 4e^-$$

Oxygen relights a glowing splint.

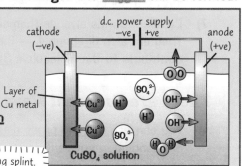

Here's How to Set Up an Electrochemical Cell

PRACTICAL

You'll probably have to do an experiment using electrolysis in the lab, so you need to know how to <u>set up</u> an electrochemical cell. Here's how you'd set up a sodium chloride cell:

1) Get <u>two electrodes</u> (you should use inert electrodes, e.g. <u>platinum</u> or <u>carbon</u>). Clean the surfaces of the electrodes using a piece of <u>emery paper</u> (or sandpaper).

2) From this point on, be careful not to touch the surfaces of the electrodes with your hands — you could transfer <u>grease</u> back onto the strips.

3) Place both electrodes into a <u>beaker</u> filled with your <u>electrolyte</u> — here it's sodium chloride solution.

The electrode that's attached to the negative end of the power supply becomes the cathode. The one that's attached to the positive end is the anode.

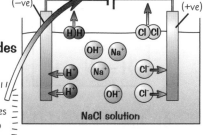

4) Connect the electrodes to a power supply using <u>crocodile clips</u> and <u>wires</u>.

A solution of <u>sodium chloride</u> (NaCl) contains <u>four different ions</u>: Na^+, Cl^-, H^+ and OH^-.

- <u>Sodium</u> metal is more reactive than hydrogen. So at the cathode, <u>hydrogen gas</u> is produced. $2H^+ + 2e^- \rightarrow H_2$
- <u>Chloride ions</u> are present in the solution. So at the anode, <u>chlorine gas</u> is produced. $2Cl^- \rightarrow Cl_2 + 2e^-$

Chlorine and hydrogen gas are released in the example above. You can <u>collect</u> these gases using the set-up shown on p.238 and then <u>test</u> them in the lab:

For more on tests for gases, see page 86.

- Chlorine <u>bleaches</u> damp <u>litmus paper</u>, turning it white. (It may turn <u>red</u> for a moment first though — that's because a solution of chlorine is <u>acidic</u>.)
- Hydrogen makes a "<u>squeaky pop</u>" when burnt with a <u>lighted splint</u>.

A Chemists Book of Poetry, page 34 — An Ode to Electrolysis...

Electrolysis can be used to extract the metals from the aqueous solutions produced by bioleaching and phytoextraction.

Q1   An aqueous solution of potassium chloride, KCl, is electrolysed using inert electrodes. Name the product formed at the anode.

[1 mark]

Covalent Bonding

Some elements bond ionically (see page 100) but others <u>share</u> electrons to form strong <u>covalent</u> bonds.

Covalent Bonds — Sharing Electrons

1) When <u>non-metal</u> atoms bond together, they <u>share</u> pairs of electrons to make <u>covalent bonds</u>.

2) Covalent bonding happens in <u>compounds</u> of <u>non-metals</u>, such as the alkanes (e.g. ethane, C_2H_6) and water (H_2O), and in <u>non-metal elements</u> (e.g. Cl_2).

I don't want to share electrons with you.

Mg   N

3) The positively charged nuclei of the bonded atoms are attracted to the shared pair of electrons by <u>electrostatic forces</u>, making covalent bonds very <u>strong</u>.

4) Atoms only share electrons in their <u>outer shells</u> (highest energy levels).

5) Each single <u>covalent bond</u> provides one <u>extra</u> shared electron for each atom.

6) Each atom involved generally makes <u>enough</u> covalent bonds to <u>fill up</u> its outer shell. Having a full outer shell gives them the electronic structure of a <u>noble gas</u>, which is very <u>stable</u>.

7) Covalent bonds arrange themselves so that they're as <u>far apart</u> from each other as possible. They are also <u>directional</u> — the electron shells overlap in a particular direction. Both of these factors contribute to the molecule's <u>3D structure</u> which you can see in ball and stick diagrams (see below).

There are Different Ways of Drawing Covalent Bonds

The dots show the H electrons and the crosses show the N electrons.

1) You can use <u>dot and cross diagrams</u> to show the bonding in covalent compounds.

Nitrogen has <u>five</u> outer electrons...

Strong covalent bond.

2) Electrons drawn in the <u>overlap</u> between the outer shells of two atoms are <u>shared</u> between those atoms.

3) Dot and cross diagrams are useful for showing <u>which atoms</u> the electrons in a covalent bond come from, but they <u>don't</u> show the relative sizes of the atoms, or how the atoms are <u>arranged</u> in space.

...so it needs to form <u>three covalent bonds</u> to make up the extra <u>three</u> electrons needed.

You can also draw dot and cross diagrams showing the inner electron shells.

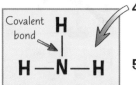
Covalent bond
H — N — H

4) <u>Displayed formulas</u> show the covalent bonds as single lines between atoms.

5) This is a great way of showing <u>how</u> atoms are connected in <u>large</u> molecules. However, they <u>don't</u> show the <u>3D structure</u> of the molecule, or <u>which atoms</u> the electrons in the covalent bonds have come from.

6) Three dimensional ball and stick models show the <u>atoms</u>, the <u>covalent bonds</u> and their <u>arrangement</u> in space next to each other. But 3D models can quickly get <u>confusing</u> for large molecules where there are lots of atoms to include. They also don't show <u>where</u> the electrons in the bonds have <u>come from</u>, either. 3D models also suggest that there are <u>gaps</u> between the atoms, when in fact, this space is where the <u>shared electrons</u> are.

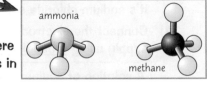
ammonia
methane

7) A <u>molecular formula</u> shows you how many <u>atoms</u> of each element are in a molecule. You can find the <u>molecular formula</u> of a simple molecular compound from <u>any</u> of these diagram by <u>counting up</u> how many atoms of each element there are.

Molecular formulas can be simplified to empirical formulas — see next page.

> **EXAMPLE:** A diagram of the molecule ethane is shown on the right. Use the diagram to find the molecular formula of ethane.
>
> In the diagram, there are two carbon atoms and six hydrogen atoms. So the molecular formula is C_2H_6.

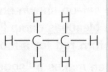

Sharing is caring...

So, there are several different ways to represent covalent bonding in molecules, but you can't get all the structural or electronic information from just one of them. Make sure you can describe the limitations of each type.

Q1   Using the diagrams above, give the molecular formula of ammonia.   [1 mark]

Simple Covalent Substances

These molecules might be <u>simple</u>, but you've still gotta know about them. I know, the world is a cruel place.

Simple Covalent Substances Contain Just a Few Atoms

Substances that have <u>simple covalent structures</u> are made from molecules containing a <u>few atoms</u> joined together by <u>covalent bonds</u>. Here are some <u>common examples</u>...

<u>Oxygen, O_2</u>
Each oxygen atom needs <u>two more electrons</u> to complete its outer shell so, in <u>oxygen gas</u>, two oxygen atoms share <u>two pairs</u> of electrons with each other, making a <u>double covalent bond</u>.

<u>Water, H_2O</u>
In <u>water molecules</u>, the oxygen atom shares a pair of electrons with two hydrogen atoms to form two <u>single covalent bonds</u>.

<u>Methane, CH_4</u>
Carbon has <u>four outer electrons</u>, which is <u>half</u> a full shell. It can form <u>four covalent bonds</u> with <u>hydrogen</u> atoms to fill up its outer shell.

Make sure you know how to draw dot and cross diagrams for simple covalent substances.

Properties of Simple Covalent Substances

1) Substances containing <u>covalent bonds</u> usually have <u>simple molecular structures</u>.

2) The atoms within the molecules are held together by <u>very strong covalent bonds</u>. By contrast, the forces of attraction <u>between</u> these molecules are <u>very weak</u>.

3) To melt or boil a simple molecular compound, you only need to break these <u>feeble intermolecular forces</u> and <u>not</u> the covalent bonds. So the melting and boiling points are <u>very low</u>, because the molecules are <u>easily parted</u> from each other.

4) <u>Bigger</u> molecules have <u>stronger</u> intermolecular forces, so the melting and boiling points are <u>higher</u> because <u>more energy</u> is need to break the forces (see p.78).

5) Molecular compounds <u>don't conduct electricity</u>, simply because they <u>aren't charged</u>, so there are <u>no free electrons</u> or ions.

Weak intermolecular forces

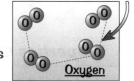

Oxygen

Most molecular substances are gases or liquids at room temperature.

The Empirical Formula is the Simplest Ratio of Atoms

An <u>empirical formula</u> of a compound tells you the <u>smallest whole number ratio</u> of atoms in the compound.

EXAMPLE: Find the empirical formula of ethane, C_2H_6.

The numbers in the <u>molecular formula</u> of <u>ethane</u> are <u>2</u> and <u>6</u>.
To simplify the ratio, divide by the largest number that goes into 2 and 6 <u>exactly</u> — that's <u>2</u>.

C: $2 \div 2 = 1$
H: $6 \div 2 = 3$
The empirical formula of ethane is CH_3.

You can use the <u>empirical formula</u> of a compound, together with its relative formula mass, M_r (see p.130), to find its molecular formula.

EXAMPLE: Compound X has the empirical formula C_2H_6N. The M_r of compound X is 88.0. Find the molecular formula of compound X.

1) Start by finding the M_r of the <u>empirical formula</u> by adding up all the relative atomic masses (A_r)of the atoms in the formula. The A_r of carbon is <u>12.0</u>, the A_r of hydrogen is <u>1.0</u> and the A_r of nitrogen is <u>14.0</u>.

M_r of $C_2H_6N = (2 \times C) + (6 \times H) + N$
$= (2 \times 12.0) + (6 \times 1.0) + 14.0$
$= 24.0 + 6.0 + 14.0$
$= 44.0$

2) Divide the M_r of compound X by the M_r of the empirical formula.

$88.0 \div 44.0 = 2$

3) From this you can see that the molecular formula of compound X contains two lots of the empirical formula, so to get the <u>molecular formula</u> you just <u>multiply</u> everything in the empirical formula by <u>2</u>.

C: $2 \times 2 = 4$
H: $6 \times 2 = 12$ The molecular formula of
N: $1 \times 2 = 2$ compound X is $C_4H_{12}N_2$.

May the intermolecular force be with you...

Never forget that it's the weak forces between molecules that are broken when a simple molecular substance melts.

Q1 Explain why oxygen, O_2, is a gas at room temperature. [2 marks]

Homologous Series and Alkanes

Alkanes — the simplest homologous series, but we'd be nowhere without them...

Compounds in a Homologous Series Share Similar Chemical Properties

1) A homologous series (e.g. alkanes and alkenes) is a family of molecules which share the same general formula. Molecules in the same homologous series share similar chemical properties.

2) The molecular formulas of neighbouring compounds in a homologous series differ by a CH_2 unit.

3) Trends can be seen in the physical properties of compounds in a homologous series. For example, the bigger a molecule is, the higher the boiling point will be.

Alkane	Molecular formula	Boiling point (°C)
Methane	CH_4	–162
Ethane	C_2H_6	–89
Dodecane	$C_{12}H_{26}$	216
Icosane	$C_{20}H_{42}$	343
Tetracontane	$C_{40}H_{82}$	524

Properties Change as the Carbon Chain Gets Longer

As the length of the carbon chain changes in a homologous series, the properties of the molecules change.

1) The shorter the carbon chains, the more runny they will be — that is, the less viscous (gloopy) they are.

2) Molecules with shorter carbon chains are also more volatile, i.e. they have lower boiling points.

3) Also, the shorter the carbon chains, the more flammable (easier to ignite) the compounds will be.

4) The properties of these compounds affect how they're used for fuels. E.g. compounds with short carbon chains and lower boiling points are used as 'bottled gases' — stored under pressure as liquids in bottles.

Alkanes Have All C–C Single Bonds

1) Alkanes are the simplest homologous series you can get. The atoms in alkanes are held together by single covalent bonds. They have the general formula C_nH_{2n+2}.

2) Alkanes are hydrocarbons — compounds containing only hydrogen and carbon atoms.

3) The first four alkanes are methane, ethane, propane and butane.

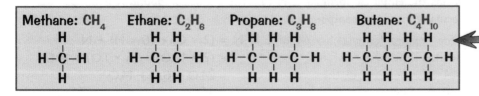

Methane: CH_4 Ethane: C_2H_6 Propane: C_3H_8 Butane: C_4H_{10}

A drawing showing all the atoms and bonds in a molecule is called a displayed formula.

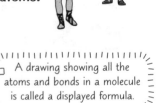

Alkane, Al saw, Al conquered.   Give it a rest, Alan!

Alkanes — full of bonds just looking for love...

So alkanes only contain two ingredients — carbon and hydrogen. Jamie Oliver would not be happy.

Q1   Draw the structural formula for propane, C_3H_8. [1 mark]

Q2   A student has two alkanes, C_5H_{12} and $C_{10}H_{22}$. Compare the following properties of the alkanes:
a) viscosity,   b) boiling point,   c) flammability. [3 marks]

Fractional Distillation of Crude Oil

Don't panic — not those types of <u>fractions</u>, I'm not going to inflict maths on you. Well, not here anyway...

Fractional Distillation can be Used to Separate Hydrocarbon Fractions

Crude oil is a <u>mixture</u> of <u>lots of different hydrocarbons</u>, most of which are <u>alkanes</u>. The different compounds in crude oil are <u>separated</u> by <u>fractional distillation</u>. Here's how it works:

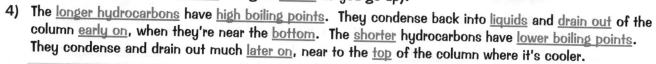

Approximate Number of Carbons in the Hydrocarbons in that Fraction

~3 ~8 ~15 ~20 ~40

LPG
COOL
Petrol
Kerosene
Diesel oil
Heavy fuel oil
VERY HOT
Bitumen

1) The oil is <u>heated</u> until most of it has turned into <u>gas</u>. The gases enter a <u>fractionating column</u> (and the liquid bit is drained off).

2) The fractionating column is a <u>tall</u> column which has <u>condensers</u> coming off at various points.

3) The column is heated from the bottom so there's a <u>temperature gradient</u> (it's <u>hot</u> at the <u>bottom</u> and gets <u>cooler</u> as you go up).

4) The <u>longer hydrocarbons</u> have <u>high boiling points</u>. They condense back into <u>liquids</u> and <u>drain out</u> of the column <u>early on</u>, when they're near the <u>bottom</u>. The <u>shorter</u> hydrocarbons have <u>lower boiling points</u>. They condense and drain out much <u>later on</u>, near to the <u>top</u> of the column where it's cooler.

When the crude oil mixture is <u>heated</u>, the molecules are supplied with <u>extra energy</u>. This makes the molecules <u>move about</u> more. Eventually, a molecule might have enough energy to <u>overcome</u> the <u>intermolecular forces</u> that keep it with the other molecules and so it can <u>whizz off</u> as a <u>gas</u>. The intermolecular forces break a lot more <u>easily</u> between <u>small</u> molecules than they do between bigger molecules because they're much <u>weaker</u>. That's why <u>small</u> molecules generally have <u>lower boiling points</u> than big molecules do.

There are two types of bond in crude oil — strong covalent bonds between the atoms within hydrocarbon molecules and weaker intermolecular forces of attraction between hydrocarbon molecules in the mixture.

5) You end up with the crude oil mixture separated out into <u>different fractions</u>. Each fraction contains a mixture of mainly alkanes that have a <u>similar</u> number of <u>carbon atoms</u>, so have similar <u>boiling points</u>.

Fractional Distillation can also Separate Crude Oil in the Lab

PRACTICAL

If you've got a <u>mixture of liquids</u> you can separate it using <u>fractional distillation</u>. Here's a practical you can do that models the <u>fractional distillation of crude oil</u> at a <u>refinery</u>:

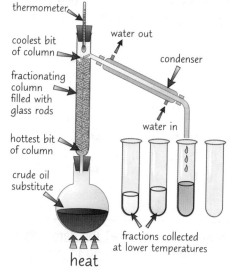

thermometer
coolest bit of column
water out
condenser
fractionating column filled with glass rods
water in
hottest bit of column
crude oil substitute
fractions collected at lower temperatures
heat

1) Put your <u>crude oil substitute</u> in a flask. Attach a <u>fractionating column</u> and <u>condenser</u> above the flask as shown.

2) Gradually <u>heat</u> the flask. The liquids with the <u>lowest boiling points</u> will evaporate first. Collect this fraction in a <u>collection vessel</u>.

3) Liquids with <u>higher boiling points</u> may start evaporating. But they'll only get part of the way up before <u>condensing</u> and running back down towards the flask.

4) When the temperature on the thermometer reaches 50 °C, <u>replace</u> the collection vessel and collect the <u>next fraction</u>.

5) Collect further fractions, changing the collection vessel each time the temperature is raised by <u>50 °C</u>.

To separate a mixture of liquids with distinct boiling points, you'd need to gradually heat the flask and collect each liquid in a separate vessel at each of their boiling points.

How much petrol is there in crude oil? Just a fraction...

So whether you're doing fractional distillation in industry or the lab, they both work using the same principle — separation depends on the boiling points of the different molecules and the boiling points depends on their size.

Q1 Outline why short-chain hydrocarbons drain out of the top of the fractionating column. [3 marks]

Uses of Crude Oil

Crude oil really <u>improves</u> our lives in lots of ways but we're using up our supplies way too <u>quickly</u>...

Crude Oil has Various Important Uses in Modern Life...

1) Most of the hydrocarbons that are in use today have come from <u>crude oil</u>.

2) <u>Crude oil</u> provides the <u>fuel</u> for most modern <u>transport</u> — cars, trains, planes, the lot.

3) The <u>petrochemical industry</u> uses some of the hydrocarbons from crude oil as a <u>feedstock</u> to make <u>new compounds</u> for use in things like <u>polymers</u>, <u>solvents</u>, <u>lubricants</u>, and <u>detergents</u>.

4) Almost all of the <u>consumer products</u> we use, from cleaning products to smart phones, use crude oil, whether it's for their <u>manufacture</u> or for their <u>transport</u>.

...But It Will Run Out Eventually... Eeek

1) Crude oil is a <u>finite</u> resource — our supplies are <u>limited</u> and <u>non-renewable</u> so if we keep using it at the current rate, we will eventually <u>run out</u>.

2) <u>New reserves</u> are sometimes found, and new <u>technology</u> helps us get to oil that was once too <u>difficult</u> to extract. But it's still not enough.

Alternative energy sources include, wind power, ethanol and solar energy.

3) Our use of crude oil is <u>not sustainable</u>, so we should continue developing <u>alternative energy sources</u>. These alternatives aren't without their own <u>problems</u>, but we'll need them when the oil runs out.

4) Some people think we should use <u>alternatives</u> for <u>fuel</u> where we can and keep the oil for making <u>plastics</u> and other <u>chemicals</u>. This could lead to conflict for resources between the fuel and chemical industries.

5) We need to balance the <u>short-term</u> benefits of using crude oil with the need to conserve it for the future.

Cracking Means Splitting Up Long–Chain Hydrocarbons

1) Fractional distillation produces many <u>large</u> alkane molecules which are <u>not in great demand</u> — we don't need them nearly as much as some of the smaller hydrocarbon fractions like petrol and diesel.

2) A lot of the longer alkane molecules produced from <u>fractional distillation</u> are <u>turned</u> into <u>smaller, more useful</u> ones by a process called <u>cracking</u>.

3) During cracking, the hydrocarbons are <u>heated</u> until they become a <u>vapour</u> and are either passed over a <u>powdered catalyst</u> or mixed with <u>steam</u>, which causes them to <u>split apart</u>.

4) Cracking is a form of <u>thermal decomposition</u> — the hydrocarbon <u>breaks down</u> when it is <u>heated</u>. You need lots of energy for this because you're breaking the strong <u>covalent bonds</u> within the molecule.

5) As well as alkanes, cracking also produces another type of hydrocarbon called <u>alkenes</u>. Alkenes are used as a <u>starting material</u> (feedstock) when making lots of other compounds and can be used to make polymers.

The number of C and H atoms in the large alkane should equal the total number of C and H atoms in the products. So when writing a cracking equation, make sure both sides balance.

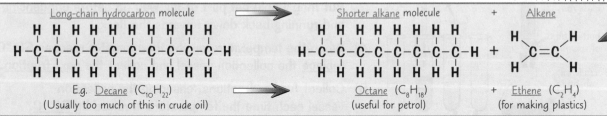

Long-chain hydrocarbon molecule → Shorter alkane molecule + Alkene

E.g. Decane $(C_{10}H_{22})$ → Octane (C_8H_{18}) + Ethene (C_2H_4)
(Usually too much of this in crude oil) (useful for petrol) (for making plastics)

6) If we didn't use cracking — lots <u>more</u> crude oil would need to be extracted to <u>meet the demands</u> for certain hydrocarbons (e.g. petrol) and a lot of the longer chain hydrocarbons would go to <u>waste</u>.

I'm not one to brag, but this really is a cracking page...

Alternative fuels are great but we're definitely not in the position to fully rely on them just yet. That's why cracking's so important — we can eke out our resources until we've developed our technology to run on alternatives.

Q1 A molecule of dodecane, $C_{12}H_{26}$, was cracked, producing two products. One of the products had the molecular formula C_9H_{20}. Give the molecular formula for the other product. [1 mark]

Revision Questions for Chapter C3

All good things must come to an end — Chapter C3 included. So make the most of these questions...
- Try these questions and <u>tick off each one</u> when you <u>get it right</u>.
- When you've done <u>all the questions</u> for a topic and are <u>completely happy</u> with it, tick off the topic.

The Reactions and Reactivity of Metals (p.103-105) ☑

1) Describe the bonding in metals. ☑
2) Do metals higher up in the reactivity series form positive ions more
   or less easily than metals further down the reactivity series? ☑
3) What will happen if you put a less reactive metal into a solution of a more reactive metal salt? ☑
4) A student adds some potassium to dilute acid. Will a reaction take place? ☑
5) A student has a piece of sodium and a piece of silver. Which metal will react with cold water? ☑

Extracting Metals from their Ores (p.106-109) ☑

6) Where do metals need to be positioned in the reactivity series
   in order to be extracted by reduction by carbon? ☑
7) Some metals can be extracted from their ore using reduction by carbon.
   What happens to the metal ore when it is reduced? ☑
8) Name two biological methods that scientists have developed to extract metals. ☑
9) Does the following half equation show oxidation or reduction? $Na \rightarrow Na^+ + e^-$ ☑
10) During electrolysis, which electrode do the negative ions in the electrolyte move towards? ☑
11) In the electrolysis of aluminium oxide, is aluminium produced at the anode or the cathode? ☑
12) Name the product formed at the cathode during the electrolysis of copper(II) sulfate solution. ☑

Covalent Bonds (p.110-111) ☐

13) What is a covalent bond? ☑
14) Give a limitation of using dot and cross diagrams to display the covalent bonding in a molecule. ☑
15) Which bonds/forces are broken when a simple covalent substance is boiled? ☐
16) Why don't simple covalent substances conduct electricity? ☑
17) What does an empirical formula show? ☑

Alkanes and Crude Oil (p.112-114) ☑

18) What is the general formula of alkanes? ☑
19) Where in a fractionating column do long-chain hydrocarbons drain off? ☑
20) What is the purpose of cracking? ☑

Polymers

Polymers are made up of <u>lots</u> of the same molecule <u>joined together</u> in one long chain. They're what make up plastics. They have lots of weird and wonderful properties which make them darn useful to modern society.

Plastics are Made Up of Long-Chain Molecules Called Polymers

1) <u>Polymers</u> are long molecules formed when lots of small molecules called <u>monomers</u> join together. This reaction is called <u>polymerisation</u>.

2) They can occur <u>naturally</u> or be made <u>synthetically</u>. For example, the <u>alkenes</u> made by cracking crude oil (see p.114) can be used to make polymers.

Polymers Are Held Together by Covalent Bonds and Intermolecular Forces

1) In polymers, all the atoms in a chain are joined by strong <u>covalent bonds</u>.

2) There are <u>intermolecular forces</u> between the chains.

3) The intermolecular forces between polymer molecules are <u>stronger</u> than between simple molecules, so <u>more energy</u> is needed to break them. This means most polymers are <u>solid</u> at room temperature.

4) The intermolecular forces are still <u>weaker</u> than ionic or covalent bonds, so polymers generally have <u>lower</u> melting points than <u>ionic</u> or <u>giant covalent</u> compounds.

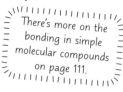
There's more on the bonding in simple molecular compounds on page 111.

5) Before polymers melt, they become <u>soft</u>. The weaker the forces between the chains, the lower the <u>softening point</u> of a polymer.

The Forces Between Chains Influence the Properties of a Polymer

Polymers have different properties depending on their <u>structure</u> and the <u>forces between</u> the chains.

- <u>Low density</u> (LD) poly(ethene) is made from ethene. There's lots of space between the polymer chains, so the forces between the chains are relatively <u>weak</u>. This means it's <u>flexible</u> and so is used for bags and bottles.

- <u>High density</u> (HD) poly(ethene) is also made from ethene but under different conditions. The chains are packed more <u>closely</u> together, so the forces between them are <u>stronger</u>. So it's <u>stiff</u> and is used for water tanks and drainpipes.

As well as intermolecular forces between the chains, some <u>polymers</u> also form <u>covalent</u> or <u>ionic crosslinks</u>.

Polymers that only have intermolecular forces between the chains are made up of <u>individual tangled chains</u> that can <u>slide</u> over each other. The forces between the chains can be overcome, so the polymers can be <u>melted</u>.

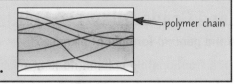
polymer chain

In polymers that have <u>crosslinks</u> between the chains as well as intermolecular forces, the chains are held together very strongly. These polymers <u>don't soften</u> when they're heated. The chains are held together in a rigid structure, making them <u>strong, hard</u> and <u>stiff</u>.

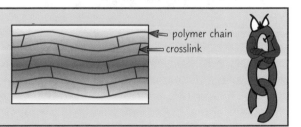
polymer chain
crosslink

Revision's like polymers — it's all about stringing facts together...

Make sure you understand that it's the forces between the chains in a polymer that decide what properties it has.

Q1   A polymer contains crosslinks. State four properties you would expect it to have.   [4 marks]

Giant Covalent Structures

If you though <u>polymers</u> were large, just wait til you meet these beauties... And I'm not joking about them being beautiful — <u>sparkly diamonds</u> are giant covalent structures. Ooooh... Sparkles...

Giant Covalent Structures Contain Many Covalent Bonds

1) <u>Giant covalent structures</u> are similar to giant ionic lattices <u>except</u> that there are <u>no charged ions</u>.

2) The atoms are <u>bonded</u> to <u>each other</u> by <u>strong</u> covalent bonds.

3) This means that they have <u>very high</u> melting and boiling points.

4) They <u>don't conduct electricity</u> — not even when <u>molten</u> (except for graphite and graphene — see below).

> Giant covalent structures are sometimes called 'macromolecules'. 'Macro-' means 'big'. They're called that because they're molecules, and they're big. Big for molecules, anyway.

5) They tend to be <u>insoluble</u> in water.

6) The examples of <u>giant covalent structures</u> you need to know about are made from <u>carbon atoms</u>.

7) <u>Carbon</u> can form <u>lots</u> of different types of molecule (including the ones below), because carbon atoms can form up to <u>four covalent bonds</u>, and, unusually, carbon atoms can bond <u>to each other</u> to make <u>chains</u> and <u>rings</u>. Alkanes, a <u>family</u> (<u>homologous series</u>) of <u>organic</u> compounds, are covered on p.112.

Diamond

1) Pure diamonds are <u>lustrous</u> (sparkly) and <u>colourless</u>. Ideal for jewellery.

2) Each carbon atom forms <u>four covalent bonds</u> in a <u>very rigid</u> giant covalent structure, which makes diamond <u>really hard</u>. This makes diamonds ideal as cutting tools.

3) All those <u>strong covalent bonds</u> take a lot of energy to break and give diamond a <u>very high melting point</u>, which is another reason diamond is a good <u>cutting tool</u>.

4) It <u>doesn't conduct electricity</u> because it has <u>no free electrons</u> or ions.

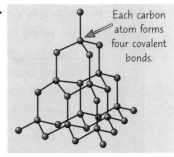

Each carbon atom forms four covalent bonds.

Graphite and Graphene

1) Graphite is <u>black</u> and <u>opaque</u>, but still kind of <u>shiny</u>.

2) Each carbon atom only forms <u>three covalent bonds</u>, creating <u>sheets of carbon atoms</u> which are free to <u>slide over each other</u>.

3) The layers are held together weakly so they are slippery and can be <u>rubbed off</u> onto paper to leave a black mark — that's how a pencil works. This also makes graphite ideal as a <u>lubricating material</u>.

> Diamond, graphite and graphene are <u>allotropes</u> of carbon — different forms of the same element.

Each carbon atom forms three covalent bonds.

Weak forces between the layers.

4) Graphite's got a <u>high melting point</u> — the covalent bonds need <u>loads of energy</u> to break.

5) Since only three out of each carbon's four outer electrons are used in bonds, there are lots of <u>delocalised</u> (free) <u>electrons</u> that can move. This means graphite <u>conducts electricity</u>.

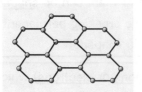

6) <u>Graphene</u> is a <u>single sheet</u> of graphite. The carbon atoms are arranged in hexagons, and each atom forms <u>three</u> covalent bonds. Graphene's a bit of a wonder material — its covalent bonds make it extremely <u>strong</u> and a sheet of graphene is so thin that it's <u>transparent</u> and incredibly <u>light</u>. Its delocalised electrons are <u>completely free</u> to move about, which makes it even better at <u>conducting electricity</u> and <u>thermal energy</u> than graphite.

So that pencil I gave her was just the same as a diamond, really...

Graphene's got loads of possible uses. As a strengthening material, in batteries, even to make inks that conduct electricity. It's all quite new and snazzy, so scientists have to use their imagination when developing uses for it.

Q1 Give two similarities and two differences between diamond and graphite, in terms of their structure and properties. [4 marks]

Q2 Describe the structure of graphene. [2 marks]

Bulk Properties of Materials

The way a material behaves is all to do with its <u>structure</u> and the type of <u>bonding</u> it contains.

Different Materials Have Different Structures

The properties of materials are related to their <u>bonding</u> and <u>structure</u>. That's why some materials have <u>different properties</u> even though they're made of the <u>same elements</u> (e.g. alkenes and polymers). These are the <u>types of structure</u> you need to know about:

Chemists use information about bonding and structure to predict the properties of materials.

Structure	Ionic (p.101)	Simple Molecular (p.111)	Metallic (p.103)	Polymer (p.116)	Giant Covalent (p.117)
Example	NaCl	CO_2	Iron	poly(ethene)	Diamond
Type of bonding	Electrostatic attractions between oppositely charged ions in all directions.	Strong covalent bonds between atoms. Weak intermolecular forces between particles.	Electrostatic attractions between positive metal ions and delocalised 'sea' of electrons.	Strong covalent bonds between atoms. Intermolecular forces between chains (stronger than between simple molecules). Can contain crosslinks.	Covalent bonds between atoms.

Different Materials Have Different Bulk Properties

Melting point

1) Most materials that are pure chemicals have a <u>melting point</u>. At this temperature the <u>solid</u> material turns to <u>liquid</u>. The <u>stronger</u> the forces between particles, the <u>higher</u> the melting point.

Strength

1) <u>Strength</u> is how good a material is at <u>resisting</u> a <u>force</u>. The stronger something is, the <u>greater</u> the force that's needed to either <u>break</u> it or <u>permanently</u> change its <u>shape</u> (<u>deform</u> it).

2) The strength of a material depends on how <u>firmly</u> the particles are <u>held in place</u>. <u>Pure metals</u> aren't strong because the layers of atoms can <u>slide</u> over each other. <u>Ionic compounds</u> are strong because the ions in the lattice are held <u>firmly in place</u> by the ionic bonds acting in all directions.

3) There are <u>two</u> types of strength you need to know about:
   - <u>TENSILE STRENGTH</u> — how much a material can resist a <u>pulling</u> (stretching) <u>force</u>.
   - <u>COMPRESSIVE STRENGTH</u> — how much a material can resist a <u>pushing</u> (squashing) <u>force</u>.

Stiffness

1) <u>Stiff</u> materials don't bend when a force is applied. This <u>isn't</u> the same as strength — <u>flexible</u> materials can be strong if the force doesn't <u>permanently</u> deform them.

2) The stronger the forces between particles, the <u>stiffer</u> a material is.

Hardness

1) The hardness of a material is how <u>difficult</u> it is to <u>cut</u> into.

2) The <u>stronger</u> the forces between particles, the <u>harder</u> it tends to be. Diamond is the <u>hardest known</u> natural material.

Brittleness

1) <u>Brittle</u> materials <u>break</u> if they're hit by a sudden <u>force</u> (e.g. being hit by a hammer).

2) Materials that are brittle tend to have structures where the particles <u>can't move</u> without the <u>bonds</u> between them <u>breaking</u> permanently. For example, <u>diamond</u> is brittle because if the particles move suddenly, the covalent bonds will break. <u>Ionic compounds</u> are also brittle. <u>Metals aren't</u> brittle because the layers can <u>slide</u> over each other without the bonds breaking permanently.

Ease of reshaping

1) Materials that <u>deform</u> but don't break when a force is applied to them can be <u>shaped</u>.

2) These materials have particles that can <u>move</u> without the bonds breaking permanently.

3) <u>Metals</u> and polymers that <u>don't</u> form <u>crosslinks</u> are often easily shaped.

Conductivity

1) To conduct <u>electricity</u>, a material must have <u>charged particles</u> (<u>ions</u> or <u>electrons</u>) which can <u>move</u>.

2) Materials with free electrons are often good <u>thermal conductors</u> as the electrons can transfer energy <u>quickly</u> through the material. Materials without free electrons transfer energy via their <u>bonds</u>, which is <u>slow</u>, so they're often <u>thermal insulators</u>.

Hulk properties — green, strong, and able to reshape...

The properties above are bulk properties. They're characteristic of the material and depend on how lots of particles interact together. This means the individual particles in the material don't have these properties.

Q1   What characteristic of a material allows it to conduct electricity?   [1 mark]

Types of Materials

I can tell you now that this page is going to be smashing. At least the bit about ceramics will be...

Ceramics are Stiff but Brittle

Ceramics are made by baking substances, such as clay, to produce a brittle, stiff material.

Ceramics include glass, porcelain and bone china.

- Clay is soft when it's wet, so it's easy to mould into different shapes e.g. for pottery or bricks.
- It is hardened by firing at very high temperatures. It has a high compressive strength so it's used as a building material — clay bricks can withstand the weight of lots more bricks on top of them.

- Glass is generally transparent and strong, can be moulded when hot and can be brittle when thin.
- The majority of glass made is soda-lime glass which is made by heating lime, sand and sodium carbonate (soda) until they melt. When the mixture cools it comes out as glass.

Composites are Made of Different Materials

Composites, such as fibreglass, are made of one material (the reinforcement) embedded in another (the matrix/binder). The materials could be embedded on a bulk scale, such as with concrete that's reinforced with steel, or they could be made up of nanoparticles of one substance embedded in another. The properties of a composite depend on the properties of the materials it is made from. For example:

Carbon fibre composites have been made using carbon atoms bonded together to make carbon fibres or carbon nanotubes (see p.124) held together in a polymer resin matrix. These polymers are expensive to make but they're strong and have a low density so they're used to make aeroplanes and sports cars.

Some Materials are Damaged by Corrosion

1) Some materials, such as metals, can be destroyed by a process called corrosion.

2) If iron comes into contact with air and water, it will slowly corrode (rust). This limits the lifetime of iron objects. Iron only corrodes when it's in contact with both oxygen (e.g. from the air) and water.

3) Fortunately, there ways to help prevent the corrosion of metals. For example, you can create a barrier (e.g. with paint) to stop the metal coming into contact with water or oxygen. You can also attach a more reactive metal to the metal you want to protect. The more reactive metal will react with oxygen and water instead of the metal you're protecting. This is sacrificial protection.

If you put an iron nail in a test tube with air and water, it will rust. If the test tube contains just air or just water, then no rusting will happen.

Corrosion is a Redox Reaction

1) Corrosion of iron is a redox reaction — so it involves both oxidation and reduction.

2) Oxidation can be described as the loss of electrons, and reduction can be described as the gain of electrons (see p.107).

3) When it corrodes, iron loses electrons as it reacts with oxygen. Each Fe atom loses three electrons to become Fe^{3+}, so iron's oxidised. Simultaneously, oxygen gains electrons when it reacts with iron. Each O atom gains two electrons to become O^{2-}. Oxygen's reduced.

Remember OIL RIG — Oxidation is Loss, Reduction is Gain (of electrons).

Oxidation can also mean the addition of oxygen to an element or compound. The removal of oxygen is called reduction.

Copper gains oxygen so is oxidised.
$$2Cu + O_2 \rightarrow 2CuO$$

$$2CuO + C \rightarrow 2Cu + CO_2$$
Copper oxide loses oxygen to form copper metal, so copper is reduced.

Porcelain jugs never cry — they've got a stiff upper lip...

So many materials, but my favourite type of material will always be the soft, fluffy kind...

Q1   Name two composite materials.   [2 mark]

Materials and their Uses

It's all very well making a material, but it needs to be fit for purpose. You need to be able to understand why a certain material is used and not another material. For example, a fire guard made of iron instead of chocolate.

Different Materials are Suited to Different Jobs

What purposes materials are used for depends on their properties. In the exam they might ask you to interpret information about the properties of materials and assess the suitability of these materials for different purposes.

You should know all about the bonding in metals (see page 103) and polymers (see page 116).

Polymers are really adaptable — for example, some are flexible, so they can be bent without breaking, and can be easily moulded into almost any shape. They're often cheaper than most other materials, and they also tend to be less dense than most metals or ceramics, so they're often used when designing products that need to have a low mass. They're also thermal and electrical insulators. But, polymers can degrade over time, so polymer products don't always last as long as those made from other materials.

Ceramics, like polymers, are insulators of heat and electricity. They're much more brittle and stiff than most other materials, but they're also strong and hard wearing. They don't degrade or corrode like other materials can, so they can last longer — that's why we still use glass in windows instead of clear plastic.

Metals are good conductors of heat and electricity — which can be an advantage or a disadvantage, depending on what the material is needed for. They generally have high melting points. They're malleable, so they can be formed into a variety of shapes. Some metals corrode easily, but products made from corrosion resistant metals can last for a very long time. Metals are usually less brittle than either ceramics or some polymers, so they're likely to deform but stay in one piece where other materials may shatter.

Composites have different properties depending on the matrix/binder and the reinforcement. The combination of component materials used can be altered, so composites can be designed to have specific properties for a specific purpose. The main disadvantage of composites is that they tend to be much more expensive to produce than other materials.

You Need to Be Able to Interpret Information about Materials

Chemists use information about the properties of materials and assess their suitability for different uses.

EXAMPLE: A company is investigating the best material to make a camping cup. The cup needs to be lightweight, able to withstand the temperature of hot drinks and shouldn't be brittle. Using the data in the table, suggest which material from the table the company should use.

Material	Melting point (°C)	Density (g/cm³)	Brittleness
Aluminium	660	2.7	Low
Glass	700 (softens)	2.6	High
Poly(propene)	171	0.94	Medium
LDPE	110 (but softens from 80)	0.92	Medium

Aluminium can be ruled out — it has a high melting point and isn't brittle but it's the densest material.

Glass has a high softening point and is less dense than aluminium, but it's brittle, so breaks easily.

The density and brittleness of LDPE and poly(propene) are similar, but LDPE starts softening at 80 °C. A hot drink could be up to 100 °C, so LDPE wouldn't be any good.

Poly(propene) melts above 100 °C, is lightweight and not too brittle.
So poly(propene) is the best material for the job.

As well as making sure a product is fit for its purpose, life-cycle assessment data (see page 122) is also used to work out how environmentally friendly manufacturing, using and disposing of a product is.

Compost-sites — piles of old vegetables embedded in muck...

So, you can't use any old material for any old job. My steel pillow and my glass duvet taught me that.

Q1 Look at the table in the example above. Given that glass, poly(propene) and LDPE are fairly unreactive and aluminium is fairly reactive, which of the four materials would you use to make a piece of equipment for heating chemicals to 300 °C? Explain your answer. [3 marks]

Reuse and Recycling

Recycling's a hot topic. It's really important to make sure we <u>don't run out</u> of lots of important raw materials.

Extracting Raw Materials Requires Energy

1) Instead of throwing products away, some things can be <u>reused</u> or <u>recycled</u> instead.
2) <u>Reusing</u> means using the product again in the <u>same form</u>. E.g. <u>glass milk bottles</u> can be used again.
3) <u>Recycling</u> means using the materials in a product to make new things.
   For example, <u>paper</u> can be recycled to make the paper for <u>newspapers</u>.
4) Recycling and reusing can affect factors in the <u>life cycle assessment</u> of a product (see next page).
5) Extracting raw materials can take large amounts of <u>energy</u>, lots of which comes from burning <u>fossil fuels</u>.
6) Fossil fuels are <u>running out</u> so we need to <u>conserve</u> them. Burning them also causes <u>pollution</u> (p.84).
7) Recycling often only uses a <u>small fraction</u> of the energy needed to extract and refine the material from scratch. <u>Reusing</u> takes <u>even less</u> energy. Energy is expensive, so recycling and reusing can <u>save money</u>.
8) Recycling and reusing <u>conserves</u> the finite amounts of many <u>non-renewable</u> raw materials, e.g. metal ores and crude oil. However, recycling and reusing materials can't completely meet our demand for these materials. To stop us from <u>running out</u> of finite resources, society also needs to <u>use less</u>.
9) Recycling and reusing means less waste is sent to <u>landfill</u>. Landfill takes up space and <u>pollutes</u> the area.

- Plastic drinks bottles are usually made from a polymer called <u>PET</u>. They can be recycled to make other packaging materials.
- Plastic waste is first <u>sorted</u> to separate out PET objects from other plastic materials. The PET objects are then <u>shredded</u> and cleaned, before being <u>melted down</u> and then processed to make <u>new objects</u>.
- Recycling PET is <u>viable</u> because it uses <u>fewer resources</u> and <u>less energy</u> than making 'new' PET.
- 'New' PET is made by polymerising <u>alkenes</u>, which are made by distilling and cracking <u>crude oil</u> (see pages 113-114). All this processing takes <u>lots of energy</u> — recycling PET uses up to <u>75%</u> less energy.
- Recycling also saves crude oil, a <u>finite resource</u>. For every 1 kg of PET that's recycled, you save about 2.4 dm³ of crude oil.
- If PET isn't recycled, it's usually thrown away in <u>landfill</u> which takes up lots of <u>space</u>.
- PET bottles can also be <u>reused</u>, for example to <u>sterilise water</u>. They're filled with <u>water</u> and left in the <u>sunlight</u>. PET lets <u>UV radiation</u> through, which <u>sterilises</u> the water.

Sometimes Recycling isn't Straightforward

1) Recycling needs <u>energy</u> and <u>resources</u> to <u>collect</u> the materials, to <u>sort</u> them and to remove any <u>impurities</u> from them (e.g. food waste). You also need energy to <u>reprocess</u> the materials into new forms.
2) Often, items will need <u>sorting</u> to separate out different materials. E.g. <u>glass</u> may need to be sorted into <u>different colours</u>. If the materials are <u>hard</u> to separate, this step can take lots of <u>time</u> or <u>energy</u>.
3) Weighing up whether <u>recycling</u> a material is better than just <u>disposing</u> of it and starting from scratch, therefore requires you to think about the <u>environmental impact</u> for both these different processes.
4) Generally, you want to go for the option which has the <u>smallest</u> impact on the environment. This means working out which method uses the <u>least energy</u> and the <u>fewest resources</u>. You should also think about the consequences of putting materials in <u>landfill</u>, and whether the material comes from a <u>non-renewable</u> or a <u>renewable</u> source.
5) But the environment isn't the only thing to think about. Materials may not be recycled if it's too <u>expensive</u>, if not <u>enough</u> of the material is thrown away for it to be recycled on an <u>industrial scale</u>, or if there's not much <u>demand</u> for the products made from the recycled material. Similarly, things might be recycled if it's <u>cheaper</u> than making them from scratch, even if the environmental impact is <u>worse</u>.

Compost-sites — piles of old vegetables embedded in muck...

Great jokes like this grow on trees you know. So to save trees, I've reused that hilarious pun from page 120.

Q1 Material X is a metal. To recycle material X you need 110% of the energy used to extract and refine it. Explain why it might still be better to recycle material X than dispose of it in landfill. [2 marks]

Life Cycle Assessments

If a company wants to manufacture a new product, it will carry out a life cycle assessment (LCA).

Life Cycle Assessments Show Total Environmental Costs

A life cycle assessment (LCA) looks at each stage of the life of a product — from making the material from natural raw materials, to making the product from the material, using the product and disposing of the product. It works out the potential environmental impact of each stage.

Choice of material
1) Metals have to be mined and extracted from their ores (see p.106). These processes need a lot of energy and cause a lot of pollution.
2) Materials for chemical manufacture often come from crude oil. Crude oil is a non-renewable resource, and supplies are decreasing. Also, obtaining crude oil from the ground and refining it into useful raw materials requires a lot of energy and generates pollution.

Manufacture
1) Manufacturing products uses a lot of energy and other resources such as water.
2) It can also cause a lot of pollution, e.g. harmful gases such as CO or HCl.
3) Manufacture produces waste which has to be disposed of. Some waste can be recycled and turned into other useful chemicals, reducing the amount that ends up polluting the environment.
4) Most chemical manufacture needs water which needs to be treated before it's put back into rivers.

Product Use
Using the product can also damage the environment. For example:
1) Paint gives off toxic fumes.
2) Burning fuels releases greenhouse gases and other pollutants.
3) Fertilisers can leach into rivers and damage ecosystems.

Companies may have to make assumptions and estimations when making LCAs. For example, an object may be recyclable, but they don't know how many users will actually recycle it.

Disposal
1) Products are often disposed of in a landfill site at the end of their life. This takes up space and can pollute land and water.
2) If the products are biodegradeable, they'll decompose quite quickly, but if they're non-biodegradeable, they'll hang around in landfill for years.
3) Products might be incinerated (burnt), which causes air pollution. But the energy released by burning can be used to generate electricity, which reduces the need for fossil fuels.
4) Recycling or reusing a product reduces the impact of disposing of it. The amount of resources needed to make new products from the recycled material is also reduced.

EXAMPLE:
A company is carrying out life cycle assessments of three cars, A, B and C. The table shows some data on the useful life of each car. Use it to explain which car the company should produce to minimise the environmental impact.

Car	CO_2 emissions (tonnes)	Waste solid produced (kg)	Water used (m^3)	Expected life span of product (years)
A	26	10 720	8.2	11
B	26	5900	6.0	17
C	34	15 010	9.5	12

- Car A produces the joint least CO_2, but produces the second highest amount of waste solids and uses the second highest amount of water. It also has the shortest life span.
- Car B produces same amount of CO_2 as car A, but produces by far the least waste solid, uses the least water and also has the longest life span. On balance, this looks a better choice than car A.
- Car C produces the most CO_2, the most waste solid, uses the most water, and has almost as short a life span as car A. This looks like the worst choice.

So, on balance, **car B** looks like the one that will have the least environmental impact.

My cycle assessment — two wheels, a bell, an uncomfortable seat...

Don't get your bike-cycle and life cycle assessments confused. Life cycle assessments are the ones you'll need.

Q1   For the example above, suggest four further things (that aren't outlined in the table) that the company should consider when forming a life cycle assessment for the cars.   [4 marks]

Nanoparticles

Just time to squeeze in something <u>really small</u> before the end of the chapter...

Nanoparticles Are Really Really Really Really Tiny...

...smaller than that.

1) The sizes of very small particles are often given in <u>nanometers</u> or '<u>nm</u>'.
2) 1 nm is the same as <u>0.000000001 m</u>.
3) Rather than writing lots of zeros, it can be easier to write very small numbers like this in <u>standard form</u>.

This number must always be greater or equal to 1 and less than 10. → $A \times 10^n$ ← This number is the number of places the decimal point moves.

4) If 'n' is <u>positive</u>, the number is <u>greater than 1</u>. More positive values of 'n' mean <u>larger</u> numbers.
   If 'n' is <u>negative</u> the number is <u>less than 1</u>. More negative values of 'n' mean <u>smaller</u> numbers.
5) So, in standard form, <u>1 nm = 1×10^{-9} m</u>.
6) <u>Nanoparticles</u> have a diameter between 1 nm (1×10^{-9} m) and 100 nm (1×10^{-7} m). These particles contain between a <u>few hundred</u> and <u>tens of thousands</u> of atoms — so they're <u>bigger</u> than <u>atoms</u> (0.1-0.5 nm) and <u>simple molecules</u> (e.g. methane is about 0.4 nm), but smaller than most other things.

Nanoparticles Have a Large Surface Area to Volume Ratio

1) The surface area to volume ratio is an important factor as it can <u>affect</u> the way that a particle <u>behaves</u>.
2) As particles <u>decrease</u> in size, the size of their surface area <u>increases</u> in relation to their volume (assuming their shape doesn't change much). This causes the surface area to volume ratio to <u>increase</u>.
3) You can see this happening by using two <u>cubes</u> as an example:

EXAMPLE:

The drawings of the cubes aren't to scale. Obviously.

Find the surface area to volume ratio for each of the cubes below.

This cube has sides of length 1 mm.

Each face has a surface area of 1 mm × 1 mm = 1 mm^2

The cube has six faces, so the total surface area is 6 × 1 mm^2 = 6 mm^2

The volume of the cube is 1 mm × 1 mm × 1 mm = 1 mm^3

The surface area to volume ratio = 6 : 1

To be able to compare the cubes, the lengths need to have the same units.

10 nm = 1×10^{-8} m = 1×10^{-5} mm

Each face has a surface area of (1×10^{-5}) mm × (1×10^{-5}) mm = 1×10^{-10} mm^2

The cube has six faces, so the total surface area is 6 × $(1 \times 10^{-10}$ mm$^2)$ = 6×10^{-10} mm^2

The volume of the cube is (1×10^{-5}) mm × (1×10^{-5}) mm × (1×10^{-5}) mm = 1×10^{-15} mm^3

The surface area to volume ratio = 6×10^{-10} : 1×10^{-15} = **600 000 : 1**

These two ratios are the same, we've just simplified the first one so that it's easier to compare with the ratio for the 1 mm cube.

4) Nanoparticles have a very <u>high</u> surface area to volume ratio — this means the surface area is very <u>large</u> compared to the volume.
5) This can cause the properties of a material to be <u>different</u> when it's in the form of <u>nanoparticles</u> to when it's in <u>bulk</u>. This is because, in a nanoparticle, a <u>higher proportion</u> of the atoms are <u>at the surface</u> and able to <u>interact</u> with substances than in the bulk material.
6) For example, you'll often need <u>less</u> of a material that's made up of nanoparticles to work as an effective <u>catalyst</u> compared to a material made up of 'normal' sized particles (containing billions of atoms rather than a few hundred).

Nannyparticles

Nano nano nano nano nano nano nano nano — particles...

Nanoparticles are between ten and one thousand times larger than atoms and simple molecules. That's teeny tiny.

Q1   Would you expect the surface area to volume ratio to be greater for a nanoparticle
      with a diameter of 20 nm or for a molecule of a similar shape with a diameter of 0.2 nm?   [1 mark]

Uses of Nanoparticles

'What's the use of something so small that not even a <u>gnat</u> can see it?' I hear you cry. Well, as you're about to find out, <u>scientists</u> have developed some pretty swanky uses for nanoparticles.

Fullerenes are Nanoparticles of Carbon

1) <u>Fullerenes</u> are a form of <u>carbon</u>. They're large <u>molecules</u> shaped like <u>hollow balls</u> or <u>tubes</u>. Different fullerenes contain <u>different numbers</u> of carbon atoms but they're all <u>nanoparticles</u>.

2) The carbon atoms in fullerenes are arranged in <u>rings</u>, similar to those in graphite (see page 117).

3) Their <u>melting</u> and <u>boiling points</u> aren't anything like as high as those of diamond and graphite, but they're <u>pretty high</u> for <u>molecular substances</u> because they're relatively big molecules (and bigger molecules have more <u>intermolecular forces</u>).

There's more about the other forms of carbon on p.117.

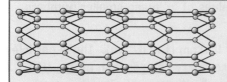

Fullerenes can form <u>nanotubes</u> — tiny carbon <u>cylinders</u>.
Nanotubes have <u>delocalised electrons</u> so they can conduct both <u>electricity</u> and <u>thermal energy</u> (heat).
They also have a high <u>tensile strength</u>.

Nanoparticles Can Modify the Properties of Materials

Using nanoparticles is known as <u>nanotechnology</u>. Many <u>new uses</u> of nanoparticles are being developed:

1) They have a <u>huge surface area to volume ratio</u>, so they can make good <u>catalysts</u> (see p.145).

2) New cosmetics, e.g. <u>sun creams</u> and <u>deodorants</u>, have been made using nanoparticles. The small particles do their job but don't leave <u>white marks</u> on the skin.

3) Fullerenes could be used to <u>cage</u> small drug molecules and are <u>absorbed</u> more easily by the body than most particles. This means that they could <u>deliver drugs</u> right to the cells where they're needed.

4) Fullerenes can also be used as <u>molecular sieves</u> — <u>small molecules</u> can pass through pores in the material, but larger molecules get trapped on the other side.

5) New <u>lubricant coatings</u> are being developed using fullerenes. These coatings reduce friction — a bit like really tiny <u>ball bearings</u> and could be used in all sorts of places from <u>artificial joints</u> to <u>gears</u>.

6) Nanotubes <u>conduct</u> electricity, so they can be used in tiny <u>electric circuits</u> for computer chips.

7) Nanoparticles are added to <u>plastics</u> to make <u>composite materials</u> (see page 119) which are used to make <u>sports equipment</u>, e.g. tennis rackets, golf clubs and golf balls. They make the plastic much <u>stronger</u> and <u>more durable</u>, without adding much <u>mass</u> (hardly any in fact).

8) <u>Silver nanoparticles</u> are added to the <u>polymer fibres</u> used to make <u>surgical masks</u> and <u>wound dressings</u>. This gives the fibres <u>antibacterial properties</u>.

The Effects of Nanoparticles on Health Aren't Fully Understood

1) Although nanoparticles are useful, they might have risks that aren't fully understood.

2) For example, they're so <u>small</u> that they can get into cells deep within the body. Their high surface area means they could react in <u>unknown ways</u> with cells, leading to unexpected <u>side-effects</u>.

3) So it's important that any new nanoparticle products are <u>tested</u> thoroughly to minimise the risks.

4) The <u>benefits</u> of using products with nanoparticles need to be <u>weighed up</u> against the potential risks.

5) For example, a new drug that could be delivered to the right area of the body using fullerenes could save someone's life. It's likely to be used if the benefit <u>outweighs</u> the side effects of using it.

6) Using nanoparticles is a relatively <u>new</u> technology. This means that whilst lots of uses have been developed, there hasn't yet been <u>time</u> to investigate the <u>long-term impacts</u> of nanoparticles on health.

7) So some people are worried that <u>products</u> containing nanoparticles have been made available <u>before</u> any possible <u>harmful</u> effects on <u>human health</u> have been investigated <u>properly</u>.

Not to be confused with my Irish granny, Nan O'Flaherty...

It seems like small particles are big business — but as with any new tech there are pros and cons.

Q1   Give three examples of uses of nanoparticles.   [3 marks]

Revision Questions for Chapter C4

Phew. That's almost it for Chapter C4. But before you run off, time to have a go at a few questions.

- Try these questions and <u>tick off each one</u> when you <u>get it right</u>.
- When you've done <u>all the questions</u> for a topic and are <u>completely happy</u> with it, tick off the topic.

Polymers (p.116) ☑

1) What type of bonds are there between the atoms in a polymer chain? ☑
2) Give one difference between the properties of a polymer that forms crosslinks and one that doesn't. ☑

Giant Covalent Structures (p.117) ☑

3) What is a giant covalent structure? ☑
4) Explain how the structure of graphite gives rise to:
   a) its electrical conductivity,   b) its high melting point. ☑

Properties and Uses of Materials (p.118-120) ☑

5) Name three types of bonding that can form between particles. ☑
6) What factor determines the melting point of a substance? ☑
7) What is stiffness? ☑
8) Describe how soda-lime glass is made. ☑
9) Name a composite material and outline its properties. ☑
10) Explain why the corrosion of iron is a redox reaction. ☑
11) Define reduction in terms of:
    a) oxygen,   b) electrons. ☑
12) Are metals thermal conductors or insulators? ☑

Reuse, Recycling and Life Cycle Assessments (p.121-122) ☑

13) What is reuse? ☑
14) Give two benefits of recycling. ☑
15) Give one reason why it might not be beneficial to recycle a material. ☑
16) What is a life cycle assessment? ☑

Nanoparticles (p.123-124) ☑

17) What is a nanoparticle? ☑
18) Give three uses of nanoparticles. ☑
19) Explain why people may be wary of using products that contain nanoparticles. ☑

Purity and Mixtures

Mixtures in chemistry are like mixtures in baking, lots of separate things all mixed together. Just don't eat them.

Purity Has a Specific Meaning in Chemistry

1) Usually when you refer to a substance as being pure you mean that nothing has been added to it, so it's in its natural state. For example: pure milk or beeswax.

2) In chemistry, a pure substance is something that only contains one compound or element throughout — not mixed with anything else.

Having impure thoughts again, Henry?

The Melting Point Tells You How Pure a Substance Is

1) A chemically pure substance will melt at a specific temperature.

2) You can test the purity of a sample by measuring its melting point and comparing it with the reference melting point of the pure substance (which you can find from a data book).

3) The closer your measured value is to the actual melting point, the purer your sample is.

4) Impurities in your sample will lower the melting point and increase the melting range of your substance.

A Substance that isn't Pure is a Mixture

1) Substances that contain more than one element or compound which aren't chemically bonded together are known as mixtures.

2) The parts of a mixture can be either elements or compounds, and they can be separated out by physical methods such as filtration (p.129), crystallisation (p.129), simple distillation (p.129), fractional distillation (p.113) or chromatography (p.127).

A physical method is one that doesn't involve a chemical reaction.

3) For example, crude oil is a mixture of different length hydrocarbon molecules.

4) The properties of a mixture are just a mixture of the properties of the separate parts — the chemical properties of a substance aren't affected by it being part of a mixture.

Formulations are Mixtures with Exact Amounts of Components

1) Formulations are useful mixtures with a precise purpose that are made by following a 'formula' (a recipe). Each component in a formulation is present in a measured quantity, and contributes to the properties of the formulation so that it meets its required function.

2) For example, paints are formulations. They contain a pigment to give the paint colour, a solvent to dissolve the other components, a binder which holds the pigment in place after it's been painted on and other additives to change the physical and chemical properties of the paint. Depending on the purpose of the paint, the chemicals used and their amounts will be changed so the paint is right for the job.

3) Lots of everyday products are formulations. For example, many medicines are formulations, as are cleaning products, fuels, cosmetics, hygiene products, fertilisers, alloys and even food and drink.

4) It's important that the substances used to make a formulation such as drugs and cosmetics are pure. If impurities get into the formulation, people could be harmed when they use them.

5) Ratios can be used to describe the composition of formulations:

In a certain formulation made from water and ethanol, the ratio of water to ethanol is 2 : 1. What volume of ethanol is present in 15 cm³ of the formulation?

$$\text{proportion of ethanol} = \frac{\text{parts of ethanol in the ratio}}{\text{total number of parts in the ratio}} = \frac{1}{1+2} = \frac{1}{3}$$

$$\text{volume of ethanol} = \text{proportion of ethanol} \times \text{total volume} = \frac{1}{3} \times 15 \text{ cm}^3 = 5 \text{ cm}^3$$

I was hoping for pure joy, but this page was a real mixture...

All formulations are mixtures, but not all mixtures are formulations. To be a formulation, a mixture has to have been made for a precise purpose and have its components present in particular, carefully measured quantities.

Q1   The melting point of pure aspirin is 136 °C. The melting point of a sample of aspirin is measured as being between 128-132 °C. Give two reasons why this suggests that the sample is not pure aspirin.   [2 marks]

Chromatography

Chromatography sounds weird and complicated, but read on and you'll find that it's actually pretty nifty.

Chromatography uses Two Phases

Chromatography is an analytical method used to separate the substances in a mixture. You can then use it to identify the substances. There are different types of chromatography, but they all have two 'phases':

- A mobile phase — where the particles of the phase can move. This is always a liquid or a gas.
- A stationary phase — where the particles of the phase can't move. This can be a solid or a very thick liquid.

1) During a chromatography experiment, the substances in the sample constantly move between the mobile and the stationary phases — an equilibrium is formed between the two phases.

2) Different chemicals will have different distributions between the same phase — they'll spend different amounts of time dissolved in the mobile phase or attracted to the stationary phase.

3) The mobile phase moves through the stationary phase, and anything dissolved in the mobile phase moves with it. The more time a chemical spends in the mobile phase, the further through the stationary phase it'll move.

4) So chemicals with different distributions will separate into different spots on the chromatogram.

5) The number of spots may change in different solvents as the distribution of the chemical will change depending on the solvent. A pure substance will only ever form one spot in any solvent as there is only one substance in the sample. If the chromatogram has more than one spot then it's a mixture.

You Need to Know How to Do Paper Chromatography

PRACTICAL

1) One type of chromatography is paper chromatography. Here, the stationary phase is the chromatography paper (often filter paper) and the mobile phase is the solvent.

2) The amount of time the molecules spend in each phase depends on how soluble they are in the solvent and how attracted they are to the paper.

3) Molecules with a higher solubility in the solvent, and which are less attracted to the paper, will spend more time in the mobile phase — and they'll be carried further up the paper.

4) Paper chromatography can be used to work out whether something's pure. Here's how you can do it:

- Draw a line near the bottom of a sheet of filter paper. (Use a pencil to do this — pencil marks are insoluble and won't dissolve in the solvent.)

  If the mixture that contains substances that are insoluble in the solvent, they won't move up the paper, so they won't separate and you won't be able to identify them.

- Add a spot of the test substance to the line and place the sheet in a beaker of solvent so that the solvent is just below, but not touching the spot.

- The solvent used depends on what's being tested. Some compounds dissolve in water, or in solutions where water is the solvent (aqueous solutions), but sometimes other solvents (known as non-aqueous solvents), like ethanol, are needed.

- Place a lid on top of the container to minimise the evaporation of solvent.

- The solvent seeps up the paper, carrying the test substance with it.

- When the solvent has nearly reached the top of the paper, take the paper out of the beaker, mark the point that the solvent reached with a pencil and leave the paper to dry.

- The end result is a pattern of spots called a chromatogram.

- If the chromatogram has more than one spot, the substance is impure. If it contains only one spot it may well be pure (but you'll have to check that only one spot's produced in other solvents too).

The point the solvent has reached as it moves up the paper is the solvent front.

Chromatography revision — it's a phase you have to get through...

You can't see the chemicals moving between the two phases, but it does happen. You'll just have to trust me.

Q1   Explain how paper chromatography separates mixtures.   [4 marks]

Interpreting Chromatograms

Chromatograms can tell you all sorts of things. <u>How many</u> components are in a mixture, <u>what</u> the components might be... It's like looking into a <u>crystal ball</u>. Only more reliable. And slightly less fun.

You Need to Identify the Spots

1) If the chemicals in the mixture are <u>coloured</u> (such as the dyes that make up an ink) then you'll see them as a set of coloured dots at different heights on the chromatogram...

2) If there are colourless chemicals in the mixture, you'll need to use <u>locating agents</u> to make them visible.

- If the mixture contains amino acids, you can spray <u>ninhydrin solution</u> on the completed chromatogram, which should turn the spots purple.

- You could also dip the completed chromatogram into a jar containing a few <u>iodine</u> crystals. Iodine vapour sticks to the chemicals on the paper and they'll show up as <u>purple spots</u>.

You can Calculate the Rf Value for Each Chemical

1) An Rf value is the <u>ratio</u> between the distance travelled by the dissolved substance (the solute) and the distance travelled by the solvent.

2) You need to know how to work out the <u>Rf values</u> for <u>spots</u> (solutes) on a chromatogram.

3) You can find Rf values using the formula:

$$Rf = \frac{\text{distance travelled by solute}}{\text{distance travelled by solvent}}$$

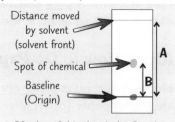

Distance moved by solvent (solvent front)

Spot of chemical

Baseline (Origin)

Rf value of this chemical = B ÷ A

4) To find the distance travelled by the solute, measure from the <u>baseline</u> to the <u>centre of the spot</u>.

EXAMPLE:

During a chromatography experiment, the solvent moves 4.8 cm up the paper, and a solute moves 1.2 cm. Calculate the Rf value of the solute.

$$Rf = \frac{\text{distance travelled by solute}}{\text{distance travelled by solvent front}} = \frac{1.2}{4.8} = 0.25$$

Rf values should always be less than 1. So if you get an answer that's greater than 1, you should go back and check your working.

5) Chromatography is often carried out to see if a certain substance is present in a mixture. You run a <u>pure sample</u> of the substance alongside the unknown mixture. If the Rf values match, the substances may be the <u>same</u> (although it doesn't definitely prove they are the same).

Rf Values can Change if the Conditions are Different

1) The <u>Rf value</u> of a substance can <u>change</u> if the method used in the chromatography experiment changes, for example if a different <u>solvent</u> (or concentration of solvent), a different <u>temperature</u> or a different <u>stationary phase</u> is used.

2) This can be useful if you get spots on a chromatogram that don't <u>separate properly</u> — repeating the chromatography experiment with different conditions could cause them to separate.

3) It's also useful if two <u>reference compounds</u> have similar Rf values in a particular solvent. If you run the experiment again in conditions where the reference compounds have very different Rf values, you'll be able to identify <u>which one's</u> in the mixture.

Please welcome to the stage Dennis and Abi, who will be interpreting a chromatogram through the medium of dance.

Leopard, cheetah, dalmatian — I love identifying spots...

Make sure you know the equation for calculating Rf values. It could save the day in the exam.

Q1 The solvent front on a chromatogram is at 6.0 cm. There is one visible spot at 4.8 cm.
   a) Calculate the Rf value of the visible spot. [2 marks]
   b) Suggest how you could find out whether there are any colourless spots on the chromatogram. [1 mark]

Separating Mixtures

When chemists make substances, they'll often be part of a <u>mixture</u> or will contain <u>impurities</u> so need <u>purifying</u>.

Filtration is Used to Separate an Insoluble Solid from a Liquid

Filter paper folded into a cone shape.

The solid is left in the filter paper.

1) To separate an <u>insoluble solid</u> from a liquid, you can use <u>filtration</u>.

2) This means it can be used in <u>purification</u>. For example, <u>solid impurities</u> can be separated out from a reaction mixture using <u>filtration</u>.

3) All you do is pop some <u>filter paper</u> into a <u>funnel</u> and pour your mixture into it. The liquid part of the mixture <u>runs through</u> the paper, leaving behind a <u>solid residue</u>.

Crystallisation Separates a Soluble Solid from a Solution

evaporating dish

To separate a <u>solute</u> (dissolved solid) from a <u>solution</u> you'll need to crystallise it...

1) Pour the solution into an <u>evaporating dish</u> and gently <u>heat</u> the solution. This technique is called <u>evaporation</u>. Some of the <u>solvent</u> (which will usually be water) will evaporate and the solution will get more <u>concentrated</u>. You could just evaporate all the solvent, but you'll end up with <u>tiny</u> crystals and your substance could <u>decompose</u>.

2) Instead, once some of the solvent has evaporated, <u>or</u> when you see crystals start to form (the <u>point of crystallisation</u>), you should remove the dish from the heat and leave the solution to <u>cool</u>.

3) The salt should start to form <u>crystals</u> as it becomes <u>insoluble</u> in the cold, highly concentrated solution.

4) <u>Filter</u> the crystals out of the solution, and leave them in a warm place to <u>dry</u>. You could also use a <u>drying oven</u> or a <u>desiccator</u> (a desiccator contains chemicals that remove water from the surroundings).

Simple Distillation is Used to Separate Out Mixtures of Liquids or Solutions

<u>Simple distillation</u> is used for separating out a <u>liquid</u> from a <u>solution</u>, or to separate liquids that have <u>very different</u> boiling points. Here's how to use simple distillation to get <u>pure water</u> from <u>seawater</u>:

1) Set up the <u>apparatus</u> as shown in the diagram. Connect the bottom end of the <u>condenser</u> to a cold tap using <u>rubber tubing</u>. Run <u>cold water</u> through the condenser to keep it cool.

2) Gradually heat the distillation flask. The part of the solution that has the lowest boiling point will <u>evaporate</u> — in this case, that's the water.

3) The water <u>vapour</u> passes into the condenser where it <u>cools</u> and <u>condenses</u> (turns back into a liquid). It then flows into the beaker where it is <u>collected</u>.

4) Eventually you'll end up with just the <u>salt</u> left in the flask.

The <u>problem</u> with simple distillation is that it only separates things with <u>very different</u> boiling points. If you have a <u>mixture of liquids</u> with <u>similar boiling points</u>, you should use <u>fractional distillation</u> — see page 113.

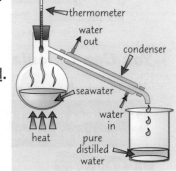

thermometer
water out
condenser
seawater
water in
heat
pure distilled water

Choose the Right Purification Method

The best technique to separate a mixture will depend on the <u>properties</u> of the <u>substances</u> in the mixture.

> A <u>mixture</u> is composed of two substances, **X** and **Y**. <u>Substance X</u> is a <u>liquid</u> at room temperature. It has a <u>melting point</u> of 5 °C and a <u>boiling point</u> of 60 °C. <u>Substance Y</u> is a <u>solid</u> at room temperature. It has a <u>melting point</u> of 745 °C and a <u>boiling point</u> of 1218 °C. Substance Y <u>dissolves completely</u> in substance **X**.
>
> • To get **X** on its own, you need to <u>distil it</u> from the solution. You can use <u>simple distillation</u> here — there's no need for fractional distillation as there's only <u>one liquid</u> in the solution.
>
> • To get **Y** on its own, you need to get a <u>soluble solid</u> from a solution, so you should use <u>crystallisation</u>.

Its mum calls it Philliptration...

The product of separation may not be completely pure first time, so scientists may carry out the same technique a couple of times before it's pure enough. Or they'll use a combination of techniques to remove all the impurities.

Q1   Describe a method to extract pure copper sulfate crystals from a copper sulfate solution.   [4 marks]

Relative Mass

The mass of an atom is really, really tiny. To make it easier to calculate with and compare the masses of different atoms, you usually use relative masses instead of their actual masses.

Relative Atomic Mass, A_r — Easy Peasy

In the periodic table, the elements all have <u>two</u> numbers next to them. The <u>bigger one</u> is the <u>relative atomic mass</u> (A_r) of the element.

relative atomic mass

$$^4_2\text{He} \qquad ^{12}_6\text{C}$$

> The <u>relative atomic mass</u> of an element is the <u>average mass</u> of <u>one atom</u> of the element, compared to $\frac{1}{12}$ of the <u>mass</u> of <u>one atom</u> of <u>carbon-12</u>.

1) If an element only has <u>one isotope</u> (see p.91), its A_r will be the same as its <u>mass number</u>.
2) If an element has <u>more than one</u> isotope, you have to take into account <u>how much</u> of each isotope there is when you work out the relative atomic mass of the element.

$$\text{relative atomic mass} = \frac{\text{sum of (isotope abundance} \times \text{isotope mass number)}}{\text{sum of abundances of all the isotopes}}$$

 **EXAMPLE:** Copper has two stable isotopes. Cu-63 has an abundance of 69.2% and Cu-65 has an abundance of 30.8%. Calculate the relative atomic mass of copper to 1 decimal place.

$$\text{Relative atomic mass} = \frac{(69.2 \times 63) + (30.8 \times 65)}{69.2 + 30.8} = \frac{4359.6 + 2002}{100} = \frac{6361.6}{100} = 63.616 = \textbf{63.6}$$

Relative Formula Mass, M_r — Also Easy Peasy

The <u>relative formula mass</u>, M_r (or RFM), of a compound is all the relative atomic masses in its formula <u>added together</u>.

> For simple covalent compounds, the relative formula mass is usually called the relative molecular mass (RMM).

 EXAMPLE:

Find the relative formula mass of magnesium chloride, $MgCl_2$. Use the <u>periodic table</u> to find the <u>relative atomic masses</u> of magnesium and chlorine.

$Mg + (2 \times Cl) = 24.3 + (2 \times 35.5) = 24.3 + 71.0 = 95.3$

M_r of $MgCl_2 = \textbf{95.3}$

You Can Calculate the % Mass of an Element in a Compound

This is actually <u>dead easy</u> — so long as you've learnt this <u>formula</u>:

$$\text{Percentage mass of an element in a compound} = \frac{A_r \times \text{number of atoms of that element}}{M_r \text{ of the compound}} \times 100$$

EXAMPLE:

a) Find the percentage mass of sodium in sodium carbonate, Na_2CO_3.

A_r of sodium = 23.0, A_r of carbon = 12.0, A_r of oxygen = 16.0

M_r of $Na_2CO_3 = (2 \times 23.0) + 12.0 + (3 \times 16.0) = 106.0$

$$\text{Percentage mass of sodium} = \frac{A_r \times \text{number of atoms of that element}}{M_r \text{ of the compound}} \times 100 = \frac{23.0 \times 2}{106.0} \times 100 = \textbf{43.4\%}$$

b) Use your answer to part a) to calculate the mass of sodium in 5.00 g of sodium carbonate.

% mass of sodium in sodium carbonate = 43.4%

mass of sodium in 5.00 g of sodium carbonate = 43.4% of 5.00 g = $5.00 \times \frac{43.4}{100} = \textbf{2.17 g}$

Have you mastered this page? Relatively...

The best way to get to grips with all this stuff is by practising. Start by having a go at these questions...

Q1 Calculate the relative formula mass (M_r) of: a) H_2O b) LiOH c) H_2SO_4 [3 marks]

Q2 Calculate the percentage composition by mass of potassium in potassium hydroxide (KOH). [2 marks]

Conservation of Mass

You've probably realised by now that you can't magic stuff out of thin air, and you can't make it magically disappear, either. This fact is pretty useful for working out the amounts of substances in chemical reactions.

In a Chemical Reaction, Mass is Always Conserved

1) During a chemical reaction, even though the way atoms are arranged in compounds changes, no atoms are destroyed and no atoms are created.

2) This means there are the same number and types of atoms on each side of a reaction equation.

3) Because of this, no mass is lost or gained — we say that mass is conserved during a reaction.
   E.g.

   $$2Li + F_2 \rightarrow 2LiF$$

   In this reaction, there are 2 lithium atoms and 2 fluorine atoms on each side of the equation.

4) By adding up the relative formula masses of the substances on each side of a balanced symbol equation, you can see that mass is conserved. The total M_r of all the reactants equals the total M_r of the products.

There's more about balanced symbol equations on p.80.

EXAMPLE:

Show that mass is conserved in this reaction: $2Li + F_2 \rightarrow 2LiF$.
1) Add up the relative formula masses on the left-hand side of the equation.
   $2 \times A_r(Li) + M_r(F_2) = (2 \times 6.9) + (2 \times 19.0) = 13.8 + 38.0 = 51.8$
2) Add up the relative formula masses on the right-hand side of the equation.
   $2 \times M_r(LiF) = 2 \times (6.9 + 19.0) = 2 \times 25.9 = 51.8$

The total M_r on the left-hand side of the equation is equal to the total M_r on the right-hand side, so mass is conserved.

If the Mass Seems to Change, There's Usually a Gas Involved

If the reaction vessel isn't sealed, the system is 'open' because particles can get in or out.

In some experiments, you might observe a change of mass of an unsealed reaction vessel during a reaction. There are usually two explanations for this:

Explanation 1: If the mass increases, it's probably because some of the atoms in gaseous reactants end up in solid, liquid or aqueous products.

- Before the reaction, the gas is floating around in the air. It's there, but it's not contained in the reaction vessel, so you can't account for its mass.
- When the gas reacts to form part of the product, it becomes contained inside the reaction vessel — so the total mass of the stuff inside the reaction vessel increases.

For example, when a metal reacts with oxygen in an unsealed container, the mass of the container increases. The mass of the metal oxide produced equals the total mass of the metal and the oxygen that reacted from the air.

$$metal_{(s)} + oxygen_{(g)} \rightarrow metal\ oxide_{(s)}$$

Explanation 2: If the mass decreases, it's probably because some (or all) of the atoms in the solid, liquid or aqueous reactants end up in gaseous products.

- Before the reaction, all the reactants are contained in the reaction vessel.
- If the vessel isn't enclosed, then the gas can escape from the reaction vessel as it's formed. It's no longer contained in the reaction vessel, so you can't account for its mass — the total mass of the stuff inside the reaction vessel decreases.

For example, when a metal carbonate thermally decomposes to form a metal oxide and carbon dioxide gas, the mass of the reaction vessel will decrease if it isn't sealed. But in reality, the mass of the metal oxide and the carbon dioxide produced will equal the mass of the metal carbonate that decomposed.

$$metal\ carbonate_{(s)} \rightarrow metal\ oxide_{(s)} + carbon\ dioxide_{(g)}$$

Remember from the particle model on page 77 that a gas will expand to fill any container it's in. So if the reaction vessel isn't sealed, the gas expands out from the vessel, and escapes into the air around.

Leaving all the potatoes on your plate — that's mash conservation...

Never, ever forget that, in a reaction, the total mass of reactants is the same as the total mass of products.

Q1 Predict whether the mass of the contents in an open reaction vessel will increase, decrease or stay the same for the following reaction: $2Na_{(s)} + 2H_2O_{(l)} \rightarrow 2NaOH_{(aq)} + H_{2(g)}$. Explain your answer. [3 marks]

The Mole

The mole might seem a bit confusing. I think it's the word that puts people off. But it's not that hard really...

"The Mole" is Simply the Name Given to a Certain Number

1) Just like a million is this many: 1 000 000, or a billion is this many: 1 000 000 000, a mole is given by Avogadro's constant, and it's this many: 600 000 000 000 000 000 000 000 or 6.0×10^{23}.

2) But what does Avogadro's constant show? The answer is that it's the number of atoms in 12 g of carbon-12. Conveniently, when you get that number of atoms or molecules, of any element or compound, then their mass is exactly the same number of grams as the relative atomic mass, A_r (or relative formula mass, M_r) of the element or compound.

> One mole of particles (atoms, ions, molecules etc.) of any substance will have a mass in grams equal to the relative formula mass (A_r or M_r) for that substance.

Examples:

Neon has an A_r of 20.2.

Nitrogen gas, N_2, has an M_r of 28.0 (2×14.0).

Hexane, C_6H_{14}, has an M_r of 86.0 ((6×12.0) + (14×1.0)).

The mass of one mole of neon is 20.2 g.

The mass of one mole of N_2 is 28.0 g.

The mass of one mole of hexane is 86.0 g.

So 12 g of carbon, 28 g of N_2 and 86 g of hexane all contain the same number of particles, namely one mole or 6.0×10^{23} particles.

EXAMPLE: How many atoms are there in 5.0 moles of oxygen gas (O_2)?

1) Multiply Avogadro's constant by the number of moles you have to find the number of particles.

$6.0 \times 10^{23} \times 5.0 = 3.0 \times 10^{24}$

2) There are two atoms in each molecule of oxygen gas, so multiply your answer by 2.

$3.0 \times 10^{24} \times 2 = 6.0 \times 10^{24}$

Give your answer in standard form (in terms of $\times 10^x$) to save you having to write out lots of O's.

3) To find the average mass of an atom of a certain element, just divide its relative atomic mass by Avogadro's constant.

EXAMPLE: What is the mean mass of one atom of iron?

Mass of one atom = A_r ÷ Avogadro's constant
= $55.8 ÷ (6.0 \times 10^{23}) = 9.3 \times 10^{-23}$ g

You Can Find the Number of Moles in a Given Mass

There's a nifty formula you can use to find the number of moles in a certain mass of something. You need to know how to use it, and be able to rearrange it to find mass or M_r.

You can rearrange an equation using a formula triangle. Just cover the thing you want to find, and you're left with the expression you need to calculate it.

$$\text{Number of Moles} = \frac{\text{Mass in g (of element or compound)}}{M_r \text{ (of element or compound)}}$$

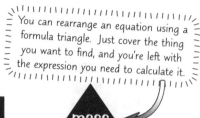

To find the number of moles of atoms in a certain mass of an element, just replace M_r in the formula with A_r.

EXAMPLE:

How many moles are there in 66 g of carbon dioxide?

M_r of carbon dioxide (CO_2) = 12.0 + (2×16.0) = 44.0

moles = mass ÷ M_r = 66 ÷ 44.0 = 1.5 moles

EXAMPLE: What mass of carbon is there in 4.0 moles of carbon dioxide?

mass = moles × A_r
= 4.0×12.0 = 44 g

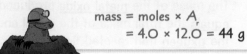

What do moles do for fun? Moller skate...

Moles can give you a bit of a headache — so spend a bit of time getting your head round all this if you need to.

Q1 Calculate the number of moles in 90 g of water. M_r of water = 18.0. [1 mark]

Q2 Calculate the mass of 0.200 moles of potassium bromide. M_r of KBr = 119.0. [1 mark]

Q3 0.500 moles of substance X has a mass of 87.0 g. What is the relative formula mass of X? [1 mark]

Calculations Using Balanced Equations

Unlimited. Together we're unlimited. Unless you're a <u>limiting reactant</u>, in which case you're a big ol' limiter.

Reactions Stop When One Reactant is Used Up

1) A reaction stops when all of one of the reactants is <u>used up</u>. Any other reactants are said to be in <u>excess</u>.

2) The reactant that's <u>used up</u> in a reaction is called the <u>limiting reactant</u> (because it limits the amount of product that's formed).

3) The amount of product formed is <u>directly proportional</u> to the amount of <u>limiting reactant</u>. This is because if you add <u>more of the limiting reactant</u> there will be <u>more reactant particles</u> to take part in the reaction, which means <u>more product particles</u> are made (as long as the other reactants are in excess).

The Amount of Product Depends on the Limiting Reactant

You can use a <u>balanced chemical equation</u> to work out the <u>mass of product formed</u> from a given <u>mass of a limiting reactant</u>. Here's how...

> The mass of product is the 'yield' of a reaction. Masses you calculate in this way are 'theoretical yields'. In practice you never get 100% of the yield, so the amount of product you get will be less than you calculated.

1) Write out the <u>balanced equation</u>.
2) <u>Work out relative masses</u> (M_r or A_r) of the reactant and product you want.
3) Find out <u>how many moles</u> there are of the substance you <u>know</u> the mass of.
4) Use the balanced equation to work out <u>how many moles</u> there'll be of the <u>other</u> substance (i.e. how many moles of product will be made by this many moles of reactant).
5) Use the number of moles to calculate the <u>mass</u>.

EXAMPLE: Calculate the mass of aluminium oxide formed when 135 g of aluminium is burned in air.

1) Write out the <u>balanced equation</u>: $4Al + 3O_2 \rightarrow 2Al_2O_3$

2) Calculate the relative formula masses of the reactants and products you're interested in.   Al: 27.0 Al_2O_3: $(2 \times 27.0) + (3 \times 16.0) = 102.0$

3) <u>Calculate the number of moles</u> of aluminium in 135 g: moles = mass ÷ M_r = 135 ÷ 27.0 = 5.00

4) Look at the <u>ratio</u> of moles in the equation: 4 moles of Al react to produce 2 moles of Al_2O_3 — half the number of moles are produced. So 5.00 moles of Al will react to produce 2.50 moles of Al_2O_3.

5) <u>Calculate the mass</u> of 2.5 moles of aluminium oxide: mass = moles × M_r = 2.50 × 102.0 = **255 g**

You can also use this method to find the <u>mass of a reactant</u> needed to produce a known mass of product...

EXAMPLE: Magnesium oxide can be made by burning magnesium in air. What mass of magnesium is needed to make 100 g of magnesium oxide?

> In industry, it's useful to know the amount of reactant that's needed to make a given amount of product, so that as little waste as possible is created. This makes the processes more efficient.

1) Write out the balanced equation. $2Mg + O_2 \rightarrow 2MgO$

2) Work out the relative formula masses of the reactants and products you're interested in.   Mg: 24.3   MgO: 24.3 + 16.0 = 40.3

3) <u>Calculate the number of moles</u> of magnesium oxide in 100 g: moles = mass ÷ M_r = 100 ÷ 40.3 = 2.48...

4) Look at the <u>ratio</u> of moles in the equation to work out the no. moles of reactant used, compared to the no. moles of product made.   2 moles of MgO are made from 2 moles of Mg. So 2.48... moles of MgO will be formed from 2.48... moles of Mg.

5) <u>Calculate the mass</u> of 2.48... moles of Mg.   mass = moles × A_r = 2.48... × 24.3 = **60.3 g**

Where do moles live? Edinburrow...

A specially organically grown, hand-picked question for you my dear. Don't say I don't spoil you.

Q1   Chlorine and potassium bromide react according to this equation: $Cl_2 + 2KBr \rightarrow Br_2 + 2KCl$. Calculate the mass of bromine produced when 23.8 g of potassium bromide reacts in an excess of chlorine.   [4 marks]

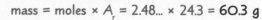

Calculations Using Moles

You've already seen how to <u>balance equations</u> back on page 80. But, sometimes, you may have to balance equations given the <u>masses</u> of the reactants and products. Your good old friend the <u>mole</u> will come in handy...

You Can Balance Equations Using Reacting Masses

If you know the <u>masses</u> of the <u>reactants</u> and <u>products</u> that took part in a reaction, you can work out the <u>balanced symbol equation</u> for the reaction. Here are the steps you should take:

1) Divide the <u>mass</u> of each substance by its <u>relative formula mass</u> to find the <u>number of moles</u>.

You may need to work out some unknown masses first (see below).

2) Divide the number of moles of each substance by the <u>smallest number of moles</u> in the reaction.

3) If needed, multiply all the numbers by the same amount to make them all <u>whole numbers</u>.

4) Write the <u>balanced symbol equation</u> for the reaction by putting these numbers in front of the formulas.

EXAMPLE:

Noor burns a metal, X, in oxygen. There is a single product, an oxide of the metal.
Given that 25.4 g of X burns in 3.2 g of oxygen, write a balanced equation for this reaction.
A_r of X = 63.5 and M_r of X oxide = 143.0.

1) Work out the <u>mass of metal oxide produced</u>. Because it's the only product, the mass of metal oxide produced must equal the <u>total mass of reactants</u>.   25.4 + 3.2 = 28.6 g of X oxide

2) Divide the mass of each substance by its M_r or A_r to calculate how many <u>moles</u> of each substance reacted or were produced:

X: $\frac{25.4}{63.5}$ = 0.40 mol O_2: $\frac{3.2}{32.0}$ = 0.10 mol   X oxide: $\frac{28.6}{143.0}$ = 0.20 mol

3) Divide by the <u>smallest number of moles</u>, which is 0.10:   X: $\frac{0.40}{0.10}$ = 4.0 O_2: $\frac{0.10}{0.10}$ = 1.0   X oxide: $\frac{0.20}{0.10}$ = 2.0

4) The numbers are all whole numbers, so you can write out the <u>balanced symbol equation</u> straight away. $4X + O_2 \rightarrow 2(X\ oxide)$

5) The oxide of X must have a <u>chemical formula</u> containing X and O atoms. In order for the equation to balance, each molecule of X oxide must contain <u>one O atom</u> and <u>2 X atoms</u>. $4X + O_2 \rightarrow 2X_2O$

You Can Work Out Limiting Reactants

EXAMPLE:

8.14 g of zinc oxide (ZnO, M_r = 81.4) were put in a crucible with 0.30 g of carbon and heated until they reacted. Given that the balanced chemical equation for this reaction is: $2ZnO + C \rightarrow CO_2 + 2Zn$, work out the limiting reactant in this reaction.

1) Divide the mass of each substance by its M_r or A_r to find how many <u>moles</u> of each substance were reacted: ZnO: $\frac{8.14}{81.4}$ = 0.10 mol C: $\frac{0.30}{12.0}$ = 0.025 mol

2) Divide by the <u>smallest number of moles</u>, which is 0.025:   ZnO: $\frac{0.10}{0.025}$ = 4.0 C: $\frac{0.025}{0.025}$ = 1.0

3) Compare the ratios between the moles of products with the balanced chemical equation.   In the balanced equation, ZnO and C react in a ratio of 2 : 1. Using the masses, there is a 4 : 1 ratio of ZnO to C. So, ZnO is in excess, and C must be the limiting reactant.

What do moles have for pudding? Jam moly-poly...

The best way to get to grips with the maths on this page is by practising. By coincidence, there's a question below to get you started. You lucky bean. Better get cracking...

Q1   86.4 g of solid boron are sealed in a vessel with 228 g of fluorine gas. They react to make bromine trifluoride.
The equation for the reaction is: $2B + 3F_2 \rightarrow 2BF_3$. What is the limiting reactant?   [3 marks]

Chapter C5 — Chemical Analysis

Acids, Alkalis and Concentrations

Acids and alkalis — some people love 'em, some people hate 'em. I'm fairly <u>neutral</u>, to be honest.

Acids and Alkalis Neutralise Each Other

1) An <u>acid</u> is a substance that dissolves in water to release <u>H^+ ions</u>.

2) An <u>alkali</u> is a substance that produces <u>hydroxide (OH^-) ions</u> when it <u>dissolves in water</u>.

3) Acids and alkalis react together in <u>neutralisation reactions</u>:

> acid + alkali → salt + water

You can tell whether a solution is acidic, alkaline or neutral by measuring its pH. There's more about this on page 140.

4) The salt that forms contains the <u>negative ion</u> from the <u>acid</u> and the <u>positive ion</u> from the <u>alkali</u>.

> <u>Examples</u>: $HCl + NaOH \rightarrow NaCl + H_2O$ (Sodium chloride)
> $H_2SO_4 + Ca(OH)_2 \rightarrow CaSO_4 + 2H_2O$ (Calcium sulfate)
> $HNO_3 + KOH \rightarrow KNO_3 + H_2O$ (Potassium nitrate)

5) Neutralisation between acids and alkalis can be seen in terms of <u>H^+</u> and <u>OH^- ions</u> like this:

> $H^+_{(aq)} + OH^-_{(aq)} \rightarrow H_2O_{(l)}$

Concentration is a Measure of How Crowded Things Are

1) The <u>amount</u> of a substance in a given <u>volume</u> of a solution is called its <u>concentration</u>.

2) The <u>more solute</u> (the thing that's dissolved) there is in a set volume, the <u>more concentrated</u> the solution.

3) One way to <u>measure</u> the concentration of a solution is by calculating the <u>mass</u> of a substance in a given <u>volume</u> of solution. The units will be <u>units of mass/units of volume</u>.

4) Here's how to calculate the concentration of a solution in g/dm³:

You can rearrange these formulas to calculate the mass or number of moles of a solute in solution.

Concentrations in mol/dm³ are often easier to work with than g/dm³, as they relate directly to the numbers of moles in a balanced reaction equation (e.g. in titration calculations, see p.138).

$$\text{concentration} = \frac{\text{mass of solute (in g)}}{\text{volume of solvent (in dm}^3)} \quad (\text{in g/dm}^3)$$

5) Concentration can also be given in <u>mol/dm³</u>:

$$\text{concentration} = \frac{\text{number of moles of solute (in mol)}}{\text{volume of solvent (in dm}^3)} \quad (\text{in mol/dm}^3)$$

EXAMPLES:

1) What's the concentration in g/dm³ of a solution of sodium chloride where 30 g of sodium chloride is dissolved in 0.20 dm³ of water?

$\text{concentration} = \frac{30}{0.20} = 150 \text{ g/dm}^3$

1 dm³ = 1000 cm³

2) What's the concentration, in mol/dm³, of a solution with 2 moles of salt in 500 cm³?

• Convert the volume to <u>dm³</u> by dividing by 1000:   500 cm³ ÷ 1000 = 0.5 dm³

• Now you've got the number of moles and the volume in the right units, just stick them in the formula: $\text{Concentration} = \frac{2}{0.5} = 4 \text{ mol/dm}^3$

Gavin wasn't great at concentration.

CGP Revision Guides — not from concentrate...

The equation showing neutralisation in terms of H^+ and OH^- is an ionic equation. There's more on these on p.104.

Q1 a) A student dissolves 2.7 g of sulfuric acid in 0.03 dm³ of water.
   Calculate the concentration of the sulfuric acid solution in g/dm³. [1 mark]

   b) The student reacts the sulfuric acid solution with a solution of the alkali sodium hydroxide.
   Write a word equation for this reaction. [1 mark]

Quantitative Tests and Standard Solutions

Standard solutions deserve a bit more credit than their name suggests. High standard solutions, more like.

A Standard Solution Has a Known Concentration

You can prepare a standard solution (a solution with a known concentration) in the lab.

If the concentration is given in mol/dm³, work out how many moles of solid you need, then convert it to grams.

Example: Make 250 cm³ of a 31.4 g/dm³ solution of sodium hydroxide.
1) First work out how many grams of solute you need using the formula:
   mass = concentration × volume. Here, it's 31.4 g/dm³ × 0.250 dm³ = 7.85 g
2) Now weigh out this mass — put an empty weighing container on a mass balance and reset it to zero, then add the correct mass. [0.00 grams] [7.85 grams]
3) Add the solid to a beaker containing about 100 cm³ of deionised water and stir until all the solute has dissolved. Use some deionised water to wash the weighing container and pour the washings into the beaker — this makes sure all the solid is transferred.
4) Tip the solution into a volumetric flask of the right size. Use a funnel to make sure it all goes in.
5) Rinse the beaker and stirring rod with deionised water and add that to the flask too. This makes sure there's no solute clinging to the beaker or rod.
6) Top the flask up to the correct volume (250 cm³) with more deionised water. Make sure the bottom of the meniscus is on the line. When you get close to the line, use a dropping pipette to add the last bit of water one drop at a time.
7) Stopper the flask and turn it upside down a few times to mix the solution.

You could also make a standard solution by diluting a more concentrated solution with deionised water. The method for doing this is very similar to the one above, except that you measure out a volume of the concentrated solution using a pipette, rather than weighing out a mass of the solute.

Here's how to calculate the volume of the concentrated solution you'd need:

You can use a similar method to work out how to dilute a solution with a concentration in g/dm³. Just work out how many grams of solute are in the required volume of the standard solution, and then work out what volume of the concentrated solution contains this mass of solute.

EXAMPLE: What volume of 0.50 mol/dm³ hydrochloric acid would you need to dilute to make 250 cm³ of 0.010 mol/dm³ hydrochloric acid?
1) Work out how many moles of HCl are in 250 cm³ of the 0.010 mol/dm³ solution.
moles = conc. × volume = 0.010 × 0.250 = 0.0025 mol
2) Work out what volume of 0.50 mol/dm³ solution contains this number of moles.
volume = moles ÷ conc. = 0.0025 ÷ 0.50 = 0.0050 dm³ = 5.0 cm³

The Way You Choose Samples can be Important

1) Standard solutions can be used in titrations (see page 137), which are a type of quantitative test.
2) Quantitative tests measure numerical data and let you work out the amount of a substance in a sample.
3) When you're doing a test, you shouldn't test the whole substance — instead you should choose some representative samples. This means you take a number of samples at random from the thing you're testing so that you can account for any variations in its composition.

Taking just a small sample means you can also carry out other tests on different samples from the substance if you need to.

4) For example, if you're testing water in an area, you should take a number of different samples in slightly different places and test them all. If you're testing a chemical that's been made in industry, you should take a number of samples at random from each batch to test.
5) If you want to test the purity of a substance you've crystallised by testing its melting point, take a couple of samples to test, in case there's some variation across the substance.

Katherine's solution was premium, but mine was only standard...

The concentration of the standard solution needs to be accurate, otherwise it'll muck up your titration calculations.

Q1 What mass of hydrochloric acid would you need to make 300 cm³ of a 24 g/dm³ solution? [2 marks]

Titrations

Titrations are used to analyse the <u>concentrations</u> of solutions. They're pretty important. I secretly love them.

Titrations are Used to Find Out Concentrations

<u>Titrations</u> let you find out how much acid is needed to <u>neutralise</u> a quantity of alkali or vice versa. You can then use this result to work out the <u>concentration</u> of the acid or alkali (see next page). For example:

1) Say you want to find out the concentration of some <u>alkali</u>. Using a <u>pipette</u> and <u>pipette filler</u>, add a set volume of the alkali to a <u>conical flask</u>. Add two or three drops of <u>indicator</u> too (see below).

You can also do titrations by adding alkali to acid.

2) Use a <u>funnel</u> to fill a <u>burette</u> with a <u>standard solution</u> of an acid. Make sure you do this **BELOW EYE LEVEL** — you don't want to be looking up if some acid spills over. (You should wear <u>safety glasses</u> too.) Record the <u>initial volume</u> of the acid in the burette.

① Pipette
Pipettes measure just one volume, very accurately. Fill the pipette to just above the line, then carefully drop the level down to the line.

② Burette
Burettes measure different volumes and let you add the solution drop by drop.

acid

These marks down the side show the volume of acid used.

3) Using the <u>burette</u>, add the <u>acid</u> to the alkali a bit at a time — giving the conical flask a regular <u>swirl</u>. Go especially <u>slowly</u> when you think the <u>end-point</u> (colour change) is about to be reached.

To work out when this is, do a rough titration first. For this, don't worry about recording the exact end point, just note the approximate amount of acid you need, then go slowly as you get near this amount on the next runs.

Conical flask containing alkali and indicator.

4) The indicator <u>changes colour</u> when <u>all</u> the alkali has been <u>neutralised</u>, e.g. phenolphthalein is <u>pink</u> in <u>alkaline</u> conditions, but <u>colourless</u> in <u>acidic</u> conditions.

There's more about using burettes and pipettes on page 233.

5) <u>Record</u> the <u>final volume</u> of acid in the burette, and use it, along with the initial reading, to calculate the volume of acid used to <u>neutralise</u> the alkali.

- To increase the <u>accuracy</u> of your titration and to spot any <u>outliers</u>, you need <u>several consistent readings</u>.

Outliers are ones that don't fit in with the rest (see page 224).

- The <u>first</u> titration you do should be a <u>rough titration</u> to get an <u>approximate idea</u> of the end-point.
- Then <u>repeat</u> the whole thing a few times, making sure you get (pretty much) the <u>same answer</u> each time (within 0.10 cm^3).
- Finally, calculate a <u>mean</u> of your results, ignoring the rough titration and any <u>outliers</u>.

6) If you've followed the <u>correct method</u>, the results of your titration should be <u>valid</u> (see p.222).

7) Getting the same result more than once shows that your results are <u>repeatable</u>. They'll also be <u>precise</u> if they're in close agreement with each other. Using precise equipment such as <u>burettes</u> and <u>pipettes</u> will help with the precision of your results.

If you're using titrations to analyse the composition of a substance, use the sampling techniques on page 136.

8) Taking a mean from the results which are in close agreement should help to minimise any <u>random errors</u> in the individual results, making your overall result more <u>accurate</u>.

Use Single Indicators for Titrations

Universal indicator (see p.140) is no good here — it changes colour too gradually.

1) During a titration between an alkali and an acid, you want to see a <u>sudden colour change</u>, at the end-point.

2) So you need to use a <u>single indicator</u>, such as <u>litmus</u> (blue in alkalis and red in acids), <u>phenolphthalein</u> (pink in alkalis and colourless in acids), or <u>methyl orange</u> (yellow in alkalis and red in acids).

litmus	methyl orange	phenolphthalein
acid alkali	acid alkali	acid alkali

How do you get lean molecules? Feed them tight rations...

Titrations aren't too tricky really — you just need to be careful that you're doing them as carefully as you can.

Q1   How do you determine when the end-point of a titration has been reached?   [1 mark]

Q2   Give two reasons why you should repeat a titration until you have consistent readings.   [2 marks]

Titration Calculations

I expect you're wondering what you can do with the results from a titration experiment (who wouldn't be?). Well, you'll be relieved to know that you can use them to calculate <u>concentrations</u> of acids or alkalis.

You Might Be Asked to Calculate the Concentration

Titrations let you find the <u>volumes</u> of two solutions that are needed to <u>react together completely</u>. If you know the <u>concentration</u> of one of the solutions, you can use the volumes from the titration experiment, along with the <u>reaction equation</u>, to <u>find</u> the concentration of the other solution.

Find the Concentration in mol/dm³

You might remember the formula for working out the <u>concentration</u> of a substance in mol/dm³ from page 135. Well, here it is in a handy <u>formula triangle</u>. It's dead useful in titration calculations.

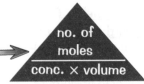

no. of moles

conc. × volume

EXAMPLE: A student analysed a sample of sulfuric acid (H_2SO_4) of unknown concentration. She found by titration that it took an average of 25.0 cm³ of 0.100 mol/dm³ sodium hydroxide (NaOH) to neutralise 30.0 cm³ of the sulfuric acid. Find the concentration of the acid in mol/dm³. The balanced symbol equation for the reaction is:

$$2NaOH + H_2SO_4 \rightarrow Na_2SO_4 + 2H_2O$$

1) Work out how many <u>moles</u> of the "<u>known</u>" substance you have using the formula: no. of moles = conc. × volume.

0.100 mol/dm³ × (25.0 / 1000) dm³ = 0.00250 moles of NaOH

2) Use the reaction equation to work out how many moles of the "<u>unknown</u>" substance you must have had. Using the equation, you can see that two moles of sodium hydroxide reacts with one mole of sulfuric acid. So 0.00250 moles of NaOH must have reacted with 0.00250 ÷ 2 = 0.00125 moles of H_2SO_4.

3) Work out the concentration of the "<u>unknown</u>" substance.

Concentration = number of moles ÷ volume

= 0.00125 mol ÷ (30.0 ÷ 1000) dm³ = 0.041666... mol/dm³ = **0.0417 mol/dm³**

Make sure the volume is in dm³ by dividing volumes in cm³ by 1000.

Converting mol/dm³ to g/dm³

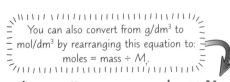

You can also convert from g/dm³ to mol/dm³ by rearranging this equation to: moles = mass ÷ M_r

1) To find the concentration in <u>g/dm³</u>, start by finding the concentration in mol/dm³ using the steps above.

2) Then, <u>convert</u> the concentration in mol/dm³ to g/dm³ using the equation <u>mass = moles × M_r</u>.

EXAMPLE: What's the concentration, in g/dm³, of the sulfuric acid solution in the example above?

1) Work out the <u>relative formula mass</u> for the acid.

$M_r(H_2SO_4)$ = (2 × 1.0) + 32.1 + (4 × 16.0) = 98.1

2) Convert the concentration in <u>moles</u> (that you've already worked out) into concentration in <u>grams</u>. So, in 1 dm³:

Don't round your answer until right at the end.

Mass in grams = moles × relative formula mass = 0.041666... × 98.1 = 4.0875 g

So the concentration in g/dm³ = **4.09 g/dm³**

Titrations — you gotta concentrate...

These calculations look pretty scary. But if you get enough practice, then the fear will evaporate and you can tackle them with a smile on your face and a spring in your step. Better get cracking...

Q1 In a titration, 22.5 cm³ of 0.150 mol/dm³ potassium hydroxide (KOH) was needed to neutralise 25.0 cm³ of nitric acid (HNO_3). The balanced equation for the reaction is: $HNO_3 + KOH \rightarrow KNO_3 + H_2O$
Calculate the concentration of nitric acid in mol/dm³. [3 marks]

Revision Questions for Chapter C5

Well, what a Chapter that was. And you can relive all the highlights by having a go at the questions below.

* Try these questions and tick off each one when you get it right.
* When you've done all the questions for a topic and are completely happy with it, tick off the topic.

Purity and Mixtures (p.126-129) ✓

1) Give the definition of a pure substance in chemistry.
2) What is a formulation?
3) What are the names of the two phases in chromatography?
4) How can you tell that a substance is a mixture using paper chromatography?
5) Give the equation for calculating the Rf value of a spot in paper chromatography.
6) Describe how you could separate an insoluble solid from a liquid.

Masses and Moles (p.130-134) ✓

7) How do you calculate the relative formula mass, M_r of a substance?
8) What does conservation of mass mean?
9) Suggest why the mass of the contents of a reaction vessel might decrease during a reaction.
10) State the value of the Avogadro constant.
11) What is the formula that relates the number of moles of a substance to its mass and M_r?
12) Explain what is meant by the term 'limiting reactant'.
13) How can you find the limiting reactant from a balanced equation and the masses of reactants present?

Solutions and Titrations (p.135-138) ✓

14) What is an acid?
15) Write the general equation for the reaction between H^+ and OH^- ions in a neutralisation reaction.
16) What is concentration?
17) Give the equation for working out the concentration of a solution in g/dm^3.
18) Give the equation for working out the concentration of a solution in mol/dm^3.
19) Describe how you would prepare a standard solution from a solid solute.
20) Describe the steps involved in carrying out a titration.
21) Why should you first carry out a rough titration when carrying out a titration experiment?
22) Outline the steps you'd take to calculate the concentration of an alkali
    from the result of a titration with an acid of known concentration.

Acids, Alkalis and pH

Testing the pH of a solution means using an <u>indicator</u> — and that means pretty <u>colours</u>...

The pH Scale Goes From 0 to 14

1) You might remember from page 135 that <u>acids</u> form H^+ ions in water, and <u>alkalis</u> form OH^- ions in water.

2) You can tell how acidic or alkaline a solution is from its pH. A <u>neutral</u> substance has <u>pH 7</u>.

3) An <u>acid</u> is a substance with a <u>pH less than 7</u>. Alkaline solutions have a pH <u>greater than 7</u>.

4) The value of the pH is <u>inversely proportional</u> to the <u>concentration of hydrogen ions</u> in a solution. So, as the concentration of hydrogen ions <u>increases</u>, the <u>pH decreases</u>. This makes sense, because the higher the hydrogen ion concentration, the <u>more acidic</u> something is, so the lower the pH.

5) In <u>neutral</u> solutions, the concentration of H^+ ions is <u>equal</u> to the concentration of OH^- ions.

6) If the concentration of <u>H^+ ions</u> is <u>greater</u> than the concentration of OH^- ions, then the solution is <u>acidic</u>. The higher the concentration of H^+ ions compared to OH^- ions, the lower the pH.

7) If the concentration of <u>OH^- ions</u> is <u>greater</u> than the concentration of H^+ ions, then the solution is <u>alkaline</u>. The higher the concentration of OH^- ions compared to H^+ ions, the higher the pH.

> Acids are found in lots of everyday products. They're used in cleaning products to help break down dirt, added to food to stop mould from growing and can play roles in medicines.

You Can Measure the pH of a Solution

An <u>indicator</u> is a <u>dye</u> that <u>changes colour</u> depending on whether it's <u>above or below a certain pH</u>. <u>Universal indicator</u> is a <u>combination of dyes</u>. It's very useful for <u>estimating</u> the pH of a solution. Indicators are simple to use — <u>add a few drops</u> to the solution you're testing, then compare the colour the solution goes to a <u>pH chart</u> for that indicator. Here's a pH chart for Universal indicator:

pH   0   1   2   3   4   5   6   7   8   9   10   11   12   13   14

ACIDS   NEUTRAL   ALKALIS

◄━━━━ CONCENTRATION OF H^+ IONS INCREASES ━━━━

A <u>pH probe</u> attached to a <u>pH meter</u> can be used to measure pH <u>electronically</u>. The probe is placed in the solution you are measuring and the pH is given on a digital display as a <u>numerical value</u>. This gives a <u>higher level</u> of accuracy than an indicator. When using a pH probe, it's important you <u>calibrate it correctly</u> (by setting it to read set values against a couple of solutions of known pH), and rinse the probe with deionised water in between readings.

Changing the Concentration of an Acid Affects its pH

If the concentration of H^+ ions <u>increases</u> by a factor of <u>10</u>, the pH <u>decreases</u> by <u>1</u>. So if the H^+ ion concentration <u>increases</u> by a factor of <u>100</u> (= 10 × 10), the pH <u>decreases</u> by <u>2</u> (= 1 + 1), and so on. Decreasing the H^+ ion concentration has the opposite effect — a <u>decrease</u> by a factor of <u>10</u> in the H^+ concentration means an <u>increase</u> of <u>1</u> on the pH scale.

 **EXAMPLE:** A solution with a hydrogen ion concentration of 0.001 mol/dm^3 has a pH of 3. Predict the new pH if you increased the hydrogen ion concentration to 0.01 mol/dm^3. The H^+ concentration has increased by a factor of 10, so the pH would decrease by 1. So the new pH would be 3 − 1 = 2.

You can <u>estimate</u> the pH of a solution from the concentration of H^+ ions. If the concentration's given in mol/dm^3, the pH will be roughly equal to the <u>number of zeroes</u> before the first <u>non-zero number</u>.

 **EXAMPLE:** Estimate the pH of a solution with a hydrogen ion concentration of 0.0002 mol/dm^3. There are 4 zeroes before the 2, so the pH is approximately 4.

Indie 'gators — hipster crocodiles...

pHew, you got to the end of the page, so here's an interesting(ish) fact — your skin is slightly acidic (pH 5.5).

Q1   a) The pH of an unknown solution is found to be 6. Is the solution acidic or alkaline?   [1 mark]

     b) By how many times would the concentration of H^+ change if the pH went from 3 to 6?   [2 marks]

Strong and Weak Acids

Right then. More on acids. Brace yourself.

Acids Produce Protons in Water

The thing about acids is that they ionise — they produce hydrogen ions, H^+.
For example,

$$HCl \rightarrow H^+ + Cl^-$$
$$HNO_3 \rightarrow H^+ + NO_3^-$$

An H^+ ion is just a proton.

HCl and HNO_3 don't produce hydrogen ions until they meet water.

Acids Can be Strong or Weak

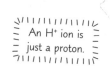

1) Strong acids (e.g. sulfuric, hydrochloric and nitric acids) ionise completely in water. All of the acid molecules dissociate to release H^+ ions.

2) Weak acids (e.g. ethanoic, citric and carbonic acids) do not fully ionise in solution. Only a small proportion of acid molecules dissociate to release H^+ ions.

3) The ionisation of a weak acid is a reversible reaction, which sets up an equilibrium mixture. Since only a few of the acid molecules release H^+ ions, the equilibrium lies well to the left.

Strong acid: $HCl \longrightarrow H^+ + Cl^-$

Weak acid: $CH_3COOH \rightleftharpoons H^+ + CH_3COO^-$

For more on equilibria turn to page 148.

4) You saw on the previous page that the pH of a solution depends on the concentration of H^+ ions. This means that the pH of a strong acid is always less than the pH of a weaker acid if they have the same concentration (see below), as a greater proportion of the strong acid will have dissociated.

5) Reactions of acids involve the reactions of the H^+ ions with other substances (you can see this from ionic equations). If the concentration of H^+ ions is higher, the rate of reaction will be faster. This means that if you have a strong acid and a weak acid of the same concentration, the strong acid will be more reactive. You can see this from the different reactions of acids.

> Example: Magnesium will react with 1 mol/dm³ hydrochloric acid and with 1 mol/dm³ solution of ethanoic acid.
> The reaction with hydrochloric acid fizzes vigorously as hydrogen gas is formed. In the reaction with ethanoic acid, bubbles of hydrogen gas form at a slower rate than in the reaction with hydrochloric acid.

Don't Confuse Strong Acids with Concentrated Acids

1) Acid strength (i.e. strong or weak) tells you what proportion of the acid molecules ionise in water.

2) The concentration of an acid is different. Concentration measures how much acid there is in a litre (1 dm³) of water. Concentration is basically how watered down your acid is.

3) An acid with a high proportion of acid molecules compared to the volume of water is said to be concentrated. An acid with a low proportion of acid molecules compared to the volume of water is said to be dilute.

Concentration is measured in g/dm³ or mol/dm³.

4) Note that concentration describes the total number of dissolved acid molecules — not the number of molecules that produce hydrogen ions.

5) The more grams (or moles) of acid per dm³, the more concentrated the acid is.

6) So you can have a dilute but strong acid, or a concentrated but weak acid.

Weak acid or strong acid? I know which goes better with chips...

Acids are acidic because of H^+ ions. And strong acids are strong because they let go of all their H^+ ions at the drop of a hat... Well, at the drop of a drop of water.

Q1   Explain the difference between a strong acid and a weak acid, in terms of dissociation.   [2 marks]

Reactions of Acids

You saw on page 135 that acids will react with alkalis in <u>neutralisation reactions</u> to form a <u>salt</u> and <u>water</u>. So I'm sure you'll be overjoyed to hear there are more of these reactions coming up.

Salts Form in Neutralisation Reactions

1) A <u>salt</u> is formed during a <u>neutralisation reaction</u>. <u>Salts</u> are ionic compounds.

2) In general, <u>hydrochloric acid</u> produces <u>chloride</u> salts, <u>sulfuric acid</u> produces <u>sulfate salts</u> and <u>nitric acid</u> produces <u>nitrate salts</u>.

3) You need to be able to remember what happens when you add acids to various substances...

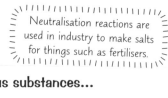
Neutralisation reactions are used in industry to make salts for things such as fertilisers.

Acid + Metal Hydroxide → Salt + Water

<u>Examples</u>: $HCl + NaOH \rightarrow NaCl + H_2O$ (Sodium chloride)
$H_2SO_4 + Zn(OH)_2 \rightarrow ZnSO_4 + 2H_2O$ (Zinc sulfate)
$HNO_3 + KOH \rightarrow KNO_3 + H_2O$ (Potassium nitrate)

Acid + Metal → Salt + Hydrogen

<u>Examples</u>: $2HCl + Mg \rightarrow MgCl_2 + H_2$ (Magnesium chloride)
$H_2SO_4 + Mg \rightarrow MgSO_4 + H_2$ (Magnesium sulfate)

The reaction of nitric acid with metals can be more complicated — you get a nitrate salt, but instead of hydrogen gas, the other products are usually a mixture of water, NO and NO_2.

Some metals, such as copper and silver, are very <u>unreactive</u> so <u>don't react</u> with acids at all.

Acid + Metal Carbonate → Salt + Water + Carbon Dioxide

<u>Examples</u>: $2HCl + Na_2CO_3 \rightarrow 2NaCl + H_2O + CO_2$ (Sodium chloride)
$H_2SO_4 + K_2CO_3 \rightarrow K_2SO_4 + H_2O + CO_2$ (Potassium sulfate)
$2HNO_3 + ZnCO_3 \rightarrow Zn(NO_3)_2 + H_2O + CO_2$ (Zinc nitrate)

You can Make Soluble Salts Using Acid/Alkali Reactions

PRACTICAL

1) Soluble salts (salts that dissolve in water) can be made by reacting an acid with an <u>alkali</u>.

2) But you can't tell whether the reaction has <u>finished</u> — there's no signal that all the acid has been neutralised. You also can't just add an <u>excess</u> of alkali to the acid and filter out what's left because the salt is <u>soluble</u> and would be contaminated with the excess alkali.

3) Instead, you have to add <u>exactly</u> the right amount of alkali to <u>neutralise</u> the acid. You can carry out a <u>titration</u> (see page 137) using an <u>indicator</u> to work out the <u>exact amount</u> of alkali needed.

4) Then, carry out the reaction using exactly the right proportions of alkali and acid but with no <u>indicator</u> (because you now know the volumes needed), so the salt <u>won't be contaminated</u> with indicator.

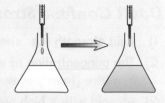

5) The <u>solution</u> that remains when the reaction is complete contains only the <u>salt</u> and <u>water</u>. Slowly <u>evaporate</u> off some of the water and then leave the solution to crystallise. Filter off the solid (see page 129 for more on crystallisation).

6) Finally, <u>dry</u> the salt. To do this, you could leave it in a fume cupboard until all the solvent has evaporated. A faster method would be to put the salt in a <u>drying oven</u>, which gently warms the substance, so the solvent evaporates. You can also use a <u>desiccator</u>, which is a flask that contains a compound that <u>absorbs water</u> from the air (a drying agent) and speeds up the drying process.

Nitrates — much cheaper than day-rates...

What a lot of reactions. Better take a peek back at page 80 for help with writing and balancing chemical equations.

Q1   Write a balanced chemical equation for the reaction of hydrochloric acid with calcium carbonate ($CaCO_3$).   [2 marks]

Making Salts

Making salts can be tricky. You need a different method depending on whether the salt's insoluble or soluble. You met one technique for making salts on the previous page. Time for some more...

Making Soluble Salts Using an Acid and an Insoluble Reactant

1) You can make soluble salts by reacting an acid with a metal, an insoluble metal hydroxide or a metal carbonate. To get a particular salt, you need to pick the right reactants.

2) Add the insoluble substance to the acid — they will react to produce a soluble salt (plus either water, hydrogen or water and carbon dioxide).

3) You will know when all the acid has been reacted because the excess solid will just sink to the bottom of the flask.
   You sometimes need to heat the reaction mixture during this step to get the acid and base to react.

4) Then filter off the excess solid to get a solution containing only salt and water.

5) Heat the solution gently to slowly evaporate off some of the water, then leave the more concentrated solution to cool and allow the salt to crystallise (see page 129). Filter off the solid and leave it to dry.

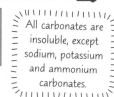

filter paper

filter funnel

excess solid

salt and water

> **Example:** You can add copper carbonate to hydrochloric acid to make copper chloride:
> $$CuCO_{3(s)} + 2HCl_{(aq)} \rightarrow CuCl_{2(aq)} + H_2O_{(l)} + CO_{2(g)}$$

All carbonates are insoluble, except sodium, potassium and ammonium carbonates.

Making Insoluble Salts — Precipitation Reactions

1) To make a pure, dry sample of an insoluble salt, you can use a precipitation reaction. To do this, you just need to pick the right two soluble salts, which react to give your insoluble salt (the precipitate).

2) E.g. to make lead chloride (insoluble), mix lead nitrate and sodium chloride (both soluble).

> lead nitrate + sodium chloride → lead chloride + sodium nitrate
> $$Pb(NO_3)_{2\,(aq)} + 2NaCl_{(aq)} \rightarrow PbCl_{2\,(s)} + 2NaNO_{3\,(aq)}$$

Soluble salts dissolve in water. Insoluble salts don't.

Method

1) Add 1 spatula of lead nitrate to a test tube. Add deionised water to dissolve the lead nitrate. Use deionised water to make sure there are no other ions about. Bung the tube, then shake it thoroughly to ensure that all the lead nitrate has dissolved. Then, in a separate test tube, do the same with 1 spatula of sodium chloride.

2) Tip the two solutions into a small beaker, and give them a good stir to make sure they're mixed together. The lead chloride should precipitate out.

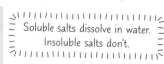

precipitate

filter paper

filter funnel

3) Put a folded piece of filter paper into a filter funnel, and stick the funnel into a conical flask.

4) Pour the contents of the beaker into the middle of the filter paper. Make sure that the solution doesn't go above the filter paper — otherwise some of the solid could dribble down the side.

5) Swill out the beaker with more deionised water, and tip this into the filter paper — this makes sure you get all the wanted product from the beaker.

lead chloride

6) Rinse the contents of the filter paper with deionised water to make sure that all the soluble sodium nitrate has been washed away.

7) Then just scrape the lead chloride onto fresh filter paper and leave to dry.

I was attacked by a nasty lead chloride — it was a-salt...

The theory may seem dull, but you'll probably get to make some nice salts in your class, and that's pretty cool.

Q1 Iron nitrate is a soluble salt that can be made from iron oxide (an insoluble substance) and nitric acid. Suggest a method you could use to make a pure, dry sample of iron nitrate from these reactants. [4 marks]

Rates of Reactions

Reactions can be <u>fast</u> or <u>slow</u> — you've probably already realised that. It's exciting stuff. Honest.

The Rate of Reaction is a Measure of How Fast the Reaction Happens

The <u>rate of a reaction</u> is how quickly a reaction happens. It can be observed <u>either</u> by measuring how quickly the reactants are used up or how quickly the products are formed.

Particles Must Collide with Enough Energy in Order to React

Reaction rates can be explained using <u>collision theory</u>. This states that the <u>rate</u> of a reaction depends on:

1) The <u>collision frequency</u> of reacting particles (how <u>often</u> they collide). The <u>more frequent</u> the collisions are, the <u>faster</u> the reaction is.

2) The energy <u>transferred</u> during a collision. Particles have to collide with <u>enough energy</u> for the collision to be successful.

You might remember from page 81 that the <u>minimum</u> amount of energy that particles need to react is called the <u>activation energy</u>. Particles need this much energy to <u>break the bonds</u> in the reactants and start the reaction.

A successful collision is a collision that ends in the particles reacting to form products.

The More Successful Collisions, the Higher the Rate of Reaction

Reactions only happen if <u>particles collide</u>. So if you <u>increase</u> the <u>frequency</u> of collisions, the reaction happens <u>more quickly</u> (the rate increases). The three factors below all lead to more frequent collisions...

Increasing the Temperature Increases Rate

1) When the <u>temperature is increased</u> the particles <u>move faster</u>. If they move faster, they're going to have <u>more frequent collisions</u>.

2) Higher temperatures also increase the <u>energy</u> of the collisions, since the particles are moving <u>faster</u>. Reactions <u>only happen</u> if the particles collide with <u>enough energy</u>.

3) This means that at <u>higher</u> temperatures there will be more frequent <u>successful collisions</u> (<u>more particles</u> will <u>collide</u> with <u>enough energy</u> to react). So <u>increasing</u> the temperature <u>increases</u> the rate of reaction.

Cold | Hot

Increasing Concentration (or Pressure) Increases Rate

1) If a <u>solution</u> is made more <u>concentrated</u>, it means there are more particles of <u>reactant</u> in the same volume. This makes collisions <u>more likely</u>, so the reaction rate <u>increases</u>.

2) In a <u>gas</u>, increasing the <u>pressure</u> means that the particles are <u>more crowded</u>. This means that the frequency of <u>collisions</u> between particles will <u>increase</u> — so the rate of reaction will also <u>increase</u>.

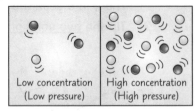
Low concentration (Low pressure) | High concentration (High pressure)

Smaller Solid Particles (or Higher Surface Area) Means a Higher Rate

1) If one reactant is a <u>solid</u>, breaking it into <u>smaller</u> pieces will <u>increase its surface area to volume ratio</u> (i.e. more of the solid will be exposed, compared to its overall volume).

2) The particles around it will have <u>more area to work on</u>, so the frequency of collisions will <u>increase</u>.

3) This means that the rate of reaction is faster for solids with a larger <u>surface area to volume</u> ratio.

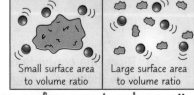
Small surface area to volume ratio | Large surface area to volume ratio

Increase your concentration — burn through that exam paper...

Revising more frequently and with more effort increases the number of successful exams. That's revision theory.

Q1   For the following reactions, state which one would have the fastest rate (A or B) and explain why:
    A: A 2 g solid piece of calcium with water.   B: 2 g of calcium granules with water.   [2 marks]

Reaction Rates and Catalysts

Catalysts are very important for commercial reasons — they increase reaction rate and reduce energy costs in industrial reactions. If that's not reason enough to learn this page, I don't know what is. (Oh, apart from "exams"...)

Using a Catalyst Increases the Rate

1) A catalyst is a substance that speeds up a reaction, but isn't used up itself — it can be recovered, unchanged, at the end of the reaction. So it's not part of the overall reaction equation.

2) Different catalysts are needed for different reactions, but they all work by decreasing the activation energy needed for the reaction to occur. They do this by providing an alternative reaction pathway with a lower activation energy.

3) By using catalysts you can speed up the rate of a reaction without needing high temperatures or pressures. This is useful in industry as, if less energy is needed to get the right conditions for the reaction, the process will be cheaper and more sustainable.

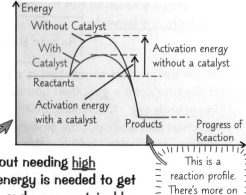

This is a reaction profile. There's more on these on p.81.

Enzymes Control Cell Reactions

1) Enzymes are proteins that act as biological catalysts. They catalyse the chemical reactions in cells.

2) Enzymes work best under specific conditions. If the temperature is too low, the enzyme's activity will be limited. If it's too high, or if the pH is too acidic or too alkaline, the enzyme can be damaged (denatured) and stop working.

3) Some industrial processes use adapted or synthesised enzymes as catalysts. This can give the reaction a reasonable rate at a much lower temperature than would otherwise be needed — making the process cheaper and more sustainable, as less energy is needed. However, there might be extra restrictions on the reaction conditions to make sure the enzyme will work.

You Need to Understand Graphs for the Rate of Reaction

You can find the rate of a reaction by recording the amount of product formed, or the amount of reactant used up over time (see next page).

1) The steeper the line on the graph, the faster the rate of reaction. Over time the line generally becomes less steep as the reactants are used up.

2) The quickest reactions have the steepest lines to begin with and become flat in the least time.

3) You can use these graphs to see how the speed of a particular reaction varies under different conditions.

- Graph 1 represents the original reaction.
- Graphs 2 and 3 represent the reaction taking place quicker, but with the same initial amounts of reactants. The slopes of the graphs are steeper than for graph 1.
- Graphs 1, 2 and 3 all converge at the same level, showing that they all produce the same amount of product although they take different times to produce it.
- Graph 4 shows more product and a faster reaction. This can only happen if more reactant(s) are added at the start.

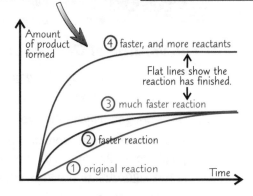

Catalysts are chemical stars — but success won't change them...

Catalysts aren't just in science labs. Enzymes are in all our cells, catalysing the reactions we need for life.

Q1 What is a catalyst? [2 marks]

Q2 On a graph of the amount of product formed against time, sketch and label the curves you would expect to see for the same reaction with and without a catalyst, if all other conditions are kept the same. [3 marks]

PRACTICAL Measuring Reaction Rates

All this talk about reaction rates is fine and dandy, but it's no good if you can't <u>measure</u> them.

Here Are Three Ways to Measure the Rate of a Reaction

The rate of a reaction can be observed either by how quickly the <u>reactants are used up</u> or how quickly the <u>products are formed</u>:

$$\text{Rate of Reaction} = \frac{\text{Amount of reactant used or amount of product formed}}{\text{Time}}$$

This is the mean rate of reaction. To find the rate of a reaction at a particular time, you'll need to plot a graph and find the gradient at that time (see next page).

When the product or reactant is a <u>solid</u> you measure the amount in <u>grams</u> (g). If the product's a <u>gas</u>, then you usually use <u>cm³</u>. Time is often measured in <u>seconds</u> (s). This means that the units for rate may be in <u>g/s</u> or in <u>cm³/s</u>. You can also work out the amount of product or reactant in <u>moles</u> — so the units of rate could also be <u>mol/s</u>. Here are <u>three ways</u> of measuring the rate of a reaction:

1) Precipitation and Colour Change

1) You can record the <u>visual change</u> in a reaction if the initial solution is <u>transparent</u> and the product is a <u>precipitate</u> which <u>clouds</u> the solution (so it becomes <u>opaque</u>).

2) You can observe a <u>mark</u> through the solution and measure how long it takes for it to <u>disappear</u> — the <u>faster</u> the mark disappears, the <u>quicker</u> the reaction.

3) If the reactants are <u>coloured</u> and the products are <u>colourless</u>, you can time how long it takes for the solution to <u>lose its colour</u>.

4) The results are <u>subjective</u> — <u>different people</u> might disagree about when the mark 'disappears' or the solution changes colour. Also, you can't plot a rate of reaction <u>graph</u> from the results.

5) You can make the results of a colour change experiment less subjective by using a <u>colorimeter</u>. This measures the amount of <u>light</u> passing through a solution (which changes as the colour changes). So you can measure <u>absorbance</u> at regular intervals throughout the reaction, and use these results to plot a <u>graph</u> to find the rate (see p.147). The faster the absorbance <u>changes</u>, the <u>faster the rate</u>.

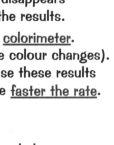

2) Change in Mass (Usually Gas Given Off)

1) Measuring the rate of a reaction that <u>produces a gas</u> can be carried out using a <u>mass balance</u>.

2) As the gas is released, the mass <u>disappearing</u> is measured on the balance.

3) The <u>quicker</u> the reading on the balance <u>drops</u>, the <u>faster</u> the reaction.

4) If you take measurements at <u>regular intervals</u>, you can plot a rate of reaction <u>graph</u> and find the rate at a given time quite easily (see next page for more).

5) This is the <u>most accurate</u> of the three methods described on this page because the mass balance is very accurate. But it has the <u>disadvantage</u> of releasing the gas straight into the room.

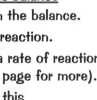

3) The Volume of Gas Given Off

1) This involves the use of a <u>gas syringe</u> to measure the volume of gas <u>given off</u>.

2) The <u>more</u> gas given off during a given time interval, the <u>faster</u> the reaction.

3) Gas syringes usually give volumes accurate to the nearest cm³, so they're quite <u>accurate</u>.

4) You can take measurements at <u>regular intervals</u> and plot a rate of reaction <u>graph</u> using this method. You have to be quite careful though — if the reaction is too <u>vigorous</u>, you can easily blow the plunger out of the end of the syringe.

5) You can also measure the volume of gas produced by bubbling it into an <u>upturned</u> <u>measuring cylinder</u> filled with <u>water</u>. There's more about this method on page 238.

I'd rate these reaction measurements as 8/10...

Make sure you've learnt the three different methods on this page, then have a go at this question:

Q1   The reaction between solid Na_2CO_3 and aqueous HCl releases CO_2 (a gas).
Describe an experiment that would allow you to measure the rate of this reaction.   [3 marks]

Finding Reaction Rates from Graphs

You might remember a bit about how to <u>interpret</u> graphs on reaction rate from page 145 — well this page shows you how to use them to <u>calculate</u> rates.

You can Calculate the Mean Reaction Rate from a Graph

1) Remember, a <u>rate of reaction graph</u> shows the amount of <u>product formed</u> or amount of <u>reactant used up</u> on the <u>y-axis</u> and <u>time</u> on the <u>x-axis</u>.

2) So to find the <u>mean rate</u> for the <u>whole reaction</u>, you just work out the <u>overall change</u> in the y-value and then <u>divide this</u> by the <u>total time taken</u> for the reaction to finish.

3) You can also use the graph to find the <u>mean rate</u> of reaction between <u>any two points</u> in time:

 The graph shows the volume of gas released by a reaction, measured at regular intervals. Find the mean rate of reaction between 20 s and 40 s.

Mean rate of reaction = change in y ÷ change in x
$$= (19 \text{ cm}^3 - 15 \text{ cm}^3) \div (40 \text{ s} - 20 \text{ s})$$
$$= 4 \text{ cm}^3 \div 20 \text{ s}$$
$$= 0.2 \text{ cm}^3/\text{s}$$

If you need to find the mean rate for the whole reaction, remember that the reaction finishes as soon as the line on the graph goes flat.

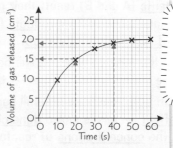

Draw a Tangent to Find the Reaction Rate at a Particular Point

If you want to find the <u>rate</u> of the reaction at a particular point in time, you need to find the <u>gradient</u> (slope) of the curve at that point. The easiest way to do this is to draw a <u>tangent</u> to the curve — a straight line that touches the curve at one point and doesn't cross it. You then work out the <u>gradient of the tangent</u>. It's simpler than it sounds, honest...

If you're asked to calculate the rate from a straight line graph, just start at step 4 and pick two points on your straight line.

 The graph below shows the mass of reactant used up measured at regular intervals during a chemical reaction. What is the rate of reaction at 3 minutes?

1) Position a <u>ruler</u> on the graph at the point where you want to know the rate — here it's <u>3 minutes</u>.

2) Adjust the ruler until the <u>space</u> between the ruler and the curve is <u>equal</u> on <u>both sides</u> of the point.

3) Draw a line along the ruler to make the <u>tangent</u>. Extend the line <u>right across</u> the graph.

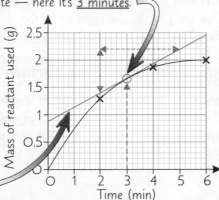

4) Pick <u>two points</u> on the line that are easy to read. Use them to calculate the <u>gradient</u> of the tangent in order to find the <u>rate</u>:

gradient = change in y ÷ change in x
$$= (2.2 - 1.4) \div (5.0 - 2.0)$$
$$= 0.8 \div 3.0$$
$$= 0.266...$$

So, the rate of reaction at 3 minutes was 0.27 g/min.

Calculate your reaction to this page. Boredom? How dare you...

There's only one way to learn this stuff properly — practise. So you'd better get going with this question.

Q1 Calcium carbonate powder was added to a conical flask containing dilute hydrochloric acid. Carbon dioxide (CO_2) was produced and collected in a gas syringe. The volume of gas released was recorded at 10 second intervals in the table on the right:

Time (s)	0	10	20	30	40	50	60
Volume of CO_2 (cm³)	0	24	32	36	38	39	40

a) Plot these results on a graph and draw a line of best fit. [3 marks]
b) Find the rate of the reaction at time = 26 s. [4 marks]

Dynamic Equilibrium

Reversible reactions — products forming from reactants and reactants forming from products. I can't keep up...

Reversible Reactions can go Forwards and Backwards

A <u>reversible reaction</u> is one where the <u>products</u> can react with each other to produce the original <u>reactants</u>. In other words, <u>it can go both ways</u>.

$$A + B \rightleftharpoons C + D$$

The '$\rightleftharpoons$' shows the reaction goes both ways.

Reversible Reactions Will Reach Equilibrium

1) As the <u>reactants</u> (A and B) react, their <u>concentrations fall</u> — so the <u>forward reaction</u> will <u>slow down</u>. But as more and more of the <u>products</u> (C and D) are made and their <u>concentrations rise</u>, the <u>backward reaction</u> will <u>speed up</u>.

2) After a while the forward reaction will be going at <u>exactly</u> the <u>same rate</u> as the backward one — this is <u>equilibrium</u>.

3) At equilibrium <u>both</u> reactions are still <u>happening</u>, but there's <u>no overall effect</u> — this is called <u>dynamic equilibrium</u>. This means the <u>concentrations</u> of reactants and products have reached a balance and <u>won't change</u>.

4) Equilibrium can only be reached if the reversible reaction takes place in a '<u>closed system</u>'. A <u>closed system</u> just means that none of the reactants or products can <u>escape</u> and nothing else can <u>get in</u>.

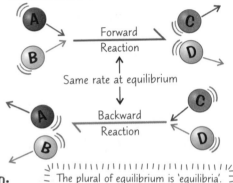

Forward Reaction

Same rate at equilibrium

Backward Reaction

The plural of equilibrium is 'equilibria'.

The Position of Equilibrium Can be on the Right or the Left

When a reaction's at equilibrium it <u>doesn't</u> mean the amounts of reactants and products are <u>equal</u>.

1) Sometimes the equilibrium will <u>lie to the right</u> — this basically means '<u>lots of the products and not much of the reactants</u>' (i.e. the concentration of products is greater than the concentration of reactants).

2) Sometimes the equilibrium will <u>lie to the left</u> — this basically means '<u>lots of the reactants but not much of the products</u>' (the concentration of reactants is greater than the concentration of products).

3) In a system that's <u>closed</u> (no matter can get in or out), there will always be a <u>mixture</u> of products and reactants, even if the equilibrium lies very far to the right or to the left. This means that the yield of a reversible reaction in a <u>closed</u> system can <u>never</u> be 100%.

A 100% yield means that all the reactants have reacted to form the products.

Three Things Can Change the Position of Equilibrium

The exact <u>position of equilibrium</u> depends on the <u>conditions</u> (as well as the reaction itself). These three things can <u>change</u> the <u>position of equilibrium</u> (which changes the amounts of products and reactants present at equilibrium):

1) Temperature
2) Pressure (only affects equilibria involving gases)
3) Concentration

Whilst <u>catalysts</u> increase the rate that a reaction <u>reaches</u> equilibrium, they <u>don't</u> have any effect on the <u>position</u> of equilibrium.

Dynamic equilibrium — lots of activity, but not to any great effect*...

Keep an eagle eye out for that arrow that shows you that a reaction is reversible. I'd hate you to miss it.

Q1 Explain what is meant by the term 'reversible reaction'. [1 mark]

Q2 What is dynamic equilibrium? [1 mark]

Q3 Name three things which can affect the position of equilibrium. [3 marks]

*Much like the England football team...

Changing the Position of Equilibrium

This stuff might feel a bit complicated to start with, but it all comes down to one simple rule — whatever you do to a <u>reversible reaction</u>, the <u>equilibrium position</u> will <u>move</u> to try to <u>undo</u> your change. How contrary...

The Equilibrium Position Moves to Minimise Any Changes You Make

If there's a <u>change</u> in concentration, pressure or temperature in a reversible reaction, the <u>equilibrium position will move</u> to help <u>counteract</u> that change.

TEMPERATURE If a reaction is <u>exothermic</u> in one direction it will be <u>endothermic</u> in the other (see p.81).

1) If you <u>decrease the temperature</u>, the equilibrium will move in the <u>exothermic direction</u> to produce more heat.

2) If you <u>increase the temperature</u>, the equilibrium will move in the <u>endothermic direction</u> to absorb the extra heat.

For example: $N_2 + 3H_2 \rightleftharpoons 2NH_3$
This reaction is exothermic in the forward direction. If you decrease the temperature, the equilibrium will shift to the right (so you'll make more product).

PRESSURE Changing this only affects equilibria involving <u>gases</u>.

1) If you <u>increase the pressure</u>, the equilibrium will move towards the side that has <u>fewer moles of gas</u> to <u>reduce</u> pressure.

2) If you <u>decrease the pressure</u>, the equilibrium will move towards the side that has <u>more moles of gas</u> to <u>increase</u> pressure.

For example:
$N_2 + 3H_2 \rightleftharpoons 2NH_3$
This reaction has 4 moles of gas on the left and 2 on the right. If you increase the pressure, the equilibrium will shift to the right (so you'll make more product).

CONCENTRATION

1) If you <u>increase the concentration</u> of the <u>reactants</u>, the equilibrium will move to the <u>right</u> to <u>use up the reactants</u> (making <u>more products</u>).

2) If you <u>increase the concentration</u> of the <u>products</u>, the equilibrium will move to the <u>left</u> to <u>use up the products</u> (making <u>more reactants</u>).

3) <u>Decreasing</u> the concentrations will have the <u>opposite effect</u>.

For example:
$N_2 + 3H_2 \rightleftharpoons 2NH_3$
If you increase the concentration of N_2 or H_2, the equilibrium will shift to the right to use up the extra reactants (so you'll make more product).

You Can Predict How the Position of Equilibrium Will Change

You can apply the rules above to any reversible reaction to work out how <u>changing the conditions</u> will affect the <u>equilibrium position</u>. This has useful applications in <u>industry</u> — you can <u>increase yield</u> by changing the conditions to shift the equilibrium position to the <u>right</u> (towards the <u>products</u>).

EXAMPLE: The compound PCl_5 can be made using this reaction: $PCl_{3(g)} + Cl_{2(g)} \rightleftharpoons PCl_{5(g)}$
Explain what would happen to the equilibrium position and to the yield of PCl_5 if you increased the pressure that the reaction was being performed at.

If you increase the pressure, the position of equilibrium will move towards the side with fewer moles of gas to reduce the pressure. In this reaction there are 2 moles of gas in the reactants and 1 in the products. The position of equilibrium will move to the right, since that is the side with fewer moles of gas. This shifts the equilibrium towards the products, so the yield of PCl_5 will increase.

Just because certain conditions give a high yield doesn't mean they'll be used for an industrial process — there are other things to consider, too. For example, a high temperature or pressure might give the best <u>yield</u>, but to maintain them <u>safely</u>, you need specialised <u>equipment</u> and lots of <u>energy</u>, both of which are <u>expensive</u>.

An equilibrium is like a particularly stubborn mule...

Reversible reactions may be able to relieve the pressure in chemical systems, but they stand a chance of giving you a right headache in the exam. So, best make sure you understand how they work now by trying these questions...

Q1　This reaction is endothermic in the forward direction: $CH_3OH_{(g)} \rightleftharpoons CO_{(g)} + 2H_{2(g)}$. What will happen to the position of equilibrium if the temperature is increased? Explain your answer. [2 marks]

Q2　What would happen to the yield of SO_3 in the reaction below if the pressure was decreased? Explain your answer. $2SO_{2(g)} + O_{2(g)} \rightleftharpoons 2SO_{3(g)}$ [3 marks]

Revision Questions for Chapter C6

<u>Chapter C6</u> was quite an adventure, and it's not over yet. Time to test what you remember...
- Try these questions and <u>tick off each one</u> when you <u>get it right</u>.
- When you've done <u>all the questions</u> for a topic and are <u>completely happy</u> with it, tick off the topic.

Acids, Alkalis and pH (p.140-143) ☑

1) What is the pH of a neutral solution?
2) If the concentration of H^+ ions in a solution increases by a factor of 10, what will happen to the pH?
3) What is a strong acid?
4) For a solution of a strong acid and a solution of a weak acid, both with the same concentration, would the pH of the strong acid or the weak acid be lower? Explain your answer.
5) What are the products of a reaction between a metal and an acid?
6) Describe a method you could use to produce a pure, insoluble salt from two soluble salts.

Rates of Reactions (p.144-147) ☑

7) Name two factors that affect the rate of a reaction.
8) Explain, using collision theory, why increasing the temperature of a reaction increases its rate.
9) Describe how catalysts increase the rate of a reaction.
10) Describe a method you could use to monitor the rate of a reaction where a precipitate is formed.
11) Describe how you'd use a tangent to find the rate of a reaction at a particular point from a graph of product formed against time.

Reversible Reactions and Equilibria (p.148-149) ☑

12) What symbol is used to show that a reaction is reversible?
13) The equilibrium of a reaction is to the right. At equilibrium, will there be higher concentration of products or reactants?
14) What would happen to the position of equilibrium if the concentration of reactants was increased?

Waves

Waves transfer <u>energy</u> from one place to another without transferring any <u>matter</u> (stuff). Clever so and so's.

Waves Transfer Energy in the Direction they are Travelling

A <u>wave</u> is a <u>regular disturbance</u> (i.e. a uniform pattern of <u>movement</u>) that <u>transfers energy</u>. For waves travelling through a medium, the <u>particles</u> (see p.213) of the medium <u>vibrate</u> and <u>transfer energy</u> between each other. BUT overall, the particles stay in the <u>same place</u> — <u>only energy</u> is transferred.

> For example, if you drop a twig into a calm pool of water, <u>ripples</u> form on the surface. The ripples <u>don't</u> carry the <u>water</u> (or the twig) away with them though.
>
> Similarly, if you strum a <u>guitar string</u> and create a <u>sound wave</u>, the sound wave travels to your <u>ear</u> but it doesn't carry the <u>air</u> away from the guitar — if it did, it would create a <u>vacuum</u>.

1) The <u>amplitude</u> of a wave is the <u>displacement</u> from the <u>rest position</u> to a <u>crest</u> or <u>trough</u>.

2) The <u>wavelength</u> is the distance between the same points on <u>two adjacent</u> (neighbouring) <u>disturbances</u> (e.g. from <u>crest to crest</u> or from <u>compression</u> to <u>compression</u>, see below), i.e. one a <u>full cycle</u> of the wave.

3) <u>Frequency</u> is the <u>number of complete waves</u> made by the source, <u>or the cycles</u> passing a certain point <u>per second</u>. Frequency is measured in <u>hertz (Hz)</u>. 1 Hz is <u>1 wave per second</u>.

4) The <u>period</u> of a wave is the <u>number of seconds</u> it takes for <u>one full cycle</u> to pass a certain point. <u>Period = 1 ÷ frequency</u>.

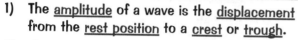

Waves (or the wave model) can be used to describe and predict how one object affects another object that is some distance away from it by transferring energy to it by waves.

Transverse Waves Have Perpendicular Disturbances

1) For <u>transverse waves</u> the disturbance of the medium is <u>perpendicular</u> (at 90°) to the <u>direction</u> the wave travels.

2) <u>Most waves</u> are transverse, including <u>electromagnetic waves</u> (p.155), waves in <u>water</u> (see p.152) and waves on a <u>rope</u>.

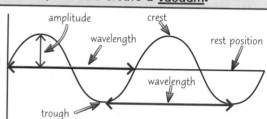

A rope wiggled <u>up and down</u> gives a <u>transverse</u> wave.

Disturbances go up and down.

Wave travels this way.

Longitudinal Waves Have Parallel Disturbances

1) For <u>longitudinal waves</u>, the disturbance of the medium is <u>parallel</u> to the <u>direction</u> the wave travels.

2) <u>Sound waves</u> in air are an example of longitudinal waves.

3) Longitudinal waves <u>squash up</u> and <u>stretch out</u> the arrangement of particles in the medium they pass through, making <u>compressions</u> (<u>high pressure</u>, lots of particles) and <u>rarefactions</u> (<u>low pressure</u>, fewer particles).

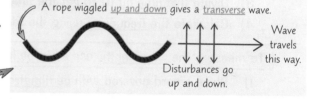

If you <u>push</u> and <u>pull</u> the end of a spring, you send a wave of <u>compression pulses</u> down the spring — a <u>longitudinal</u> wave.

Disturbances in the same direction as the wave travels.

compressions

rarefactions

A wavelength is still one complete cycle, e.g. from one compression to another.

Learn the Wave Speed Equation

It can be used for <u>all types</u> of wave, including <u>water</u>, <u>sound</u> and <u>EM waves</u>.

wave speed (m/s) = frequency (Hz) × wavelength (m)

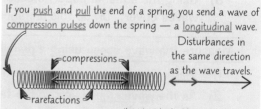

Wave frequencies are often given in <u>kHz</u> (kilohertz) or <u>MHz</u> (megahertz). Change them to Hz to use them in the equation (see p.227). <u>1 kHz = 1000 Hz</u> and <u>1 MHz = 1 000 000 Hz</u>.

What about Mexican waves...

You won't get far unless you understand these wave basics. Try a question to test your knowledge.

Q1   A wave has a speed of 0.15 m/s and a wavelength of 7.5 cm. Calculate its frequency.   [3 marks]

Wave Experiments

Time to <u>experiment</u>. Microphones and ripple tanks — sounds like fun, just don't mix them together...

Use an Oscilloscope to Measure the Speed of Sound

By attaching a <u>signal generator</u> to a speaker you can generate sounds with a specific <u>frequency</u>.
You can use <u>two microphones</u> and an <u>oscilloscope</u> to find the <u>wavelength</u> of the sound waves generated.

1) Set up the oscilloscope so the <u>detected waves</u> at each microphone are shown as <u>separate waves</u>.

2) Start with <u>both microphones</u> next to the speaker, then slowly <u>move one away</u> until the two waves are <u>aligned</u> on the display, but have moved <u>exactly one wavelength apart</u>.

3) Measure the <u>distance between the microphones</u> to find one <u>wavelength</u> (λ).

4) You can then use the formula $v = f\lambda$ to find the <u>speed</u> (v) of the <u>sound waves</u> passing through the <u>air</u> — the <u>frequency</u> (f) is whatever you set the <u>signal generator</u> to in the first place.

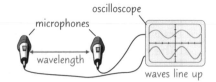

speaker attached to signal generator · microphones · oscilloscope · wavelength · waves line up

Measure Speed, Frequency and Wavelength with a Ripple Tank | PRACTICAL

You can generate <u>waves</u> in a <u>ripple tank</u> using a <u>variable power supply</u> attached to a <u>dipper</u>.
The dipper moves up and down to create water waves at a fixed frequency. Or you can use a <u>signal generator</u> which generates waves with a <u>known</u> fixed <u>frequency</u>.

The frequency is the number of waves made by the dipper (the source) per second.

To measure the <u>frequency</u>, you'll need a <u>cork</u> and a <u>stopwatch</u>:

1) <u>Float</u> the cork in the ripple tank. It should <u>bob up and down</u> as the waves pass it.

2) When the cork is at the <u>top</u> of a 'bob', <u>start the stopwatch</u>. <u>Time</u> how long the cork takes to complete <u>10 bobs</u>.

3) <u>Divide</u> this <u>time</u> by 10 to get the time for <u>one bob</u> — the <u>period</u>.

4) Calculate the <u>frequency</u> using the formula <u>frequency = 1 ÷ period</u>.

dipper attached to variable power supply

cork bobs up and down

(If you used a signal generator, your result should match its frequency.)

To measure the <u>wavelength</u>, use a <u>strobe light</u>:

1) Place a card covered with <u>centimetre-squared paper</u> behind the ripple tank.

2) Turn on the <u>strobe light</u> and <u>adjust its frequency</u> until the waves appear to '<u>freeze</u>'.

3) Using the squared paper, measure the <u>distance</u> that, e.g. <u>five</u> waves cover. Divide this distance by the number of waves to get an <u>average wavelength</u>.

strobe light · five waves · card

Measure the <u>wave speed</u> using a <u>pencil</u> and a <u>stopwatch</u>:

You need two people for this.

As $v = f\lambda$, you could measure two of these quantities and calculate the third.

1) Place a <u>large piece of paper</u> next to the tank.

2) As the <u>waves move</u> across the tank, one of you should <u>track the path</u> of one of the crests on the paper using the <u>pencil</u>. Using a ruler will help make sure your line is <u>parallel</u> to the direction the wave travels.

3) The other should <u>time</u> how long it takes the first to draw a line of a <u>certain length</u>, e.g. 20 cm.

4) <u>Calculate wave speed</u> by plugging the <u>length of the line</u> (the distance) and the <u>time taken</u> to draw it into the formula <u>speed = distance ÷ time</u>.

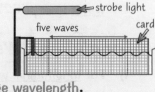

pencil tracks this wave crest

line drawn along the paper as the crest moves

As always, for <u>each</u> of these experiments make sure you do at least three <u>repeats</u> and take an <u>average</u>.
Also, make sure it's a <u>fair test</u> — keep the <u>equipment</u> the <u>same</u> and the <u>variables</u> you <u>aren't testing</u> the <u>same</u> every time, e.g. the <u>position</u> of the dipper, the <u>voltage</u> of the power supply, the <u>depth</u> of the water...

Disco time in the physics lab...

Sound waves always travel at the same speed in air — about 330 m/s. So your value should be in that ball park.

Q1   Describe an experiment in which a water wave is produced and its frequency measured.   [4 marks]

Reflection and Refraction

All waves <u>reflect</u> and <u>refract</u>. 'What does that mean?' you ask. Read on...

Waves Are Absorbed, Transmitted and Reflected at Boundaries

When a <u>wave</u> meets a <u>boundary</u> between two materials (a <u>material interface</u>), <u>three</u> things can happen:

1) The wave is <u>ABSORBED</u> by the second material — its energy is <u>transferred</u> to the material, often causing <u>heating</u>.

What actually happens depends on the wavelength of the wave and the properties of the materials involved.

2) The wave is <u>TRANSMITTED</u> through the second material — the wave <u>carries on travelling</u> through the new material. This often leads to <u>refraction</u> (see below).

3) The wave is <u>REFLECTED</u> — the wave is '<u>sent back</u>' away from the second material. There's one rule for reflection: <u>ANGLE OF INCIDENCE = ANGLE OF REFLECTION</u> — see p.154.

This is true for <u>all types of wave</u>, including EM waves (see p.155), sound waves and water waves.

Refraction — Waves Changing Direction at a Boundary

1) Waves travel at <u>different speeds</u> in different materials. So when a wave crosses a <u>boundary</u> between materials it <u>changes speed</u>.

2) The <u>frequency</u> of a wave <u>stays the same</u> (it can't change) as it crosses a boundary from one medium (material) to another. As $v = f\lambda$, this means if the speed of the wave changes, the <u>wavelength</u> must also change. The wavelength <u>decreases</u> if the wave <u>slows down</u>, and <u>increases</u> if it <u>speeds up</u>.

3) If the wave hits the boundary at an <u>angle</u> to the normal, this change of <u>speed</u> causes a <u>change in direction</u> — this is <u>refraction</u>. If the wave is travelling <u>along the normal</u> it will <u>change speed</u>, but it's <u>NOT refracted</u>.

A normal is an imaginary line at right angles to the surface at the point the wave hits it.

4) The <u>wavefront diagrams</u> below show a wave slowing down as it crosses a boundary.

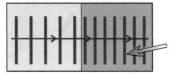

The wavefronts are closer together, showing a decrease in wavelength (and so a decrease in velocity).

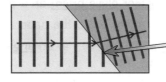

The wave hits a different medium at an angle, so the wave changes direction.

A wavefront is a line used to represent a crest (or trough) of a wave.

5) The <u>greater</u> the <u>change</u> in speed, the <u>more</u> a wave <u>bends</u> (changes direction).

6) The wave bends <u>towards the normal</u> if it <u>slows down</u>, and <u>away</u> from the normal if it <u>speeds up</u>.

Light and Sound Waves can be Modelled by Water Waves

<u>Water waves</u> show some of the behaviours of <u>light</u> and <u>sound</u> waves — and the best thing is, you can actually <u>see</u> the <u>wavefronts</u>. A <u>ripple tank</u> can be used to demonstrate reflection and refraction.

<u>REFLECTION:</u>

When water waves hit an object, they are <u>reflected</u> by it. The <u>angles</u> the incident and reflected waves make with the normal always <u>match</u> each other.

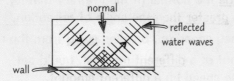

normal

reflected water waves

wall

<u>REFRACTION:</u>

When water waves pass into <u>shallower</u> water, they <u>slow down</u>. If they're at an angle to the normal, they'll <u>refract</u>.

The boundary in this diagram is where the depth of water suddenly changes.

deep water

shallow water

I'll give you some time to reflect on this page...

So the angle at which a wave hits a boundary determines whether it refracts or not. How fantabulous.

Q1   Explain what happens to the wavelength of a wave when it passes into a different medium and slows down.   [3 marks]

Reflection and Refraction Experiments

Experiments are what science is all about. And here are some beauties involving refraction and reflection.

You can Investigate Reflection Using a Ray Box and a Mirror

PRACTICAL

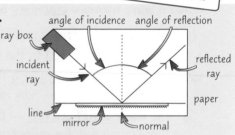

1) Take a piece of paper and draw a solid line across it using a ruler. Then draw a dotted line at 90° to the solid line (your normal).

2) Place a plane (flat) mirror so it lines up with the solid line.

3) Using a ray box, shine a thin beam of white light at the mirror, so the light hits the mirror where the normal meets the mirror.

4) Trace the incident and reflected light rays.

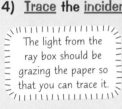

The light from the ray box should be grazing the paper so that you can trace it.

5) Measure the angle between the incident ray and the normal (the angle of incidence) and the angle between the reflected ray and the normal (the angle of reflection) using a protractor.

6) Repeat these steps, varying the angle of incidence. You should find that no matter its value, the angle of incidence ALWAYS equals the angle of reflection.

Do this experiment in a dark room. Keep the light levels the same throughout your experiment.

7) As always, keep your test fair by keeping other variables the same, e.g. same mirror, same width and brightness of beam.

8) You should see that the reflected ray is as thin and bright as the incident ray — a plane mirror gives a clear reflection and none of the light is absorbed.

You can Investigate the Refraction of Light using a Prism

PRACTICAL

You'll need a light source, such as a laser (lasers produce only a single wavelength of light), and a triangular glass prism on a piece of paper:

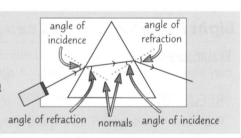

1) Draw a solid line around the prism on to the paper.

2) Then shine the laser beam into the prism at an angle to its surface. (Some light will be reflected.)

3) Trace the incident and emerging rays onto the paper and remove the prism.

4) Draw the refracted ray by joining the ends of the other two rays with a straight line.

5) You can then measure the angles of incidence and refraction:

- Draw normals at the points where the ray enters and leaves the prism. Do this by drawing dotted lines at 90° to the sides of the prism at the entry and exit points.

- You then have two sets of angles of incidence and refraction to mark and measure. There's the set where the ray enters the prism and the set where it leaves.

6) Electromagnetic (EM) waves (see p.155) like light usually travel more slowly in denser materials.

7) So, when entering glass from the air, they bend towards the normal (if they refract that is). So at the point of entry, the angle of incidence will be greater than the angle of refraction.

8) The opposite happens when they leave the prism — they speed up, bending away from the normal.

9) If you repeated the investigation using a prism made out of a different material, you'd get different angles of refraction as the wave would change speed by a different amount.

10) The speed of a wave travelling through a material may also depend on its wavelength.

Lights, camera, refraction...

Make sure you know how to conduct these experiments and what you would expect to see from the results.

Q1   Describe an investigation you could do to compare the refraction of light waves through a sapphire prism and a glass prism.   [5 marks]

The Electromagnetic Spectrum

So you know that <u>light</u> is a wave, but did you know that light's just one <u>small part</u> of the <u>EM spectrum</u>...

There's a Continuous Spectrum of EM Waves

Electromagnetic waves are vibrations of electric and magnetic fields (rather than vibrations of particles). This means they can travel through a vacuum.

1) <u>Electromagnetic (EM) waves</u> are <u>transverse</u> waves (p.151).

2) They all travel at the <u>same speed</u> through <u>space</u> (a <u>vacuum</u>). This speed is <u>very fast</u>, but <u>finite</u> (so it always takes EM waves <u>some time</u> to travel from one point to another). However, they travel at <u>different speeds</u> in <u>different materials</u>.

3) EM waves vary in <u>wavelength</u> from around 10^{-15} m to more than 10^4 m, and those with <u>shorter wavelengths</u> have <u>higher frequencies</u> (from $v = f\lambda$ on page 151).

4) We <u>group</u> them based on their <u>wavelength</u> and <u>frequency</u> — there are <u>seven basic types</u>, but the different groups <u>merge</u> to form a <u>continuous spectrum</u>.

5) Our <u>eyes</u> can only detect a <u>small part</u> of this spectrum — <u>visible light</u>. <u>Different colours</u> of light have different <u>wavelengths</u>. From <u>longest</u> to <u>shortest</u> — red, orange, yellow, green, blue, indigo, violet.

wavelength	RADIO WAVES	MICRO WAVES	INFRA RED	VISIBLE LIGHT	ULTRA VIOLET	X-RAYS	GAMMA RAYS
	1 m – 10^4 m	10^{-2} m	10^{-5} m	10^{-7} m	10^{-8} m	10^{-10} m	10^{-15} m

Long wavelength, low frequency and low energy. ⟶ Short wavelength, high frequency and high energy.

6) What we see as <u>white light</u> is actually a <u>mixture</u> of <u>all</u> of the colours across the visible spectrum.

7) EM waves <u>spread out</u> from a <u>source</u> and <u>transfer energy</u> to an <u>absorber</u>, which is some distance away. For example, when you warm yourself by an <u>electric heater</u>, <u>infrared</u> waves <u>transfer energy</u> from the <u>thermal energy store</u> of the <u>heater</u> (the source) to your <u>thermal energy store</u> (the absorber).

You might see this explanation of how energy is transferred by radiation called a radiation model.

8) The <u>higher the frequency</u> of the EM wave, the <u>more energy</u> it transfers.

EM waves are sometimes called EM radiation.

You Need to Know how Some EM Waves are Emitted...

1) A <u>wide range</u> of EM radiation can be released when <u>changes</u> occur in <u>nuclei</u>, <u>atoms</u> or <u>molecules</u>.

2) Changes in nuclei can cause <u>gamma rays</u> to be emitted — this is <u>radioactive decay</u>.

3) <u>Visible light</u>, <u>ultraviolet (UV)</u> radiation and <u>X-rays</u> are emitted when electrons <u>drop down</u> energy levels (shown on p.156).

4) The bonds holding the atoms together in <u>molecules</u> vibrate — this generates <u>infrared radiation</u>.

... and What Happens When EM Waves are Absorbed

1) When <u>any</u> type of EM wave is absorbed, it <u>ceases to exist</u> as radiation and causes <u>heating</u>. However, <u>high-energy UV</u>, <u>X-rays</u> and <u>gamma rays</u> have so much energy that they don't <u>just</u> cause heating, but can cause <u>ionisation</u> when they're absorbed by atoms (p.156).

2) <u>Infrared radiation</u> is absorbed by <u>molecules</u> (as well as being emitted by them, see above).

3) UV radiation from the Sun is absorbed by <u>oxygen molecules</u> (O_2) in the upper atmosphere, forming <u>ozone</u> (O_3). This ozone then absorbs large amounts of ionising <u>UV radiation</u> from the Sun, <u>protecting</u> living things (especially animals) from its <u>damaging effects</u>.

Learn about the EM spectrum and wave goodbye to exam woe...

Here's a handy mnemonic for the order of EM waves: 'Rock Music Is Very Useful for eXperiments with Goats'.

Q1   Put the following in order of increasing wavelength: microwaves, X-rays, visible light.   [1 mark]

Q2   Give one way in which gamma rays can be produced.   [1 mark]

Energy Levels and Ionisation

Some electromagnetic radiation can have <u>dangerous</u> effects on humans. Don't worry though, it's not all bad.

Electrons Can be Excited to Higher Energy Levels

1) <u>Electrons</u> in an atom (or molecule) sit in <u>different energy levels</u> or shells (see p.205). Each <u>energy level</u> is a different distance from the <u>nucleus</u>.

2) An electron can <u>move up</u> one or more energy levels in one go if it <u>absorbs</u> <u>electromagnetic (EM) radiation</u> with the right amount of <u>energy</u>. When it does move up, it moves to a <u>partially filled</u> (or <u>empty</u>) <u>shell</u> and is said to be '<u>excited</u>'.

3) The electron will then <u>fall back</u> to its <u>original energy level</u>, and in doing so will <u>lose</u> the <u>same amount</u> of <u>energy</u> it <u>absorbed</u>. The energy is <u>carried away</u> by EM radiation.

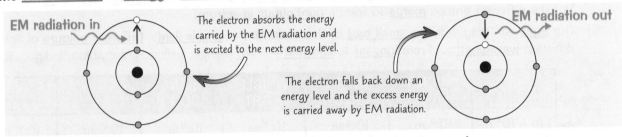

EM radiation in — The electron absorbs the energy carried by the EM radiation and is excited to the next energy level.

EM radiation out — The electron falls back down an energy level and the excess energy is carried away by EM radiation.

4) <u>Visible light</u>, <u>ultraviolet light</u> and <u>X-rays</u> are all created when atoms <u>lose energy</u> by an electron dropping <u>down</u> an energy level and emitting energy in the form of <u>EM radiation</u>.

5) The part of the <u>EM spectrum</u> the radiation is from depends on its <u>energy</u> (which depends on <u>the energy levels</u> the electron moves between). A <u>higher energy</u> means a <u>higher frequency</u> of EM radiation — which is more <u>dangerous</u> for humans.

An Atom is Ionised if it Loses an Electron

1) If an <u>outer electron</u> absorbs radiation with <u>enough energy</u>, it can move <u>so far</u> that it <u>leaves the atom</u> (or <u>molecule</u>). It is now a <u>free electron</u> and the atom is said to have been <u>ionised</u>.

2) The atom is now a <u>positive ion</u>. It's <u>positive</u> because it now consists of <u>more protons</u> than <u>electrons</u>. The positive ion can go on to take part in <u>other chemical reactions</u>.

3) Atoms can lose <u>more than one electron</u>. The <u>more</u> electrons it loses, the <u>greater</u> its positive charge.

Ionising Radiation Harms Living Cells

1) <u>Gamma rays</u>, <u>high-energy ultraviolet</u> and <u>X-rays</u> are types of <u>ionising radiation</u> — they carry enough energy to <u>knock electrons off some atoms and molecules</u>.

2) <u>High amounts</u> of <u>exposure</u> to ionising radiation is <u>dangerous</u> as ionised atoms or molecules can go on to <u>react further</u> causing <u>cell damage</u> and possible <u>cell destruction</u>. <u>Lower amounts</u> of <u>exposure</u> can <u>change</u> cells making them more likely to grow in an <u>uncontrolled way</u>, possibly <u>leading to cancer</u>.

- <u>Ultraviolet (UV)</u> is <u>absorbed</u> by the skin, where it can cause <u>damage</u> to <u>cells</u>, possibly leading to <u>skin cancer</u>. It can also damage your <u>eyes</u> and possibly even cause <u>blindness</u>.

- <u>X-rays</u> and <u>gamma rays</u> can cause mutations and damage cells too (which can lead to cancer). They can be very dangerous as they transfer <u>a lot of energy</u> and are <u>penetrating</u> — they pass through the skin and are absorbed by <u>deeper tissues</u>.

Page 209 has more on the effects of ionising radiation on living cells.

3) <u>Low energy</u> waves like <u>radio waves</u> are transmitted through the body <u>without</u> being <u>absorbed</u>.

What's an atom's favourite chore? Ioning...

So some types of EM radiation are really scary. However, other types are totally safe. It depends on their energy.

Q1 Describe how the absorption of radiation can affect the arrangement of electrons in an atom. [1 mark]

Q2 Explain why exposure to gamma radiation can lead to cancer. [2 marks]

Uses of EM Radiation

How EM waves <u>behave</u> in materials varies, which means we use <u>different types</u> of EM waves in <u>different ways</u>...

Radio Waves are used for Communications

We use <u>radio waves</u> to <u>transmit information</u> like <u>television</u> and <u>radio shows</u> from one place to another:

1) Radio waves and all EM waves are just <u>oscillating electric and magnetic fields</u> (p.178).
2) <u>Alternating currents</u> (a.c.) in electrical circuits cause <u>charges to oscillate</u>. This creates an <u>oscillating electric and magnetic field</u> — an EM wave.
   There's more on a.c. on p.168.
3) This EM wave will have the <u>same frequency</u> as the current that created it. So a current with a frequency corresponding to the <u>radio wave</u> part of the spectrum is used so that <u>radio waves</u> are produced.
4) EM waves also <u>cause</u> charged particles in a conductor to oscillate. If the charged particles are part of a <u>circuit</u>, this <u>induces</u> an <u>alternating current</u> of the same frequency as the EM wave that induced it.
5) So if you've got a <u>transmitter</u> and a <u>receiver</u>, you can <u>encode information</u> (e.g. a TV show) in an a.c. and then <u>transmit</u> it as a radio wave. The wave <u>induces</u> an a.c. in the receiver (e.g. the aerial) and bam, you've got your information.

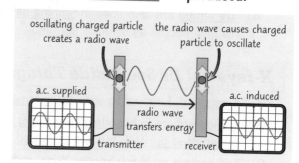

Microwaves are Used for Communications and Cooking

1) Communication to and from <u>satellites</u> (including <u>satellite TV</u> signals and <u>mobile phones</u>) uses <u>microwaves</u> with a wavelength that can <u>pass easily</u> through the Earth's <u>watery atmosphere</u>.
2) We also use microwaves of a <u>slightly different wavelength</u> to <u>cook food</u>. These microwaves penetrate up to a few centimetres into the food before being <u>absorbed</u> and <u>transferring</u> energy to <u>water molecules</u> in the food, causing the water to <u>heat up</u>. The water molecules then <u>transfer</u> this energy to the rest of the molecules in the food <u>by heating</u> — which <u>quickly cooks</u> the food.

Infrared Radiation Can be Used to Increase or Monitor Temperature

1) <u>Infrared</u> (IR) radiation is <u>given off</u> by all <u>objects</u>. The <u>hotter</u> the object, the <u>more</u> it gives off (see p.159).
2) <u>Infrared cameras</u> can detect IR radiation and <u>monitor temperature</u>. They <u>detect</u> the IR and turn it into an <u>electrical signal</u>, which is <u>displayed on a screen</u> as a picture. The <u>hotter</u> an object is, the <u>brighter</u> it appears. E.g. IR is used in <u>night-vision</u> cameras.

3) <u>Absorbing</u> IR radiation also causes objects to get <u>hotter</u>. <u>Food</u> can be <u>cooked</u> using IR radiation — the <u>temperature</u> of the food increases when it <u>absorbs</u> IR radiation, e.g. from a toaster's heating element.

Light Signals Can Travel Through Optical Fibres

1) <u>Light</u> is used to <u>look at things</u> (and to take endless selfies and holiday snaps). But it's also used for <u>communication</u> using <u>optical fibres</u>, which carry <u>data</u> over long distances as <u>pulses</u> of <u>light</u>.

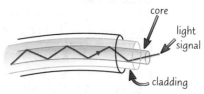

2) Optical fibres work by <u>bouncing light</u> off the sides of a very narrow <u>core</u>. The pulse of light <u>enters the core</u> at a <u>certain angle</u> at one end and is reflected <u>again and again</u> until it emerges at the other end.
3) Optical fibres are used for <u>telephone</u> and <u>internet cables</u>. They're also used for <u>medical</u> purposes to <u>see inside</u> the body — only a <u>small hole</u> is needed for the optical fibre (and any instruments) to enter the body, which is better than having <u>more major surgery</u>.
   IR can be used in optical fibres too.

Or you could just stream the radio over the Internet...

EM waves are ace — it's the difference in how they behave at boundaries that means they're suited to varied uses.

Q1 Explain how an alternating current in a transmitter produces a radio wave. [2 marks]

More Uses of EM Radiation

If you enjoyed the last page, you're in for a <u>real treat</u>. If not, well, you've just got to suck it up.

Ultraviolet is Used in Fluorescent Lamps

1) <u>Fluorescence</u> is a property of certain chemicals, where <u>ultraviolet</u> (<u>UV</u>) radiation is <u>absorbed</u> and then <u>visible light</u> is <u>emitted</u>. That's why fluorescent colours look so <u>bright</u> — they actually <u>emit light</u>.

2) <u>Fluorescent lights</u> use UV radiation to <u>emit</u> visible light. They're <u>energy-efficient</u> (p.164) so they're good to use when light is needed for <u>long periods</u> (like in your <u>classroom</u>).

3) <u>Security pens</u> can be used to <u>mark</u> property (e.g. laptops). <u>UV light</u> causes the ink to <u>fluoresce</u> (emit visible light), but the ink remains <u>invisible</u> in visible light.

4) <u>UV lamps</u> are also used in <u>tanning salons</u> to give people an artificial <u>suntan</u>.

Skin produces a brown pigment melanin in response to UV radiation — melanin absorbs UV radiation and protects the cells from damage.

X-rays Let Us See Inside Things

1) <u>X-rays</u> can be used to view the <u>internal structure</u> of <u>objects</u> and <u>materials</u>, including our <u>bodies</u>.

2) <u>Radiographers</u> in <u>hospitals</u> take <u>X-ray images</u> to help doctors diagnose <u>broken bones</u> — X-rays are <u>transmitted by flesh</u> but are <u>absorbed</u> by <u>denser material</u> like <u>bones</u> or metal.

3) To produce an <u>X-ray image</u>, X-ray radiation is directed <u>through the object</u> or <u>body</u> onto a <u>detector plate</u>. The <u>brighter bits</u> of the image are where <u>fewer X-rays</u> get through, producing a <u>negative image</u> (the plate starts off <u>all white</u>).

4) Exposure to X-rays can cause <u>cell damage</u> (p.209), so radiographers and patients are <u>protected</u> as much as possible, e.g. by <u>lead aprons</u> and <u>shields</u>, and exposure to the radiation is kept to a <u>minimum</u>.

Gamma Rays are Used for Sterilising Things

1) <u>Gamma rays</u> are used to <u>sterilise</u> medical instruments. If they're <u>absorbed</u> by microbes (e.g. bacteria), they <u>kill</u> them. They also <u>pass through</u> the instruments to reach any microbes hiding in crevices.

2) This is better than trying to <u>boil</u> plastic instruments, which might be <u>damaged</u> by high temperatures.

3) <u>Food</u> can be <u>sterilised</u> in the same way — again <u>killing microbes</u>. This keeps the food <u>fresh for longer</u>, without having to freeze it, cook it or preserve it some other way, and it's <u>perfectly safe</u> to eat.

4) Gamma radiation is also used in <u>cancer treatments</u> (p.210) — radiation is targeted at cancer cells to <u>kill them</u>. Doctors have to be careful to <u>minimise</u> the damage to <u>healthy cells</u> when treating cancer like this.

5) We also use gamma radiation in <u>medical imaging</u> (see p.210).

The Risks and Benefits of Technology Must be Evaluated

1) <u>Technology</u> has been (and continues to be) <u>developed</u> to make use of <u>every part</u> of the electromagnetic spectrum. However useful EM waves might be, they can also be <u>dangerous</u> — the <u>risks</u> involved with using them <u>need to be considered</u>.

> For example, <u>X-rays</u> were used in some <u>airport body scanners</u> that were intended to improve airport security. They were initially considered <u>safe</u> as the radiation dose from them <u>should be</u> very low. However, some scientists have <u>claimed</u> that they <u>do</u> increase the risk of <u>cancer</u>. This has contributed to that type of scanner being <u>banned</u> in many countries.

2) People often have different <u>opinions</u> about the use of <u>new technologies</u>. However, <u>decisions</u> about whether or not to use new technology need to be justified with <u>data</u> and <u>scientific explanation</u>, rather than opinion.

Phones, lights, sterilisation — what can't EM radiation do?

You've probably got the idea now that we use EM waves an awful lot — much more than the examples on the last couple of pages even. If you get asked about an example you haven't come across before in the exam, don't panic — just apply what you do know about the electromagnetic spectrum and you'll be fine.

Q1 Give two uses of gamma rays. [2 marks]

Absorbing and Emitting Radiation

All objects, including yourself, emit and absorb radiation constantly. No wonder I'm so tired all the time...

All Objects Emit Radiation

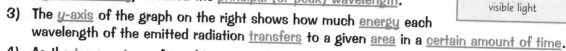

1) All objects emit electromagnetic (EM) radiation over a continuous range of wavelengths (and so over a range of frequencies).

2) The intensity (power per unit area) and wavelength (or frequency) distribution of radiation emitted depends on the object's temperature. The wavelength of radiation the object emits most of (i.e. has the highest intensity) is called the principal (or peak) wavelength.

3) The y-axis of the graph on the right shows how much energy each wavelength of the emitted radiation transfers to a given area in a certain amount of time.

4) As the temperature of an object increases, the intensity of every emitted wavelength increases.

5) However, the intensity increases more for shorter wavelengths than longer wavelengths (because shorter wavelengths of EM radiation transfer more energy, p.155). This causes the principal wavelength to decrease. So as objects get hotter, the principal wavelength gets shorter and the intensity-wavelength distribution becomes less symmetrical.

6) The principal frequency is the frequency of radiation that an object emits the most of. The principal frequency increases as the temperature of an object increases.

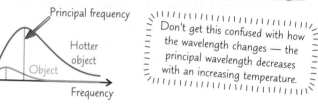

Don't get this confused with how the wavelength changes — the principal wavelength decreases with an increasing temperature.

Every Object Absorbs Radiation Too

As you saw above, all objects are continually emitting radiation, but they're also continually absorbing radiation too. The balance between absorbed and emitted radiation affects an object's temperature:

1) An object that's hotter than its surroundings emits more radiation than it absorbs. So over time, it cools down (like a cup of tea left on your desk).

2) An object that's cooler than its surroundings absorbs more radiation than it emits. Over time, the cool object warms up (e.g. ice cream on a hot day).

Hot objects give out more IR radiation than they absorb, so they cool down.

3) When an object emits the same amount of radiation as it absorbs, its temperature will stay the same.

Not all of the radiation hitting an object (incoming radiation) is absorbed — some is reflected away.

Radiation Affects the Earth's Temperature

1) The overall temperature of the Earth depends on the amount of radiation it reflects, absorbs and emits.

2) During the day, lots of EM radiation is transferred to the Earth from the Sun. The atmosphere allows some of it to pass through to be absorbed by the Earth's surface. This warms it and causes an increase in local temperature.

3) At night, less EM radiation is being absorbed than is being emitted, causing a decrease in the local temperature.

4) Overall, the temperature of the Earth stays fairly constant. This diagram shows the flow of EM radiation for the Earth.

5) Changes to the atmosphere can cause a change to the Earth's overall temperature — for example, global warming (see p.160).

Some radiation is reflected by the atmosphere, clouds and the Earth's surface.

The absorbed radiation is later emitted, some of which is absorbed by the atmosphere.

Space

Atmosphere

Earth's surface

Some radiation is absorbed by the atmosphere, clouds and the Earth's surface.

Don't let this get you hot under the collar...

The principal wavelength of radiation you emit is about 9.4×10^{-6} Hz — and you thought this page was dull...

Q1 The principal frequency of light from Star A is about 6×10^{14} Hz. The principal frequency of light from Star B is at about 3.5×10^{14} Hz. Which star is hotter? Explain your answer. [2 marks]

The Greenhouse Effect

Greenhouse gases are useful but can also cause <u>problems</u> — it's all about keeping a delicate <u>balance</u>.

Carbon Dioxide is one of the Main Greenhouse Gases

Greenhouse gases like <u>carbon dioxide</u> (CO_2), <u>methane</u> and <u>water vapour</u> trap radiation in the Earth's atmosphere — this, amongst other factors, allows the Earth to be <u>warm</u> enough to support <u>life</u>. Although CO_2 and methane are only present in <u>small amounts</u>, they have a large effect on the <u>temperature</u> of Earth:

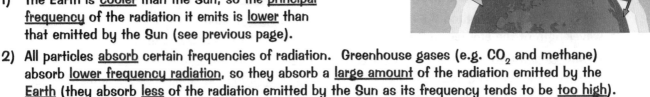

1) The Earth is <u>cooler</u> than the Sun, so the <u>principal</u> <u>frequency</u> of the radiation it emits is <u>lower</u> than that emitted by the Sun (see previous page).

2) All particles <u>absorb</u> certain frequencies of radiation. Greenhouse gases (e.g. CO_2 and methane) absorb <u>lower frequency radiation</u>, so they absorb a <u>large amount</u> of the radiation emitted by the <u>Earth</u> (they absorb <u>less</u> of the radiation emitted by the Sun as its frequency tends to be <u>too high</u>). The greenhouse gases then <u>re-emit</u> the radiation in <u>all directions</u> — including <u>back towards the Earth</u>.

3) The <u>more</u> greenhouse gases there are in the atmosphere, the <u>more</u> this happens. This is known as the <u>greenhouse effect</u> — it results in the Earth being <u>warmer</u> than it would otherwise be.

4) Some forms of <u>human activity</u> affect the amount of greenhouse gases in the atmosphere. E.g:

> • <u>Deforestation</u>: This is where humans <u>cut down</u> and <u>burn forests</u> to clear land, e.g. for farming. Fewer trees means less CO_2 is removed from the atmosphere.
>
> • Burning <u>fossil fuels</u> for energy (see p.165): carbon that was 'locked up' in these fuels is <u>released</u> as CO_2.
>
> • <u>Agriculture</u>: more <u>farm animals</u> produce more <u>methane</u> through their digestive processes.
>
> • <u>Creating waste</u>: more <u>landfill sites</u> and more waste from <u>agriculture</u> means more CO_2 and methane released as waste decays.

Increasing Carbon Dioxide is Linked to Climate Change

1) Over the last 200 years, the percentage of carbon dioxide in the atmosphere has <u>increased</u> — this is mainly due to an <u>increased burning of fossil fuels</u> as an energy source and <u>deforestation</u> by people.

2) The Earth's temperature varies naturally, but recently the average temperature of the Earth's surface has been <u>increasing</u>. Most scientists agree that the extra carbon dioxide from <u>human activity</u> is causing this increase — which is known as <u>global warming</u>.

3) Although most scientists also agree that global warming will lead to <u>climate change</u>, it's hard to <u>fully understand</u> the Earth's climate. This is because it's so <u>complex</u>, and there are so many <u>variables</u>, that it's very hard to make a <u>model</u> that isn't <u>oversimplified</u>.

4) However, the <u>computer models</u> that have been developed do show that <u>human activity</u> is <u>causing</u> global warming.

5) As more and more <u>data</u> is gathered using a large range of <u>technologies</u>, the models can be <u>refined</u> (made more accurate) and we can use them to make <u>better predictions</u>.

Eee, problems, problems — there's always summat goin' wrong...

Everyone's talking about climate change these days — and it might come up in the exam, so make sure you get it.

Q1 Give the names of three greenhouse gases present in the Earth's atmosphere. [3 marks]

Q2 Describe how human activities result in global warming. [4 marks]

Revision Questions for Chapter P1

Well, that wraps up <u>Chapter P1</u> — hopefully that got you warmed up. First chapter down, seven to go.

• Try these questions and <u>tick off each one</u> when you <u>get it right</u>.

• When you've done <u>all the questions</u> for a topic and are <u>completely happy</u> with it, tick off the topic.

Wave Basics (p.151-152) ☑

1) What is the amplitude, wavelength, frequency and period of a wave? ☑

2) What is the difference between a transverse wave and a longitudinal wave?
Give one example of each type of wave. ☑

3) State the wave speed equation. ☑

4) Describe an experiment to measure the speed of sound in air. ☑

5) Describe an experiment to measure the wavelength of a water wave. ☑

Reflection and Refraction Basics (p.153-154) ☑

6) What three things can happen to a wave when it hits a boundary between two different materials? ☑

7) Out of velocity, frequency and wavelength, which change when a wave refracts? ☑

8) Describe an experiment for investigating the reflection of light. ☑

Uses and Dangers of Electromagnetic Waves (p.155-160) ☑

9) Are EM waves transverse or longitudinal? ☑

10) List the waves in the EM spectrum, in order of increasing wavelength. ☑

11) What happens when an electron drops down an energy level? ☑

12) What is meant by ionising radiation? ☑

13) Give one use of each type of EM wave. ☑

14) Why does the local temperature of the Earth increase during the day but decrease at night? ☑

15) True or false? Only objects warmer than their surroundings emit infrared radiation. ☑

16) Compare the principal frequency of the radiation emitted by the Earth with that emitted by the Sun. ☑

17) Explain how the greenhouse effect keeps the Earth warm. ☑

18) State two ways in which human activity is leading to an increase in carbon dioxide in the atmosphere. ☑

Energy Stores and Transfers

Energy is <u>never used up</u>. Instead it's just <u>transferred</u> between different <u>energy stores</u> and different objects...

Energy is Transferred Between Stores

Energy can be held in a limited number of different <u>stores</u>. Here are the stores you need to learn:

1) <u>Thermal</u> energy stores
2) <u>Kinetic</u> energy stores — p.202
3) <u>Gravitational potential</u> energy stores — p.202
4) <u>Elastic</u> energy stores — p.218
5) <u>Chemical</u> energy stores
6) <u>Nuclear</u> energy stores

7) <u>Electromagnetic</u> energy stores — two objects will have energy in this store if they exert a magnetic force on each other.
8) <u>Electrostatic</u> energy stores — two objects will have energy in this store if they exert an electrostatic force on each other (see p.184).

<u>Energy is transferred</u> whenever a <u>system changes</u>. A <u>system</u> is just a fancy word for a <u>single</u> object (e.g. the air in a piston) or a <u>group</u> of <u>objects</u> (e.g. two colliding vehicles) that you're interested in. A system can be <u>changed</u> by <u>heating</u> or by <u>working</u>.

Energy can be Transferred by Heating...

Energy transfer <u>by heating</u> is where energy is transferred from a <u>hotter</u> region to a <u>colder</u> region. Energy can be transferred by heating in different ways:

- <u>Conduction</u> is where the <u>vibrating particles</u> of a substance transfer energy to <u>neighbouring particles</u>.
- <u>Convection</u> is where the energetic particles of a substance <u>move away</u> from <u>hotter to cooler</u> regions.

Energy can also be transferred by <u>radiation</u>, e.g. electromagnetic/sound <u>waves</u>. The energy is often transferred directly to <u>thermal energy stores</u>.

There's more about electromagnetic waves on p.155.

...or by Working

1) <u>Work done</u> is just another way of saying <u>energy transferred</u> — they're the <u>same thing</u>.
2) <u>Work</u> can be done <u>mechanically</u> (an object moving due to a <u>force</u> doing work on it, e.g. pushing, pulling or stretching) or <u>electrically</u> (a charge doing <u>electrical work</u> against resistance, e.g. charges moving round a circuit). For example:

> <u>A battery-operated heater</u> — energy is transferred <u>electrically</u> from the <u>chemical</u> energy store of the <u>battery</u> to the <u>thermal</u> energy store of the <u>electric heater</u>. This energy is then transferred to the <u>surroundings</u> by <u>heating</u>.

> A <u>motor</u> connected to the <u>mains</u> — in a <u>power station</u>, energy is transferred from the <u>chemical</u> energy store of the <u>fuel</u> to the <u>thermal</u> energy store of <u>water</u> in the boiler. This is then transferred to the <u>kinetic</u> energy stores of <u>turbines</u> and <u>generators</u> which produce electricity. Energy is transferred by the <u>electric current</u> (electrically) to the <u>kinetic</u> energy store of the <u>motor</u>.

There's more about the production of electricity on page 165.

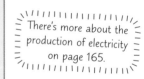

3) For both battery- and mains-operated devices (where the mains electricity has come from burning fossil fuels in a power station, see p.165), the <u>electric current</u> transfers energy from the <u>chemical energy store</u> of the fuel and <u>does work</u> on the device.
4) Transferring energy by <u>electricity</u> from a power station to consumers is <u>convenient</u> as it can travel over <u>long distances</u>. Electricity can be <u>used</u> in many ways, e.g. <u>driving motors</u> (which are used to lift or move objects) or <u>heating</u>.

All this work, I can feel my energy stores being drained...

Energy stores pop up everywhere in physics, the pesky scoundrels — make sure you've got to grips with them.

Q1   Describe the energy transfers that occur in a battery-operated motor.   [3 marks]

Conservation of Energy and Power

Repeat after me: energy is NEVER destroyed. Make sure you learn that fact, it's really important.

You Need to Know the Conservation of Energy Principle

1) The conservation of energy principle says that energy is always conserved:

> Energy can be transferred usefully, stored or dissipated, but can never be created or destroyed.

2) When energy is transferred between stores, not all of the energy is transferred usefully to the store you want. Some of the energy is dissipated (usually to the thermal energy stores of the surroundings).

3) Dissipated energy is sometimes called 'wasted energy' because the energy is being stored in a way that is not useful and that you can't access. Eventually, wasted energy ends up in thermal energy stores.

> A mobile phone is a system. When you charge the phone, energy is usefully transferred into the system to the chemical energy store of the phone's battery. But some of the energy is wasted to the thermal energy store of the phone (you may have noticed your phone feels warm if it's been charging).

4) You need to be able to describe energy transfers for closed systems (systems where neither matter nor energy can enter or leave). The net change in the total energy of a closed system is always zero.

> A cold spoon is dropped into an insulated flask of hot soup, which is then sealed. You can assume that the flask is a perfect thermal insulator so the spoon and the soup form a closed system. Energy is transferred from the thermal energy store of the soup to the useless thermal energy store of the spoon (causing the soup to cool down slightly). Energy transfers have occurred within the system, but no energy has left the system — so the net change in energy is zero.

Energy Transferred Depends on the Power

1) Power is the rate of energy transfer, i.e. how much energy is transferred between stores per second.

2) Domestic electrical appliances usually have power ratings. These are their maximum operating powers.

3) Devices with higher power ratings transfer more energy per second — e.g. a 1200 W heater will transfer twice as much energy per second than a 600 W heater. There's more on power on p.203.

4) The total energy transferred (work done) by an electrical appliance depends on its power rating and how long the appliance is on for.

Phenomenal cosmic power...

5) The amount of energy transferred electrically is given by:

$$\text{energy transferred (J)} = \text{power (W)} \times \text{time (s)} \qquad E = P \times t$$

6) Energy is usually given in joules, but for electrical devices you may also see it given in kilowatt-hours.

7) A kilowatt-hour (kWh) is the amount of energy a device with a power of 1 kW (1000 W) transfers in 1 hour of operation. It's much bigger than a joule, so it's useful for when you're dealing with large amounts of energy — 1 kWh is equal to 3 600 000 J.

8) To calculate the energy transferred in kWh, you need power in kilowatts, kW, and the time in hours, h.

9) Electricity bills are based on the number of kWh used by a household. You need to be able to calculate the cost of using an electrical device for a given amount of time:

1) Find the amount of energy transferred to the device in a certain amount of time in kWh.

2) The cost is usually given in pence per kilowatt-hour (p per kWh). So just multiply the cost per kWh by the number of kilowatt-hours used to find the total cost of running the device.

Energy can't be created or destroyed — only talked about a lot...

Make sure you get your head around kWh, they can be a bit tough until you've practised using them.

Q1   A motor transfers 4.8 kJ of energy in 2 minutes. Calculate its power in watts.   [3 marks]

Q2   A clothes dryer has a power rating of 4.0 kW. It takes 45 minutes to dry one load of clothes.
      The cost of electricity is 14p per kWh. Calculate the cost of drying one load of clothes.   [4 marks]

Efficiency and Sankey Diagrams

More! More! Tell me more about <u>energy transfers</u> please! Oh go on then, since you insist...

Most Energy Transfers Involve Some Energy Being Wasted

1) <u>No device</u> is 100% efficient — whenever <u>work is done</u>, some of the energy transferred is <u>always</u> wasted.

2) The <u>less energy</u> that is '<u>wasted</u>', the <u>more efficient</u> the device is said to be.

3) The efficiency for any energy transfer can be <u>worked out</u> using this equation:

$$\text{efficiency} = \frac{\text{useful energy transferred}}{\text{total energy transferred}}$$

You can give efficiency as a <u>decimal</u> or you can <u>multiply</u> your answer by 100 to get a <u>percentage</u>, i.e. <u>0.75</u> or <u>75%</u>.

EXAMPLE: A food blender is 70% efficient. 6000 J of energy is transferred to it. Calculate the useful energy transferred by the blender.

1) Change the <u>efficiency</u> from a <u>percentage</u> to a <u>decimal</u>. efficiency = 70% = 0.7

2) <u>Rearrange</u> the equation for <u>useful energy transferred</u>. useful energy transferred

3) <u>Stick in</u> the numbers you're given. = efficiency × total energy transferred
= 0.7 × 6000 = 4200 J

4) The <u>efficiency</u> of any energy transfer can be <u>increased</u> by <u>reducing unwanted energy transfers</u>.

5) You can increase the efficiency of a device (e.g. a motor) by <u>lubricating</u> it. You can also improve efficiency of a device by making them more <u>streamlined</u>. Both of these methods reduce unwanted energy transfers caused by <u>work done against frictional forces</u>.

<u>Reducing energy losses in buildings</u>

- Unwanted energy losses <u>by heating</u> can be reduced by using <u>thermal insulation</u>. E.g. <u>loft insulation</u>, <u>thick curtains</u> and <u>cavity walls with insulation</u> reduce <u>conduction and convection</u>. <u>Double glazed windows</u> and <u>hot water tank jackets</u> reduce <u>conduction</u> and <u>draught excluders</u> reduce <u>convection</u>.

- The <u>thickness and thermal conductivity</u> of (solid) walls also affects how <u>quickly</u> energy is <u>transferred</u> out of a building. The <u>thicker</u> the walls, the <u>lower</u> the <u>rate</u> of energy transfer. The <u>lower</u> the <u>thermal conductivity</u> of the material the walls are made from, the <u>lower</u> the rate of energy transfer. So <u>thick walls</u> with a <u>low</u> thermal conductivity <u>increase</u> the <u>time taken</u> for a building to <u>cool down</u>.

You can Use Sankey Diagrams to Show Efficiency

You can use a <u>Sankey diagram</u> like the one below. to show all the <u>energy transfers</u> made by a device. From it you can work out the <u>efficiency</u> of the device.

You can also sketch Sankey diagrams — where the width still represents the amount of energy transferred, but the diagram isn't to scale.

<u>Diagram for an electric motor with 80% efficiency:</u>

In this diagram, the <u>width</u> of <u>one square</u> on the grid represents <u>20 J</u>. The <u>thickness</u> of the arrows represents how much energy is being transferred. The <u>length</u> has nothing to do with it.

The total energy transferred by the motor equals the sum of the energy transferred to useful and wasted stores because energy is always conserved (p.163).

Total energy transferred by motor = 100 J

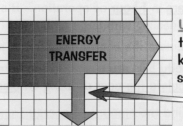

ENERGY TRANSFER

<u>Useful</u> energy transferred to kinetic energy stores = 80 J

Here, the wasted energy splits off.

Energy <u>wasted</u> to thermal energy stores (dissipated to the surroundings) = 20 J

Don't waste your energy — turn the TV off while you revise...

Unwanted energy transfers can cost you a lot in energy bills — that's why so many people invest in home insulation.

Q1 A motor in a remote-controlled car transfers 300 J of energy to the car's energy stores. 225 J is transferred to the car's kinetic energy stores. The rest is transferred to its thermal energy store. Calculate the efficiency of the motor. Give your answer as a percentage. [3 marks]

Energy Resources

We use <u>A LOT</u> of electricity (just look around you) — the energy to power it all has to come from <u>somewhere</u>.

Energy Resources Can Either be Renewable or Non-Renewable

1) We get <u>most</u> of our energy from <u>non-renewable</u> resources — resources that will <u>run out</u> one day.

2) The main non-renewable energy resources on Earth are the three <u>fossil fuels</u> (<u>coal</u>, <u>oil</u> and <u>gas</u>) and <u>nuclear fuels</u> (<u>uranium</u> and <u>plutonium</u>).

Peat (a biofuel made of decayed plants) is sometimes called a non-renewable resource too, because it can't be quickly replaced.

3) One of the <u>advantages</u> of using these energy resources is that <u>they're reliable</u>. There's enough <u>fossil</u> and <u>nuclear fuels</u> to meet <u>current demand</u>, and they are extracted from the Earth at a <u>fast enough rate</u> that power stations always have fuel in stock. This means non-renewable power stations can respond <u>quickly</u> to <u>changes in demand</u>.

4) One of the <u>disadvantages</u> of fossil fuels is they <u>damage the environment</u> when they're being used:
   - Coal, oil and gas release CO_2 into the atmosphere when they're <u>burned</u>. All this CO_2 adds to the <u>greenhouse effect</u>, and contributes to <u>global warming</u> (p.160).
   - Burning coal and oil also releases <u>sulfur dioxide</u>, which causes <u>acid rain</u>.

Some environmental problems are unpredictable, e.g. oil spillages affect mammals and birds.

5) One of the main <u>issues</u> with using <u>nuclear fuel</u> is that <u>nuclear waste</u> releases radiation, which makes it <u>dangerous</u> and difficult to <u>dispose of</u> — see p.209.

1) A <u>renewable energy resource</u> is one that will <u>never run out</u>.

2) Most of them do <u>some damage to the environment</u>, but in <u>less nasty</u> ways than non-renewables.

3) They <u>don't</u> provide as much energy as <u>non-renewables</u> and the <u>weather-dependent</u> ones can be <u>unreliable</u>.

4) The main renewable resources are <u>biofuels</u>, <u>wind</u>, the <u>Sun</u>, <u>hydroelectricity</u> and the <u>tides</u>.

Most Power Stations Use Steam to Drive a Turbine

They said turbine, Dave.

The <u>set-up costs</u> for fossil fuel power stations is <u>high</u>, but the <u>running costs</u> are <u>low</u>. We currently generate most of our electricity using <u>steam-driven turbines</u> like this:

1) As the fossil fuel <u>burns</u> the <u>water</u> is heated.

2) The water <u>boils</u> to form <u>steam</u>, which moves and <u>turns</u> a <u>turbine</u>.

Boiler | steam | Turbine | Generator
Fuel | water | Grid

3) The turbine is connected to an <u>electrical generator</u>, which generates a <u>potential difference</u> across (and so a <u>current</u> through) a wire by spinning a <u>magnet</u> near to the <u>wire</u> (you don't need to know how this works).

Only solar power doesn't use a turbine and generator to generate electricity.

4) The current produced by the generator flows through the <u>national grid</u> (p.168).

A similar set-up is used for most <u>other types</u> of electricity generation as well. In <u>nuclear</u> power stations, energy from <u>nuclear fission</u> is used to heat the water. In <u>hydroelectric</u>, <u>tidal</u> and <u>wind</u> power, the turbine is turned <u>directly</u> without needing to heat water to form steam first.

Wind Power — Lots of Little Wind Turbines

1) Each wind turbine has a <u>generator</u> inside it. The rotating <u>blades</u> turn the generator and produce <u>electricity</u>.

2) They have quite a <u>high set-up cost</u> but <u>no fuel costs</u>.

3) There's <u>no pollution</u> (except for a little bit when they're manufactured).

4) But some people think they <u>spoil the view</u> and they can be <u>very noisy</u>, which can be annoying for people living nearby. However, they can be placed <u>offshore</u> which actually generates <u>more</u> energy.

5) They <u>only</u> work when it's <u>windy</u>, so you can't always <u>supply</u> electricity, or respond to <u>high demand</u>.

It all boils down to steam...

Power stations can be made into combined heat and power stations. As they create steam, some of the energy is wasted to surrounding thermal stores. This wasted energy can be used to heat a small number of nearby homes.

Q1 State two renewable energy resources. [2 marks]

Renewable Energy Resources

Renewable energy resources see (p.165) are generally <u>better for the environment</u>, but they all have <u>drawbacks</u>...

Solar Cells — Expensive but No Environmental Damage

Time to recharge.

1) <u>Solar power</u> is often used in <u>remote places</u> where there's not much choice (e.g. the Australian outback) and to power electric <u>road signs</u> and <u>satellites</u>.
2) <u>Initial costs</u> are <u>high</u> but after that the energy is <u>free</u> and <u>running costs almost nil</u>.
3) There's <u>no pollution</u> when they're being used. (Although they do use quite a lot of energy to make.)
4) Solar cells are mainly used to generate electricity on a relatively <u>small scale</u>, e.g. in <u>homes</u>.
5) Solar power is most suitable for <u>sunny countries</u>, but it can be used in <u>cloudy countries</u> like Britain.
6) And of course, you <u>can't</u> make solar power at <u>night</u> or <u>increase production</u> when there's extra demand.

Biofuels are Made from Plants and Waste

1) <u>Biofuels</u> can be made from many different things, from <u>farm waste</u>, <u>animal droppings</u> and <u>landfill rubbish</u> to <u>specially grown crops</u> (e.g. sugar cane, vegetable oils or trees).
2) They're renewable because we can just <u>grow more</u>.
3) They can be burnt to produce <u>electricity</u> or used to run <u>cars</u> in the same way as <u>fossil fuels</u>.
4) Burning them releases CO_2, but the plants you grow (either to burn or as animal feed) <u>remove CO_2</u> from the atmosphere (so there's <u>no net change</u> in the atmosphere). There's <u>debate</u> about whether there's no net change, as this only works if you keep growing plants at <u>at least the rate</u> that you're burning things.
5) Biofuels are fairly <u>reliable</u> as they can be generated fairly quickly and easily. But it's harder to respond to <u>immediate energy demands</u>, as crops <u>take time</u> to grow (you can <u>stockpile</u> biofuels to combat this).
6) The <u>cost</u> to make <u>biofuels</u> is <u>very high</u> and some worry that growing crops specifically for biofuels could lead to there not being enough <u>space</u> or <u>water</u> to grow enough crops for <u>food</u> for everyone.
7) In some places, large areas of <u>land</u> have been <u>cleared</u> to grow <u>biofuels</u>, resulting in species losing their <u>habitats</u>. The <u>decay</u> and <u>burning</u> of this vegetation also increases CO_2 and <u>methane</u> emissions.

Hydroelectricity — Building Dams and Flooding Valleys

1) <u>Producing hydroelectricity</u> usually involves <u>flooding</u> a <u>valley</u> by building a <u>big dam</u>.
2) <u>Water</u> is stored and allowed out <u>through turbines</u>.
3) There is a <u>big impact</u> on the <u>environment</u> due to the flooding of the valley and possible <u>loss of habitat</u> for some species.
4) A <u>big advantage</u> is <u>immediate response</u> to increased electricity demand — <u>more</u> water can be let out through the turbines to generate more electricity.
5) <u>Initial costs are often high</u> but there are <u>minimal running costs</u> and it's a <u>reliable</u> energy source.

> You might see hydroelectricity referred to as HEP — this just stands for <u>hydroelectric power</u>.

Tidal Barrages — Using the Sun and Moon's Gravity

1) <u>Tidal barrages</u> are <u>big dams</u> built across <u>river estuaries</u> with <u>turbines</u> in them.
2) As the <u>tide comes in</u> it fills up the estuary. The water is then let out <u>through turbines</u> at a set speed.
3) There is <u>no pollution</u> but they <u>affect boat access</u>, can <u>spoil the view</u> and they <u>alter the habitat</u> for wildlife, e.g. wading birds.
4) Tides are pretty <u>reliable</u> (they always happen twice a day). But the <u>height</u> is <u>variable</u> and tidal barrages don't work when the water <u>level</u> is the <u>same either side</u>.
5) Even though it can only be used in <u>some estuaries</u>, tidal barrages have <u>great potential</u> as an alternative to non-renewable energy sources.

Burning poo... lovely...

Make sure you can describe the energy resources above and the effect on the environment when using them.

Q1   Give one advantage and one disadvantage of generating electricity using solar power.   [2 marks]

Trends in Energy Use

Over time, the types of energy resources we use change. There are many reasons for this...

There are Disadvantages and Benefits for Each Energy Resource

1) The risks, drawbacks and benefits need to be weighed up when deciding the best energy resource to use.

2) Which resources are easily available, their cost and how reliably they can produce the energy we need must be considered, along with their environmental impact and any opportunities (e.g. jobs) they create.

3) Of course, everyone has different priorities and opinions. This means that there's often no 'right' answer — so decisions about which resources to use vary depending on the circumstances.

- For example, a government may think hydroelectric power (p.166) is a great, reliable and (relatively) environmentally-friendly way to generate electricity. But, if there's nowhere suitable to build a hydroelectric power station then they can't use it as an energy resource. Similarly, the high cost of building the power station may put them off — even if some people think it's worth the money.

- They may decide nuclear fuel is a good, clean and reliable energy resource to use. Setting up and shutting down a nuclear power station provides many jobs but is difficult and costly. Nuclear power also always carries the small risk of a major catastrophe, which can cause lots of debate — some say the benefits outweigh the risk, whilst others say the potential damage isn't worth it.

Our Energy Demands are Changing

1) The world demand for energy is continually increasing. This is down to the population increasing, technological advances (e.g. most homes and workplaces now have computers and electronic devices) and our lifestyles.

2) The growing demand raises questions over how we will be able to keep up with it — what the future availability of energy resources will be, and how sustainable the energy resources and the methods we use to generate electricity today are.

Sustainable energy resources are those that we can keep on using in the long term. Renewable resources tend to be sustainable as they won't run out and aren't usually too damaging to the environment.

3) Concerns about sustainability have led people to make changes in their everyday lives and to put pressure on their governments in order to cause national changes. This has led to countries creating targets for using renewable resources, which in turn puts pressure on other countries to do the same.

4) Research is being done to find new energy resources, as well as looking at improving the ways we use our current ones. The research into, and development of, new energy resources provides jobs, as does the building of any new power stations.

5) These factors have all led to an increase in the use of renewable energy resources.

Currently in the UK we mostly use fossil fuels for generating electricity, heating and transport, as they're relatively cheap, efficient and reliable. But we can't keep using them long-term — they're not sustainable. So slowly, the UK is trying to increase its use of more sustainable energy resources.

6) However, it's not something that will change overnight. Research and development takes time and money. Governments need to balance this investment against spending on other areas of national interest.

7) And just like many of our current energy resources, new energy resources may also bring with them new technological and environmental challenges as well as benefits.

For example, nuclear energy was first used to generate electricity in the 1950s. It took a long time to develop the technology to release energy from nuclear fuels using a nuclear reaction. It took even longer to develop the technology to house and control the nuclear reaction to make it safe enough to generate electricity. Even though nuclear fuel is now a relatively safe and reliable energy resource, it generates radioactive waste which is highly radioactive for a very long time. This could greatly damage the environment if not treated and stored correctly — an unforseen challenge when nuclear fuel was first proposed.

Going green is on-trend this season...

So energy demands are increasing, and the energy sources we're using are changing. Just not particularly quickly.

Q1   Suggest two reasons why a government may choose to invest in nuclear power.   [2 marks]

The National Grid

Once electricity has been produced using energy resources (p.165), it has to be transported to consumers (you).

Electricity is Distributed via the National Grid

1) The national grid is a giant web of wires and transformers (p.182) that covers the UK and connects power stations to consumers (anyone who is using electricity).

2) The national grid transfers energy electrically from power stations anywhere on the grid (the supply) to anywhere else on the grid where it's needed (the demand) — e.g. homes and industry.

3) Transformers (p.182) are used to increase the generated electricity to a very high potential difference (p.d.) before it is transmitted through the network of the national grid. Transferring electrical power at a very high p.d. helps to reduce energy losses (see p.182). The p.d. is then reduced by another transformer to a level that is safe for use before being supplied to homes and businesses.

Mains Supply is a.c., Battery Supply is d.c.

1) There are two types of electric current — alternating current (a.c.) and direct current (d.c.).

2) In a.c. supplies the current is constantly changing direction. Alternating currents are produced by alternating voltages in which the positive and negative ends of the potential difference keep alternating.

3) The UK domestic (mains) supply (the electricity in your home) is an a.c. supply at around 230 V.

4) The frequency of the a.c. mains supply is 50 cycles per second or 50 Hz.

5) By contrast, cells and batteries supply direct current (d.c.).

6) Direct current is a current that is always flowing in the same direction. It's created by a direct voltage (remember — voltage is the same as p.d., p.170). This voltage is usually smoothed out to provide a straight line on a graph of p.d. (voltage) against time.

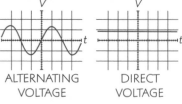

ALTERNATING VOLTAGE   DIRECT VOLTAGE

Most Plugs Contain Three Wires

Mains appliances usually have a 3-core cable, which contains three wires.

1) **LIVE WIRE — brown.**
The live wire carries the voltage (potential difference, p.d.). It alternates between a high positive and negative voltage of about 230 V.

2) **NEUTRAL WIRE — blue.**
The neutral wire completes the circuit — electricity normally flows in through the live wire and out through the neutral wire. The neutral wire is always at 0 V.

3) **EARTH WIRE — green and yellow.**
The earth wire is for safety. It carries the current away if something goes wrong. It's also at 0 V.

1) The p.d. between the live wire and the neutral wire equals the supply p.d. (230 V for the mains).

2) The p.d. between the live wire and the earth wire is also 230 V for a mains-connected appliance.

3) There is no p.d. between the neutral wire and the earth wire — they're both at 0 V.

4) Your body is an example of an earthed conductor, and is also at 0 V. This means if you touched the live wire, there'd be a large p.d. across your body and a current would flow through you. This large electric shock could injure or even kill you.

5) Even if a plug socket is off (i.e. the switch is open) there is still a danger you could get an electric shock. A current isn't flowing, but there is still a p.d. in the live part of the socket, so your body could provide a link between the supply and the earth if you made contact with it.

Why are earth wires green and yellow — when mud is brown..?

Make sure you can explain why touching a live wire is dangerous. It's all to do with our old pal, potential difference.

Q1   Explain the difference between alternating current and direct current.   [2 marks]

Q2   State the potential difference of the live, neutral and earth wires in an appliance.   [3 marks]

Revision Questions for Chapter P2

Hope you've still got some energy left to have a go at these revision questions to see what you've learnt.

• Try these questions and tick off each one when you get it right.
• When you've done all the questions for a topic and are completely happy with it, tick off the topic.

Energy Stores, Energy Transfers and Efficiency (p.162-164) ☑

1) Name the eight energy stores.
2) How can energy be transferred between stores?
3) Why is transferring energy by electricity convenient?
4) State the conservation of energy principle.
5) What does 'dissipated energy' mean?
6) True or false? The net change in the total energy of a closed system is always zero.
7) What does the power rating of an electrical appliance describe?
8) Write down the equation that links energy transferred, power and time.
9) What is a kilowatt-hour (kWh)?
10) In which energy store does wasted energy eventually end up?
11) What is the equation for calculating the efficiency of an energy transfer?
12) How can you reduce unwanted energy transfers in a motor?
13) True or false? Thicker walls make a house cool down quicker.
14) What does the thickness of an arrow in a Sankey diagram represent?

Energy Sources and Trends in their Use (p.165-167) ☑

15) Name four renewable energy resources and four non-renewable energy resources.
16) What is the difference between renewable and non-renewable energy resources?
17) Give three disadvantages of using fossil fuels. Suggest a way to reduce their negative impact.
18) Give one advantage and one disadvantage of using nuclear power.
19) Explain how a power station uses fossil fuels to produce electricity.
20) Give two advantages and two disadvantages of solar power and wind power.
21) Describe the benefits and drawbacks of using biofuels.
22) True or false? Tidal barrages are useful for storing energy to be used during times of high demand.
23) Compare the reliability of hydroelectricity and tidal barrages.
24) Describe how the energy usage in the UK has changed over recent years.
25) Suggest one reason why this change has occurred.
26) Explain why the UK plans to use more renewable energy resources in the future.

The National Grid (p.168) ☑

27) What is the national grid?
28) State the frequency and potential difference of the UK mains supply.
29) True or false? The UK mains supply is a direct current.
30) What type of current do batteries supply?
31) What is meant by a direct current?
32) State the colours of the live, neutral and earth wires in a plug.
33) Why is it dangerous to provide a link between the live wire and the ground?

Circuits — The Basics

It's pretty bad news if the word <u>current</u> makes you think of delicious cakes instead of physics. Learn what it means, as well as some handy <u>symbols</u> to show items like <u>batteries</u> and <u>switches</u> in a circuit.

Current can Only Flow Round a Closed Circuit

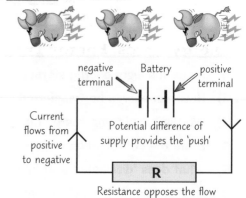

1) <u>Electric current</u> is the rate of flow of <u>electrical charge</u>. Electrical charge will <u>only flow</u> if a circuit is closed (a complete loop) and if there's a source of potential difference, e.g. a battery. The unit of current is the <u>ampere</u>, A.

2) In a <u>single</u>, closed <u>loop</u> (like the one on the right) the current has the same value <u>everywhere</u> in the circuit (see p.175).

3) <u>Potential difference</u> (or voltage) is the <u>driving force</u> that <u>pushes</u> the charge round. Its unit is the <u>volt</u>, V.

4) <u>Resistance</u> is anything that <u>resists</u> the <u>flow of charge</u>. <u>All</u> circuit components have a <u>resistance</u>, but you can usually <u>ignore</u> the resistance from <u>wires</u> connecting components as it's so small. Unit: <u>ohm</u>, Ω.

5) Resistance, current and potential difference are all <u>related</u> — if one of them <u>changes</u>, at least one of the others must <u>change too</u> (in fact there's an equation that links them, see the next page).

6) If the <u>potential difference</u> (p.d.) of a circuit is <u>increased</u> whilst the <u>resistance</u> of the circuit <u>stays the same</u>, then the <u>current will increase</u>. If the <u>resistance</u> of a circuit is <u>increased</u> whilst the <u>potential difference stays the same</u>, the <u>current</u> will <u>decrease</u>.

> You can think of an <u>electric circuit</u> as being like a set of <u>pipes</u>. The <u>current</u> is the <u>rate of flow of water</u> around the pipes and the <u>p.d.</u> is the <u>water pump</u> pushing the water around. <u>Resistance</u> is any sort of <u>narrowing</u> of the pipes which the water pressure has to <u>work against</u>. If you turn up the <u>pump</u>, more <u>force</u> is provided and the flow is <u>increased</u>. If you add more <u>narrow sections</u>, the flow <u>decreases</u>.

7) Charges going round a circuit flow in a <u>continuous loop</u>. They are <u>not used up</u>, but transfer energy to components as they do <u>work</u> (p.174).

8) <u>Metal conductors</u> (e.g. components and wires) have <u>lots of charges</u> that are free to move. A <u>battery</u> (or other p.d. source) in a circuit is what <u>causes</u> these charges to flow.

Total Charge Through a Circuit Depends on Current and Time

1) You can find the amount of <u>charge</u> that has flowed through a component in a <u>given time</u> using:

> charge (coloumbs, C) = current (A) × time (s)

2) So <u>more charge</u> passes around a circuit every second when a <u>larger current</u> flows.

Circuit Symbols You Should Know

There's more about a.c. and d.c. on p.168.

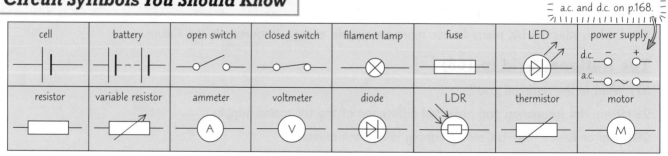

cell	battery	open switch	closed switch	filament lamp	fuse	LED	power supply
resistor	variable resistor	ammeter	voltmeter	diode	LDR	thermistor	motor

I think it's about time you took charge...

You've no doubt seen some of those circuit symbols before, but take a good look at all of them and practise drawing them. It's no good if you get asked to draw a circuit diagram and you can't tell a resistor from a thermistor.

Q1   A laptop charger passes a current of 8.0 A through a laptop battery. Calculate how long the charger needs to be connected to the battery for 28 800 C of charge to be transferred to the laptop.   [2 marks]

Resistance and $V = I \times R$

Ooh experiments, you've gotta love 'em. Here's a <u>simple experiment</u> for investigating resistance.

There's a Formula Linking Potential Difference and Current

<u>Current</u>, <u>potential difference</u> (p.d.) and <u>resistance</u> are all linked by this simple <u>formula</u>:

| potential difference (V) = current (A) × resistance (Ω) | $V = IR$ |

You can use this equation for <u>whole circuits</u> or <u>individual components</u>.

You Can Investigate the Factors Affecting Resistance   PRACTICAL

The <u>resistance</u> of a component can depend on a number of factors. One thing you can easily investigate is how the <u>length of a wire</u> affects its resistance. You can do this using the set up shown on the right, which you need to be able to draw the <u>circuit diagram</u> for.

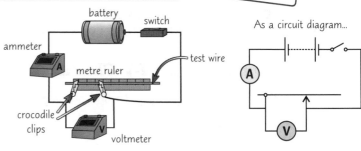

The circuit contains:

- <u>Ammeter</u> — this measures the <u>current</u> (in amps) flowing through the test wire. It can be put <u>anywhere</u> in the <u>main circuit</u> — but it must be placed <u>in series</u> (p.175) with the test wire, <u>never</u> in <u>parallel</u>.
- <u>Voltmeter</u> — this measures the <u>potential difference</u> across the test wire (in volts). It must be placed <u>in parallel</u> (p.176) with the <u>wire</u>, <u>NOT</u> any other bit of the circuit, e.g. the battery.

1) Attach a <u>crocodile clip</u> to the wire level with <u>0 cm</u> on the ruler.

2) Attach the <u>second crocodile clip</u> to the wire, e.g. 10 cm away from the first clip. Write down the <u>length</u> of the wire between the clips.

3) <u>Close the switch</u>, then record the <u>current</u> through the wire and the <u>p.d.</u> across it.

4) <u>Open the switch</u>, then move the second crocodile clip, e.g. another 10 cm, along the wire. Close the switch again, then record the <u>new length</u>, <u>current</u> and <u>p.d.</u>.

5) <u>Repeat</u> this for a number of <u>different lengths</u> of wire between the crocodile clips.

6) Use your measurements of current and p.d. to <u>calculate</u> the <u>resistance</u> for each length of wire, using $R = V \div I$ (from $V = IR$).

7) Plot a <u>graph</u> of <u>resistance</u> against <u>wire length</u> and draw a <u>line of best fit</u> (p.225).

8) You should find that the <u>longer the wire</u>, the <u>greater the resistance</u>.

9) Your graph should be a <u>straight line</u> through the <u>origin</u> — showing that resistance is <u>directly proportional</u> to length.

10) If your graph <u>doesn't</u> go through the origin, it could be because the <u>first clip</u> wasn't attached exactly at 0 cm, so all of your length readings are a <u>bit out</u>. This is a <u>systematic error</u> (p.224).

> A thin wire will give you the best results. Make sure it's as straight as possible so your length measurements are accurate.

> The wire may heat up during the experiment, which will affect its resistance. Leave the switch open for a bit between readings to let the circuit cool down.

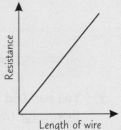

From your results you can also find the <u>resistance per unit length</u> of a wire. This is equal to the <u>gradient</u> of the graph shown above. You can use this to <u>estimate the resistance</u> of <u>any length</u> of the same wire (resistance = length × resistance per unit length).

Measure gymnastics — use a vaultmeter...

You could also investigate the effect of diameter or material on the resistance of a wire. What fun.

Q1   An appliance is connected to a 230 V source.
    Calculate the resistance of the appliance if a current of 5.0 A is flowing through it.   [2 marks]

Resistance and *I-V* Characteristics

And we're not done with the <u>experiments</u> just yet. Time to draw some sweet <u>I-V characteristics</u>...

Components are Either Linear or Non-Linear

1) The term '<u>I-V characteristic</u>' refers to a <u>graph</u> which shows how the <u>current</u> (*I*) flowing through a component changes as the <u>potential difference</u> (*V*) across it is increased.

2) *I-V* characteristics show how the <u>resistance</u> of the component changes with current. Since ***V = IR***, you can calculate the <u>resistance</u> at any <u>point</u> on an *I-V* characteristic by calculating <u>*R = V/I*</u>.

3) The <u>resistance</u> of some <u>conductors</u> remains <u>constant</u> (e.g. a <u>fixed resistor</u> at a <u>fixed temperature</u>), but the resistance of other components can <u>vary</u> (e.g. a <u>heating element</u> or a <u>filament lamp</u>).

4) <u>Linear</u> components have a <u>constant resistance</u>. Their *I-V* characteristic is a <u>straight line</u>.

5) <u>Non-linear</u> components have a <u>curved</u> *I-V* characteristic. Their resistance <u>changes</u> depending on the size of the <u>current</u> flowing through them.

You Need to Know Some I-V Characteristics

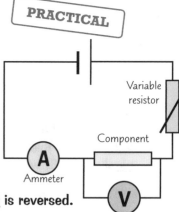

PRACTICAL

You can do the following <u>experiment</u> to find a component's <u>I-V characteristic</u>:

1) Set up the <u>test circuit</u> shown on the right.

2) Begin to vary the variable resistor. This alters the <u>current</u> flowing through the circuit and the <u>potential difference</u> across the <u>component</u>.

3) Take several <u>pairs of readings</u> from the <u>ammeter</u> and <u>voltmeter</u> to see how the <u>potential difference</u> across the component <u>varies</u> as the <u>current changes</u>. Repeat each reading twice more to get an <u>average</u> p.d. at each current.

4) <u>Swap</u> over the wires connected to the cell, so the <u>direction of the current</u> is reversed.

5) Repeat steps 2 and 3. <u>Plot a graph</u> of <u>current against voltage</u> for the component.

6) The *I-V* characteristics you get for <u>resistors</u>, a <u>filament lamp</u> and a <u>diode</u> should look like this:

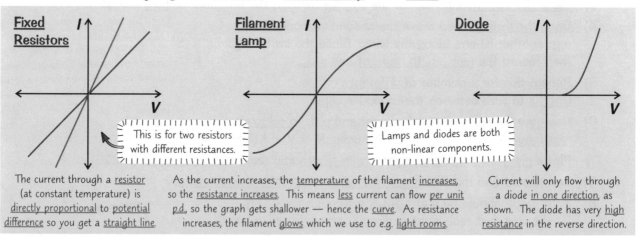

Fixed Resistors

This is for two resistors with different resistances.

The current through a <u>resistor</u> (at constant temperature) is <u>directly proportional</u> to <u>potential difference</u> so you get a <u>straight line</u>.

Filament Lamp

Lamps and diodes are both non-linear components.

As the current increases, the <u>temperature</u> of the filament <u>increases</u>, so the <u>resistance increases</u>. This means <u>less</u> current can flow per unit p.d., so the graph gets shallower — hence the <u>curve</u>. As resistance increases, the filament <u>glows</u> which we use to e.g. <u>light rooms</u>.

Diode

Current will only flow through a diode <u>in one direction</u>, as shown. The diode has very <u>high resistance</u> in the reverse direction.

7) You can find the *I-V* characteristics for an <u>LDR</u> and a <u>thermistor</u> (more about these on the next page).

8) In <u>constant conditions</u> (i.e. a constant <u>room temperature</u> or constant <u>light levels</u>) their *I-V* characteristics look like this:

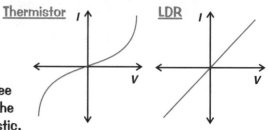

The resistance of a thermistor is dependent on its <u>temperature</u> (see p.173) — as the <u>current increases</u>, the thermistor <u>warms up</u>, so the <u>resistance decreases</u>, which is why it has a curved *I-V* characteristic.

In the end you'll have to learn this — resistance is futile...

Draw out those graphs and make sure you can tell whether they're showing a linear or non-linear component.

Q1 Draw the *I-V* characteristic for: a) an LDR in constant conditions b) a filament lamp. [2 marks]

Circuit Devices

Now it's time to see what <u>diodes</u>, <u>LDRs</u> and <u>thermistors</u> can do, and why they're so useful.

Current Only Flows in One Direction through a Diode

1) A diode is a special device made from <u>semiconductor</u> material such as <u>silicon</u>.

2) It lets current flow freely through it in <u>one direction</u>, but <u>not</u> in the other (i.e. there's a very high resistance in the <u>reverse</u> direction). This is shown by the <u>I-V characteristic</u> (see previous page).

3) This turns out to be really useful in various <u>electronic circuits</u>, e.g. in <u>radio receivers</u>. Diodes can also be used to get <u>direct current</u> from an <u>alternating</u> supply (see p.168).

current flows this way

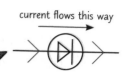

You can Use a d.c. Circuit to Test LDRs and Thermistors

1) The <u>resistance</u> of some resistors is <u>dependent</u> on the <u>environment</u>.

2) If you set up the <u>circuit</u> shown on the left, you can <u>change the environment</u> the resistor is in to see the <u>effect</u> on its <u>resistance</u>.

Direct current (d.c.) means the current always flows in the same direction.

resistor being tested

LDR Stands for Light-Dependent Resistor

1) An LDR is a resistor that's <u>dependent</u> on the <u>intensity</u> of <u>light</u>. At a <u>constant light level</u>, its <u>resistance</u> is <u>constant</u> (p.172).

2) In <u>darkness</u>, the resistance is <u>highest</u>. As light levels <u>increase</u> the resistance <u>falls</u> so (for a given p.d.) the <u>current</u> through the LDR <u>increases</u>.

3) You can <u>test</u> this by gradually <u>covering up</u> the surface of the LDR with a piece of thick paper.

4) They have lots of applications including <u>automatic night lights</u>, <u>outdoor lighting</u> and <u>burglar detectors</u>.

resistance

dark   light
light intensity

A Thermistor is a Type of Temperature-Dependent Resistor

1) In <u>hot</u> conditions, the resistance of a thermistor <u>drops</u>. In <u>cool</u> conditions, the resistance goes <u>up</u>.

You can test this by placing the thermistor into a <u>beaker of hot water</u> and taking measurements as the water cools down and the <u>temperature</u> of the thermistor <u>decreases</u>.

2) They're used as <u>temperature detectors</u>, in e.g. <u>thermostats</u>, <u>irons</u> and <u>car engines</u>.

resistance

cool   hot
temperature

You Can Use LDRs and Thermistors in Sensing Circuits

1) <u>Sensing circuits</u> can be used to <u>turn on</u> or <u>increase the power</u> to components depending on the <u>conditions</u> that they are in.

2) The circuit on the right is a <u>sensing circuit</u> in a room.

3) As the room gets hotter, the resistance of the thermistor <u>decreases</u> and it takes a <u>smaller share</u> of the p.d. from the power supply (take a look at page 175 as to why this happens). So the p.d. across the fixed resistor and the fan <u>rises</u>, making the fan go faster.

4) You can use a <u>similar</u> setup for a sensing circuit containing an LDR. You just have to connect the <u>component</u> (most likely a <u>bulb</u>) <u>across</u> the LDR.

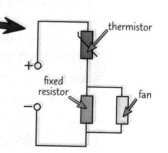

thermistor

fixed resistor   fan

Permistors — resistance decreases with curliness of hair...

Bonus fact — circuits like the ones above are called potential dividers (because they divide up p.d.).

Q1   Sketch a circuit that could be used to show how an LDR's resistance changes with light intensity. [2 marks]

Energy and Power in Circuits

All electrical devices <u>transfer energy</u> — their <u>power</u> is how <u>quickly</u> they do it.

Potential Difference is the Work Done Per Unit Charge

1) An electrical <u>current transfers energy</u> from a <u>power supply</u>, e.g. cells, batteries etc.

2) A <u>power supply</u> does <u>work</u> on a <u>charge</u> and so transfers <u>energy</u> to it.

3) <u>Charges transfer energy</u> to a <u>component</u> as they pass through it, by doing <u>work against</u> the <u>resistance</u> of the component.

> For example, in a handheld fan, energy is transferred <u>electrically</u> from the <u>battery's</u> <u>chemical energy store</u> to the <u>kinetic energy store</u> of the fan's <u>motor</u> — this is because a <u>current flows</u> and <u>does work</u> against the <u>resistance</u> of the <u>motor</u>.

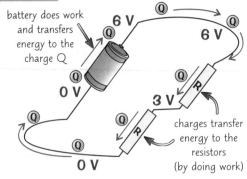

battery does work and transfers energy to the charge Q

charges transfer energy to the resistors (by doing work)

4) The <u>potential difference</u> between two points is equal to the <u>work done per unit charge</u> flowing between those two points. A power supply with a <u>bigger p.d.</u> will do <u>more work</u> on each charge, so it will transfer <u>more energy</u> to the circuit for every <u>coulomb</u> (unit) of charge which flows round it.

5) There's a simple <u>formula</u> which relates the <u>potential difference</u> (V) between <u>two points</u>, the <u>work done</u> (J) either <u>on</u> or <u>by</u> a charge passing between the points and the total <u>charge</u> (C) that passes:

> **potential difference = work done (energy transferred) ÷ charge**

6) The <u>energy transferred</u> to a <u>component</u> in an <u>electric circuit</u> is dependent on the <u>total amount of charge</u> that passes through the component and the <u>potential difference</u> across the component. It can be calculated using the formula:

> **energy transferred (work done) = charge × potential difference.**

These two equations are just the same equation rearranged.

Power is the Rate of Energy Transfer

1) Devices have <u>power ratings</u> (see p.163) which tell you the <u>rate</u> that energy is transferred <u>to them</u> from a <u>power supply</u>. Some of this energy will be transferred to the <u>surroundings</u> (see p.164).

The power rating of a device is actually the maximum power at which the device can operate, but you can usually assume that devices are operating at their maximum powers.

2) Power is measured in <u>watts</u>, <u>W</u> — <u>1 W = 1 J/s</u> (see p.203).

3) You can calculate the <u>power transfer</u> in a circuit device from the <u>amount of energy transferred</u> to the <u>device</u> in the circuit in a given amount of <u>time</u> using the formula:

> **power (W) = energy (J) ÷ time (s)** $P = E \div t$

4) The <u>higher</u> the <u>potential difference</u> across a component is, the <u>more energy</u> each charge passing through will have and the <u>faster</u> they will move (i.e. a higher current). This means there will be <u>more energy</u> transferred to the component in a <u>given time</u>, so its <u>power</u> will be <u>higher</u>. You can calculate the <u>power</u> of an electrical device using the potential difference <u>across the device</u> and the current <u>through it</u>:

> **power (W) = potential difference (V) × current (A)** $P = VI$

5) <u>Or</u> you can use the current through the device and its <u>resistance</u>:

> **power (W) = current² (A²) × resistance (Ω)** $P = I^2R$

This equation has come from substituting $V = IR$ (from p.171) into $P = VI$.

You have the power — now use your potential...

There are a lot of equations to get your head around — practise using them until you can remember them all.

Q1   A 1.5×10^3 W hairdryer is turned on for 11 minutes. Calculate the energy transferred.   [3 marks]

Series and Parallel Circuits

Ooh <u>series</u> and <u>parallel circuits</u> — my favourite. And soon to be yours too. Maybe.

Series and Parallel Circuits are *Connected Differently*

1) In <u>series circuits</u>, the different components are connected <u>in a line</u>, <u>end to end</u>, between the +ve and –ve terminals of the power supply.

2) Connecting <u>several cells</u> in <u>series</u>, <u>all the same way</u> (+ to –) gives a <u>bigger total p.d.</u> — because each charge in the circuit passes through each cell and gets a 'push' from each one. So <u>two 1.5 V</u> cells <u>in series</u> would supply <u>3 V in total</u>.

3) In <u>parallel circuits</u> (p.176) each branch is <u>separately</u> connected to the +ve and –ve terminals of the <u>supply</u>.

4) Parallel circuits are usually the most sensible way to connect things, for example in <u>cars</u> and in <u>household electrics</u>, where you have to be able to switch everything on and off <u>separately</u>.

5) <u>Connecting cells</u> in parallel <u>doesn't</u> increase the total p.d. as <u>each charge</u> will only get a 'push' from one of the cells. So <u>two 1.5 V</u> cells <u>in parallel</u> would supply <u>1.5 V in total</u>.

Series Circuits — *Everything in a Line*

Potential Difference is Shared

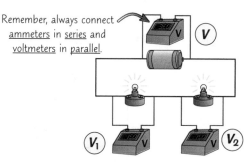

Remember, always connect <u>ammeters</u> in <u>series</u> and <u>voltmeters</u> in <u>parallel</u>.

1) In series circuits, the <u>total potential difference</u> (<u>p.d.</u>) of the <u>supply</u> is <u>shared</u> between the various <u>components</u>. So the <u>p.d.s</u> across the components in a series circuit always <u>add up</u> to equal the p.d. across the <u>power supply</u>: $V = V_1 + V_2$

2) This is because the <u>work done</u> by the <u>battery</u> on each unit of charge equals the <u>total work done</u> on the components by each unit of charge (p.174).

3) Work done and energy transferred are the same thing (see p.162), so the total <u>energy transferred</u> to the charges in the circuit by the <u>power supply</u> equals the total <u>energy transferred</u> from the charges to the <u>components</u> (p.174).

Current is the Same Everywhere

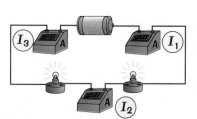

1) In a series circuit, <u>each charge</u> has to flow through <u>all</u> of the components to get round the circuit.

2) So the <u>same current</u> flows through <u>all parts</u> of the circuit: $I_1 = I_2 = I_3$

3) The <u>size</u> of the current is determined by the <u>total p.d.</u> of the power supply and the <u>net resistance</u> of the circuit, i.e. $I = V/R$ (p.171).

Resistance Adds Up

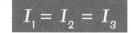

1) The resistance of <u>two</u> (or more) resistors in <u>series</u> is <u>bigger</u> than the resistance of just one of the resistors on its own. That's because the <u>battery</u> has to <u>push each charge</u> through <u>all</u> of them.

2) So the <u>net resistance</u> (R) of a series circuit is just the <u>sum</u> of the individual resistances: $R = R_1 + R_2 + R_3$

3) You might also see the net resistance called the <u>equivalent resistance</u> or the <u>effective resistance</u>.

I like series circuits so much I bought the box set...

If one of the bulbs in the diagrams above blew, it'd break the circuit, so they'd both go out. Sad times.

Q1   Calculate the net resistance of a series circuit containing three 2 Ω resistors.   [1 mark]

More on Series and Parallel Circuits

Move over series circuits, it's time for <u>parallel circuits</u> to have their say.

Parallel Circuits — Independence and Isolation

Potential Difference is the Same Across All Branches

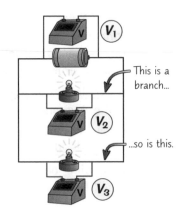

This is a branch...

...so is this.

1) In parallel circuits <u>all</u> branches have the <u>power supply p.d.</u> across them, so the p.d. is the <u>same</u> across all branches:

$$V_1 = V_2 = V_3$$

2) The <u>work done</u> (p.174) <u>per unit charge</u> in a branch is the <u>same for all branches</u> and is equal to the work done per unit charge <u>by the battery</u>.

3) This is because <u>each charge</u> can only pass down <u>one branch</u> of the circuit, so it must <u>transfer all the energy</u> supplied to it by the <u>source p.d.</u> to whatever's on that branch (see page 174).

Current is Shared Between Branches

1) In parallel circuits the <u>total current</u> flowing round the circuit equals the <u>total</u> of all the currents through the <u>separate branches</u>:

$$I = I_1 + I_2$$

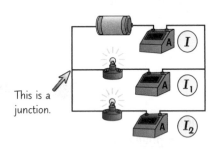

This is a junction.

2) In a parallel circuit, there are <u>junctions</u> where the current either <u>splits</u> or <u>rejoins</u>. The total current going <u>into</u> a junction has to equal the total current <u>leaving</u> it.

3) You can find the current in a branch using <u>$I = V/R$</u> (p.171), where V is the <u>p.d. across the branch</u> and R is the <u>net resistance</u> of the <u>branch</u>. All branches have the <u>same p.d.</u> as the battery across them — so the branch with the <u>lowest net resistance</u> will have the <u>largest current</u> flowing through it.

Resistance is Tricky

You <u>don't</u> need to be able to calculate the <u>net resistance</u> (see p.175) of a parallel circuit, just know that it <u>decreases</u> as you <u>add</u> resistors in parallel and why.

1) In the diagram opposite, when R_2 is added in <u>parallel</u> to R_1, the <u>charge flowing</u> round the circuit has <u>more than one</u> branch to take. This means <u>more</u> charge flows round the circuit in a <u>certain time</u> — i.e. there is a <u>higher total current</u>.

2) The p.d. of the circuit is the <u>same everywhere</u> (see above).

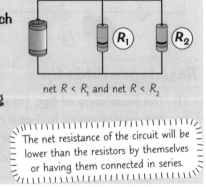

net $R < R_1$ and net $R < R_2$

3) The equation $R = V \div I$ (see page 171) shows that <u>increasing the current</u> through the circuit and keeping the <u>p.d. fixed</u> means that the <u>net resistance of the circuit</u> must <u>decrease</u>.

4) The <u>more</u> resistors added in parallel, the <u>higher</u> the current, so the <u>lower</u> the net resistance of the circuit.

The net resistance of the circuit will be lower than the resistors by themselves or having them connected in series.

After this page, your circuits knowledge will be unparalleled...

Remember, in parallel circuits, each branch has the same p.d., but the total current is shared between branches.

Q1   If 3 identical bulbs are connected in parallel to a 3.5 V battery, state the p.d. across each bulb.   [1 mark]

Investigating Series and Parallel Circuits

If you're not a fan of series and parallel circuits yet, this page is sure to <u>tickle your fancy</u>. Maybe.

Changing One Resistor Affects the Net Resistance of the Circuit

1) The <u>net resistance</u> of a circuit containing two or more components depends on the <u>resistance</u> of the components.

2) The resistance of some components <u>can change</u> (e.g. if it's a variable resistor, light-dependent resistor or thermistor). The <u>effect</u> this will have on the net resistance of the circuit depends on whether you're using a <u>series</u> or <u>parallel circuit</u>.

3) <u>Changing the resistance</u> of one component can also affect the <u>potential difference</u> and <u>current</u> within a circuit.

In series circuit

- For two components in series, the <u>bigger</u> the resistance of one of the components, the bigger its <u>share</u> of the <u>total p.d.</u> across it. This is because more <u>energy is</u> <u>transferred</u> from the charge when moving through a <u>large</u> resistance.

- So if the resistance of <u>one</u> component <u>changes</u>, the <u>potential difference</u> across all the components will <u>change</u>. The <u>net resistance</u> will also have changed, so the <u>current</u> through the components will <u>change too</u>.

Remember — the potential difference of the supply is shared out between the components in a series circuit (p.175) and is equal across parallel components in a parallel circuit.

In a parallel circuit

- For two components in a parallel circuit, if the resistance of <u>one</u> component <u>changes</u> then the current through <u>that branch</u> will <u>change</u>, but the current through the <u>other branches</u> and the <u>p.d.</u> across them will remain the <u>same</u>.

You Can Investigate Series and Parallel Circuits using Bulbs

PRACTICAL

1) Set up a <u>circuit</u> consisting of a <u>power supply</u> and a <u>bulb</u>. Use a <u>voltmeter</u> to measure the <u>p.d.</u> across the bulb, and an <u>ammeter</u> to measure the <u>current</u> in the circuit.

2) One at a time, add <u>identical bulbs</u> in <u>series</u>. Each time, measure the current through the circuit and the p.d. across each bulb. The bulbs should look <u>dimmer</u> each time.

3) You'll find that each time you <u>add a bulb</u>, the <u>p.d.</u> across each bulb <u>falls</u> — this is because the p.d.s across the bulbs in the circuit need to <u>add up</u> to the <u>source p.d.</u>.

4) The <u>current</u> also <u>falls</u> each time you add a bulb, because you're increasing the <u>resistance</u> of the circuit.

5) <u>Less current</u> and <u>less p.d.</u> means the bulbs get <u>dimmer</u> (the power of each bulb is decreasing — p.174).

6) Repeat the experiment, this time adding each bulb in <u>parallel</u> on a <u>new branch</u>. You'll need to measure the <u>current</u> on <u>each branch</u> each time you add a bulb.

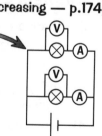

7) You should find that the bulbs <u>don't get dimmer</u> as you add more to the circuit.

8) The p.d. across <u>each bulb</u> is <u>equal</u> to the <u>source p.d.</u>, no matter the number of bulbs.

9) The <u>current</u> on each branch is <u>the same</u>, and <u>doesn't change</u> when you add more bulbs, because the resistance of and p.d. across each branch stays the same.

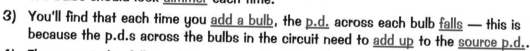

I can't resist a good practical...

Make sure you can explain the effects of changing a component's resistance, be it in a series or parallel circuit. This should include how it affects the net resistance of the circuit, the p.d. and the current.

Q1 Draw a diagram of a single circuit that could be used to investigate the effect of adding identical bulbs in parallel.

[2 marks]

Permanent and Induced Magnets

I think magnetism is an <u>attractive</u> subject, but don't get <u>repelled</u> by the exams — <u>revise</u>.

Magnets Produce Magnetic Fields

1) All magnets have <u>two poles</u> — <u>north</u> (or N-pole) and <u>south</u> (or S-pole).

2) All magnets produce a <u>magnetic field</u> — a region where <u>other magnets</u> or <u>magnetic materials</u> (e.g. iron, steel, nickel and cobalt) experience a <u>force</u>. This is the <u>magnetic effect</u> — a <u>non-contact force</u> that occurs due to interacting magnetic fields.

3) You can show a magnetic field by drawing <u>magnetic field lines</u>.

4) The lines always go from <u>north to south</u> and they show <u>which way</u> a force would act on a <u>north pole</u> of a small magnet if it was put at that point in the field.

5) The <u>closer together</u> the lines are, the <u>stronger</u> the magnetic field. The <u>further away</u> from a magnet you get, the <u>weaker</u> the field is.

6) The magnetic field is <u>strongest</u> at the <u>poles</u> of a magnet. This means that the <u>magnetic forces</u> are also <u>strongest</u> at the poles.

7) The force between a <u>magnet</u> and a <u>magnetic material</u> is <u>always attractive</u>, no matter the pole.

8) Between <u>two magnets</u> the force can be <u>attractive</u> or <u>repulsive</u>. Two poles that are the same (these are called <u>like poles</u>) will <u>repel</u> each other. Two <u>unlike</u> poles will <u>attract</u> each other.

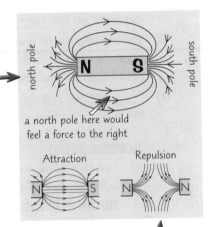

a north pole here would feel a force to the right

Attraction   Repulsion

Compasses Show the Directions of Magnetic Fields

1) Inside a compass is a tiny <u>bar magnet</u>. The <u>north</u> pole of this magnet is attracted to the south pole of any other magnet it is near. So the compass <u>points</u> in the direction of the magnetic field it is in.

2) You can move a compass around a magnet and <u>trace</u> its position on some paper to build up a picture of what the magnetic field <u>looks like</u>.

3) When they're not near a magnet, compasses always point <u>north</u>. This is because the <u>Earth</u> generates its own <u>magnetic field</u> (which looks a lot like the field of a <u>big bar magnet</u>). This is evidence that the <u>inside</u> (<u>core</u>) of the Earth must be <u>magnetic</u>.

The north pole of the magnet in the compass points along the field line towards the south pole of the bar magnet.

The <u>N-pole</u> of the compass is <u>attracted</u> towards the <u>Magnetic North Pole</u> — the <u>magnetic pole</u> near to the <u>geographic</u> North Pole. The Magnetic North Pole has a confusing name — it is actually a <u>magnetic south pole</u> but is called 'north' because it's close to <u>geographic north</u>. There's also a <u>magnetic north pole</u> near the <u>geographic South Pole</u>.

Magnets Can be Permanent or Induced

1) There are <u>two types</u> of magnet — <u>permanent</u> magnets and <u>induced</u> magnets.

2) <u>Permanent</u> magnets produce their <u>own</u> magnetic field.

3) <u>Induced</u> magnets are <u>magnetic materials</u> that <u>turn into</u> a magnet when they're put into a <u>magnetic field</u>.

4) When you <u>take away</u> the magnetic field, induced magnets quickly return to normal and <u>stop producing</u> a magnetic field (they <u>lose</u> their <u>magnetisation</u>).

magnetic material

The magnetic material becomes magnetised when it is brought near the bar magnet. It has its own poles and magnetic field:

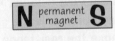 

induced poles

Magnets are like farmers — surrounded by fields...

Magnetism can get quite tough quite quickly. Learn these basics — you'll need them for the rest of the chapter.

Q1   State where the magnetic field produced by a bar magnet is strongest.   [1 mark]

Q2   Give two differences between permanent and induced magnets.   [2 marks]

Electromagnetism

On this page you'll see that a <u>magnetic field</u> is also found around a <u>wire</u> that has a <u>current</u> passing through it.

A Moving Charge Creates a Magnetic Effect

1) When a <u>current flows</u> through a <u>wire</u>, a <u>magnetic field</u> is created <u>around</u> the wire.

2) The field is made up of <u>concentric circles</u> perpendicular to the wire, with the wire in the centre.

3) You can see this by placing a <u>compass</u> near a <u>wire</u> that is carrying a <u>current</u>. As you move the compass, its needle will <u>trace</u> the direction of the magnetic field.

4) Changing the <u>direction</u> of the <u>current</u> changes the direction of the <u>magnetic field</u> — use the <u>right-hand thumb rule</u> to work out which way it goes.

5) The <u>strength</u> of the magnetic field produced <u>changes</u> with the <u>current</u> and the <u>distance</u> from the wire. The <u>larger</u> the current through the wire, or the <u>closer</u> to the wire you are, the <u>stronger</u> the field is.

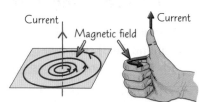

The Right-Hand Thumb Rule
Using your right hand, point your thumb in the direction of current and curl your fingers. The direction of your fingers is the direction of the field.

A Solenoid is a Coil of Wire

1) You can <u>increase</u> the <u>strength</u> of the magnetic field that a current-carrying wire produces by <u>wrapping</u> the wire into a <u>coil</u> called a <u>solenoid</u>.

2) The magnetic field strength <u>increases</u> because the fields around each <u>turn</u> (or loop) of wire <u>line up</u> with each other (and so 'add together').

4) The magnetic field <u>inside</u> a solenoid is <u>strong</u> and <u>uniform</u> (it has the <u>same strength</u> and <u>direction</u> at every point in that region).

5) <u>Outside</u> the coil, the magnetic field is just like the one round a <u>bar magnet</u>.

6) The <u>magnetic effect</u> (field strength) of a solenoid can be <u>increased</u> by: increasing the <u>current</u> through the coil, increasing the <u>number of turns</u> but keeping the <u>length</u> the <u>same</u>, and <u>decreasing</u> the <u>cross-sectional area</u> of the solenoid.

7) You can also add a block of <u>iron</u> in the <u>centre</u> of the coil. This <u>iron core</u> becomes an <u>induced</u> magnet whenever current is flowing, so the <u>magnetic effect</u> of the solenoid is <u>increased</u>.

8) A <u>current-carrying solenoid with an iron core</u> is an **ELECTROMAGNET** — a magnet with a magnetic field that can be turned <u>on</u> and <u>off</u> by turning the <u>current</u> on and off.

Electromagnets Have Many Uses

1) Magnets you can switch on and off are really <u>useful</u>. They're usually used because they're so <u>quick</u> to turn on and off or because they can create a <u>varying force</u>.

2) When electromagnets were discovered in the 19th century, it led to the creation of <u>lots of devices</u>, including the <u>electromagnetic relay</u>. This led to <u>huge advances</u> in <u>communications</u> as they allowed coded messages to be sent <u>long distances</u> as electrical signals before being translated back into words (<u>telegraphs</u>). This is how relays work:

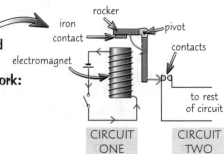

- When the <u>switch</u> in <u>circuit one</u> is <u>closed</u>, it turns on the <u>electromagnet</u>, which <u>attracts</u> the <u>iron contact</u> on the rocker.

- The <u>rocker pivots</u> and <u>pushes together</u> the contacts, <u>completing</u> circuit two and generating an electrical signal.

Strong, in uniform and a magnetic personality — I'm a catch...

Electromagnets are used in loads of everyday things from cranes to MRI machines, so learn how they work.

Q1 Draw the magnetic field for a current-carrying wire, with the current coming out of the page. [2 marks]

The Motor Effect

Time to step into the weird and wonderful world of the <u>motor effect</u> — you can do this, I believe in you.

A Current-Carrying Wire in a Magnetic Field Experiences a Force

1) When a <u>current-carrying conductor</u> (e.g. a <u>wire</u>) is put <u>near</u> a permanent magnet (or in an external magnetic field), the two <u>magnetic fields</u> interact with each other. This causes a <u>force</u> to be <u>exerted</u> on <u>both</u> the <u>wire</u> and the <u>magnet</u>. This is called the <u>motor effect</u> — this usually causes the wire to <u>move</u>.

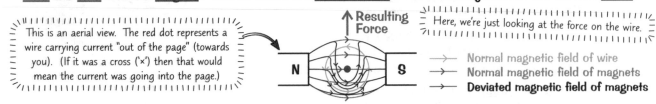

This is an aerial view. The red dot represents a wire carrying current "out of the page" (towards you). (If it was a cross ('×') then that would mean the current was going into the page.)

↑ Resulting Force

Here, we're just looking at the force on the wire.

—→ Normal magnetic field of wire
—→ Normal magnetic field of magnets
—→ **Deviated magnetic field of magnets**

2) To experience the <u>full force</u>, the <u>wire</u> has to be at <u>90°</u> (right angles) to the <u>magnetic field</u>. If the wire runs <u>along</u> the <u>magnetic field</u>, it won't experience <u>any force</u>. At angles in between, it'll feel <u>some</u> force.

3) The force always acts at <u>right angles</u> to the <u>magnetic field</u> of the magnets and the <u>direction of the current</u> in the wire.

—→ Current
—→ Magnetic field
—→ Force

4) So changing the <u>direction</u> of either the <u>magnetic field</u> or the <u>current</u> will change the direction of the <u>force</u>.

5) A good way of showing the <u>direction</u> of the force is to apply a current to a set of <u>rails</u> inside a <u>horseshoe magnet</u> (as shown). A bar is placed on the rails, which <u>completes the circuit</u>. This generates a <u>force</u> that <u>rolls the bar</u> along the rails.

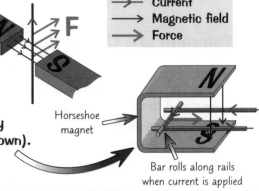

Horseshoe magnet

Bar rolls along rails when current is applied

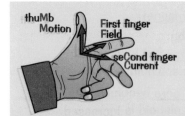

thuMb Motion
First finger Field
seCond finger Current

1) <u>Fleming's left-hand rule</u> is used to find the <u>direction of the force</u> on a current-carrying conductor that is at right-angles to a magnetic field.

2) Using your <u>left hand</u>, point your <u>First finger</u> in the direction of the magnetic <u>Field</u> and your <u>seCond finger</u> in the direction of the <u>Current</u>.

3) Your <u>thuMb</u> will then point in the direction of the <u>force</u> (Motion).

You can Calculate the Force Acting on a Current-Carrying Conductor

The <u>force</u> acting on a <u>conductor</u> at <u>90°</u> to a <u>magnetic field</u> is proportional to three things:

1) The <u>magnetic field strength</u> — this is also called the <u>magnetic flux density</u>, i.e. how many magnetic <u>field</u> (<u>flux</u>) lines there are <u>per unit area</u>.

2) The size of the <u>current</u> through the conductor.

3) The <u>length</u> of the conductor that's <u>in</u> the magnetic field.

Proportional means that increasing any of these three things will increase the force on the conductor.

You can <u>calculate</u> the force when the current is at <u>90°</u> to the magnetic field it's in using:

$$\text{force (N)} = \frac{\text{magnetic field}}{\text{strength (T)}} \times \frac{\text{current}}{\text{(A)}} \times \frac{\text{length of}}{\text{conductor (m)}} \quad \text{or} \quad F = B \times I \times l$$

A current-carrying conductor — a ticket inspector eating sultanas...

Learn the left-hand rule and use it — don't be scared of looking like a muppet in the exam.

Q1 State what the thumb, first finger and second finger each represent in Fleming's left-hand rule. [3 marks]

Q2 A 35 cm long piece of wire is at 90° to an external magnetic field. The wire experiences a force of 9.8 N when a current of 5.0 A is flowing through it. Calculate the strength of the field. [3 marks]

Electric Motors

This lot might look a bit tricky, but really it's just applying the stuff you learnt on the previous page.

A Simple Electric Motor uses Magnets and a Current-Carrying Coil

1) In a d.c. motor, a rectangular current-carrying coil sits in a uniform magnetic field between two poles.

2) Because the current is flowing in different directions on each side of the coil, and each side of the coil is perpendicular to the magnetic field, each side will experience forces in opposite directions.

3) Because the coil is on a spindle, and the forces act in opposite directions on each side, it rotates.

4) The split-ring commutator is a clever way of swapping the contacts every half turn to keep the motor rotating in the same direction.

5) The direction of the motor can be reversed by either swapping the polarity of the d.c. supply (reversing the current) or swapping the magnetic poles over (reversing the field).

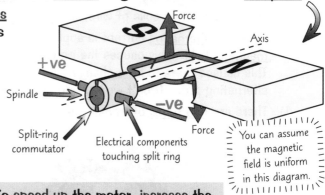

You can assume the magnetic field is uniform in this diagram.

To speed up the motor, increase the current, add more turns to the coil or increase the magnetic field strength.

You can use Fleming's left-hand rule (see the previous page) to figure out whether a coil like the one below is rotating clockwise or anticlockwise:

1) Draw in arrows to show the direction of the magnetic field lines and the current.

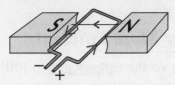

(Remember, current goes from positive to negative.)

2) Use Fleming's LHR on one side of the coil (here we've used the right-hand side).

SeCond finger Current

thuMb Motion

First finger Field

3) Draw in the direction of the force (motion) for this side of the coil.

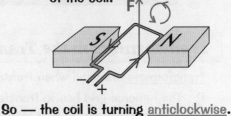

So — the coil is turning anticlockwise.

6) As a motor starts running, the current through it decreases from its initial value. As the current flows, it dissipates some energy which heats up the coil (and so increases the resistance, p.172).

Electric Motors have Lots of Uses

Electric motors are found in many everyday items, both in industry and in your home. They've had a big impact on our lives — they make many processes easier (and quicker) to complete and, in some cases, have led to almost fully-automatic production of items.

1) Factories — many machines, from ones that make paper to ones that produce chewing gum, contain large electric motors to allow them to move. Motors are also used to drive conveyor belts which transport goods between machines.

2) Electric vehicles — the driving force for these cars is provided by electricity instead of petrol or diesel.

3) Household appliances — almost all household appliances that contain moving parts contain an electric motor — hair dryers, vacuum cleaners, blenders, fans, electric toothbrushes... The list goes on.

What makes the world go round? Not an electric motor. Or love...

Practise using Fleming's LHR rule on coils, so you're super confident in working out which way they will turn.

Q1   Give one everyday use of an electric motor.   [1 mark]

Q2   State two properties that could be changed to decrease the speed of an electric motor.   [2 marks]

Transformers

Transformers are dead useful — we use them in the national grid to make transmitting electricity more efficient.

Transformers Change the p.d. — but Only for Alternating Current

1) Transformers change the size of the potential difference of an alternating current.

2) They all have two coils of wire, the primary and the secondary, joined with an iron core.

3) When an alternating current is applied through the primary coil, it creates an alternating magnetic field. This causes the iron core to magnetise and demagnetise quickly. This causes there to be a changing magnetic field through the secondary coil, which induces an alternating p.d.. (Don't worry, you don't actually need to know how this works.)

4) There are two types of transformer:

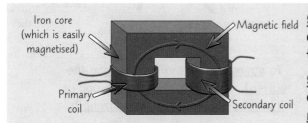

Iron core (which is easily magnetised)
Magnetic field
Primary coil
Secondary coil

STEP-UP TRANSFORMERS step the potential difference up (i.e. increase it). They have more turns on the secondary coil than the primary coil.

STEP-DOWN TRANSFORMERS step the potential difference down (i.e. decrease it). They have more turns on the primary coil than the secondary.

5) Transformers are almost 100% efficient. So you can assume that energy is conserved within them, i.e. the input power is equal to the output power. Using $P = VI$ (p.174), you can write this as:

p.d. across primary coil (V)	×	current in primary coil (A)	=	p.d. across secondary coil (V)	×	current in secondary coil (A)

Transformers make Transmitting Mains Electricity More Efficient

Transformers are used when transmitting electricity across the country via the national grid (p.168).

1) The national grid has to transfer loads of energy each second, which means it transmits electricity at a high power (as power is the rate of energy transfer).

2) Power = potential difference × current (p.174), so to transmit the huge amounts of power needed, you either need a high potential difference or a high current.

3) But a high current makes wires heat up — there are more charges in a given time doing work (transferring energy) to travel through the cable, p.174. So loads of energy is dissipated to the thermal energy stores of the cables and the surroundings.

4) The power lost (due to resistive heating) is found using power = current² × resistance ($P = I^2R$).

5) So to reduce these losses and make the national grid more efficient, high-voltage, low-resistance cables, and transformers are used.

- Step-up transformers at power stations boost the p.d. up really high (400 000 V).
- This means the current is stepped down (as power = p.d. × current, see above), so energy losses through heating are low at these relatively low currents.
- Step-down transformers then bring it back down to safe, usable levels at the consumers' end.

I once had a dream about transforming into a hamster...

...but that's a story for another time. For now, get revising what transformers do, and why they're useful.

Q1 State the type of transformer that has more turns on its primary coil than on its secondary coil. [1 mark]

Q2 A step-down transformer has a potential difference of 6.5 V across its primary coil.
The current in the primary coil is 4.0 A. The current in the secondary coil is 5.0 A.
Calculate the potential difference across the secondary coil of the transformer. [3 marks]

Revision Questions for Chapter P3

And you've struggled through to the end of electric circuits. Have a break, then test what you can remember.

- Try these questions and <u>tick off each one</u> when you <u>get it right</u>.
- When you've done <u>all the questions</u> for a topic and are <u>completely happy</u> with it, tick off the topic.

<u>Circuits (p.170-177)</u> ☑

1) Define current and state an equation that links current, charge and time, with units for each. ☑
2) Draw the circuit symbols for: a cell, a filament lamp, a diode, a thermistor and an LDR. ☑
3) What is the equation that links potential difference, current and resistance? ☑
4) Describe an experiment you could do to investigate how the length of a wire affects its resistance. ☑
5) Name one linear component and one non-linear component. ☑
6) Explain how the resistance of an LDR varies with light intensity. ☑
7) What happens to the resistance of a thermistor as it gets hotter? ☑
8) True or false? Power is the rate of energy transfer. ☑
9) Write down the equation linking power, current and resistance. ☑
10) True or false? The potential difference of a battery is shared between components in a series circuit. ☑
11) How does the current through each component vary in a series circuit? ☑
12) How does potential difference vary between components connected in parallel? ☑

<u>Magnets, The Motor Effect and Transformers (p.178-182)</u> ☑

13) Describe how you could use a compass to show the direction of a bar magnet's magnetic field lines. ☑
14) Describe the behaviour of a compass that is far away from any magnets. ☑
15) What happens to an induced magnet when it is moved far away from a permanent magnet? ☑
16) Describe an electromagnet and give one example of where it could be used. ☑
17) What is Fleming's left-hand rule? ☑
18) Name three ways you could increase the force on a current-carrying wire in a magnetic field. ☑
19) Explain how a basic d.c. motor works. ☑
20) What kind of current do transformers use? ☑
21) Explain how using transformers improves efficiency when transmitting electricity. ☑

Forces and Newton's Third Law

Clever chap Isaac Newton — he came up with three handy laws about motion. Let's start with the third...

Forces can be Contact or Non-Contact

1) A force is a push or a pull on an object that is caused by it interacting with another object.

2) Sometimes, objects need to be touching for forces to act. These are contact forces.

3) Normal contact forces are the 'push' forces that two touching objects always exert on each other.
E.g. a cat on a chair — the cat pushes down on the chair and the chair pushes up on the cat.

4) Friction is a contact force between two objects that tend to slide past each other. E.g. a book resting
on a slope — friction acts on both the slope and the book in the direction that tries to prevent motion.

5) Non-contact forces are forces between two objects that aren't touching. The forces are instead
caused by fields around the objects interacting. Some examples of non-contact forces are:

- Gravitational forces — e.g. the attractive forces between the Earth and the Sun.
- Electrostatic forces — the attraction or repulsion of charges when their electric fields interact.
- Magnetic forces — the attraction or repulsion between two magnets due to their magnetic fields (p.178).

Newton's Third Law — Reaction Forces are Equal and Opposite

1) Whenever two objects interact, they both feel a force.
This pair of forces is called an interaction pair.

2) You can represent an interaction pair with a pair of vectors (see page 186)
— arrows showing the relative size and direction of the forces.

3) The forces which make up an interaction pair are the same type of force and are the same size, but they
each act in the opposite direction and on a different object to the other. This is Newton's third law:

> Newton's Third Law: When two objects interact, the forces they exert on each other are equal and opposite.

4) The trouble with Newton's third law is understanding how anything ever goes anywhere. The important
thing to remember is that although the forces are equal and opposite, they act on different objects.

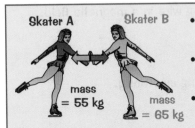

Skater A   Skater B

mass = 55 kg   mass = 65 kg

- When skater A pushes on skater B, she feels an equal and
opposite force from skater B's hand (the 'normal contact' force).
- Both skaters feel the same sized force, in opposite directions,
and so accelerate away from each other.
- Skater A will be accelerated more than skater B, though, because
she has a smaller mass, (see Newton's Second Law on page 197).

5) It's a bit more complicated for an object in equilibrium (see page 193). Imagine a book sat on a table:

The weight (p.185) of the book pulls it down, and the normal reaction force from the table pushes it up.
This is NOT Newton's Third Law as there are two interaction pairs of forces at work — normal contact
forces and gravitational forces. Each interaction pair is different and they're both acting on the book.

Each interaction pair due to Newton's Third Law in this case are:

- The weight of the book is pulled down by gravity from Earth (W_B)
and the book also pulls back up on the Earth (W_E).
- The normal contact force from the table pushing up on the book (N_B) and
the normal contact force from the book pushing down on the table (N_T).

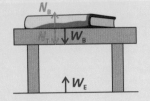

Newton's fourth law — revision must be done with cake...

For every action there is an equal and opposite reaction. Like the despair of revision and the joy of acing the exam.

Q1   Using Newton's third law of motion, explain why a ball bounces back when it hits a wall.   [2 marks]

Mass and Weight

The <u>weight</u> is finally over, it's time to talk about <u>mass</u>. And where there's mass, there's <u>gravity</u>.

Everything Made of Matter Has a Mass

1) <u>Mass</u> is just the <u>amount of matter</u> in an object
   — a measure of the total number of atoms that make it up (see page 205).

2) Mass is measured in <u>kilograms, kg</u>.

3) A given object will have the <u>same</u> mass <u>anywhere</u> in the universe.

Gravity is the Force of Attraction Between All Masses

1) <u>Everything</u> that has mass has a <u>gravitational field</u> around it. <u>Everything</u>.

2) There will be <u>gravitational forces</u> on objects whose gravitational fields interact.
   These forces are <u>always attractive</u>.

3) Isaac Newton made a <u>link</u> between the forces on <u>falling objects</u> on Earth and the forces needed
   to keep the <u>Moon</u> in <u>orbit</u> around the Earth. He realised that gravity was a <u>universal
   law of nature</u> — i.e. <u>everything</u> with mass <u>always</u> attracts everything else with mass.

4) The more <u>massive the object</u> is, the <u>greater the strength</u> of its gravitational field.

5) The <u>attraction</u> due to <u>gravity</u> only becomes noticeable when the <u>mass</u> of one object is <u>very large</u>
   — e.g. there is a noticeable attraction between <u>you</u> and <u>the Earth</u>, but not between <u>you</u> and <u>this book</u>.

6) The attractive forces between the Earth and other objects with mass is what makes
   the objects <u>fall towards the Earth's surface</u> — and keeps them there when they land.

Weight is a Downwards Force

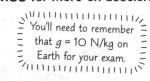

1) When an object is on a <u>planet</u> (or other <u>massive</u> body) a <u>downwards force</u> acts on
   the object due to <u>gravitational attraction</u> between the object and the planet.

2) This force is called its <u>weight</u>.

3) In most situations, <u>weight</u> is the force acting on an object as it is attracted <u>towards the Earth</u>.

4) It's measured in <u>newtons</u> (N). You can calculate weight using the equation:

> weight (N) = mass (kg) × gravitational field strength (N/kg) $W = m \times g$

5) g is called the <u>gravitational field strength</u>. It's also known as the <u>acceleration due to gravity</u>
   (i.e. it's the acceleration an object will have when falling to Earth). See p.188 for more on acceleration.

6) Near the surface of the Earth, a <u>1 kg</u> mass has a <u>weight</u> of roughly <u>10 N</u>.
   This means that g has a value of about <u>10 N/kg</u> near the Earth's surface.
   The value of g is <u>different</u> on <u>other planets</u>, so an identical
   object on another planet will have a different weight.

   You'll need to remember that g = 10 N/kg on Earth for your exam.

7) Remember, <u>mass</u> is <u>not the same</u> as weight — an object's mass is the <u>same everywhere</u>.

8) But the <u>more massive</u> an object is, the <u>larger its weight will be</u>
   — weight and mass are <u>directly proportional</u>.

9) Similarly, the <u>stronger</u> the gravitational field an object is in, the <u>larger the object's weight</u>.

10) To <u>weigh</u> an object, hold a <u>force meter</u> level and attach the object to force meter's spring, letting
    it hang freely. The <u>weight</u> of the object will <u>extend the spring</u> and the meter will show the <u>weight</u>
    of the object in <u>newtons</u>. You could also use a <u>top pan balance</u> (p.233) to measure weight.

Drag yourself away from the TV and force yourself to revise...

A common mistake is thinking that mass and weight are the same thing. They are not. Learn the difference.

Q1   A person has a weight of 820 N on Earth. Calculate their mass.   [3 marks]

Scalars and Vectors

The stuff on this page is pretty darn important. Learn it, don't forget it, and do the question at the end.

Scalars are Just Numbers, but Vectors Have Direction Too

1) Everything you measure in physics is either a scalar quantity, or a vector quantity.

2) Scalar quantities are just numbers — they simply tell you the 'size' (or 'magnitude') of the thing you're measuring, and nothing more.

3) Mass is a scalar quantity, as it only has a size. Other scalar quantities include: ➡ **Scalar quantities:** speed, distance, time, etc.

4) Vector quantities tell you both the size of the thing AND its direction.

5) Force is a vector quantity, because it is applied in a particular direction, e.g. 10 N to the right. Other vector quantities include: ➡ **Vector quantities:** velocity, displacement, acceleration, etc.

6) Vectors are usually represented by an arrow — the length of the arrow shows the magnitude, and the direction of the arrow shows the direction of the quantity.

> When we use vectors, we talk about there being a positive and a negative direction.
> E.g. a force applied in one direction could be a force of 10 N, but if it were applied in the opposite direction it would be a force of −10 N.
> In either direction the size of the force is 10 N.
> You can often pick a positive direction that makes the calculations easier.

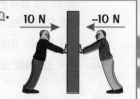

The Motion of an Object can be Described in Three Ways

1) A moving object can be described by its speed, direction of travel and whether its speed is changing.

2) Distance, displacement, speed and velocity are all terms used to describe an object's motion.

Distance is Scalar, Displacement is a Vector

1) Distance is scalar. It's how far an object has moved along the path it has taken at a given moment.

2) Displacement is a vector quantity. At a given moment, it measures the net distance and direction in a straight line from an object's starting point to its finishing point — e.g. the plane flew 5 metres north. The direction could be relative to a point, e.g. towards the school, or a bearing (a three-digit angle measured clockwise from north) e.g. 035°.

3) If you walk 5 m north, then 5 m south, your displacement is 0 m but the distance travelled is 10 m.

Speed and Velocity are Both How Fast You're Going

1) Speed is a scalar and velocity is a vector. For an object at a given moment:

> Speed is how fast the object's going (e.g. 30 mph or 20 m/s) with no regard to the direction.
> Velocity is speed of the object in a given direction, (e.g. 30 mph north or 20 m/s, 060°).

2) This means you can have objects travelling at a constant speed with a changing velocity. This happens when an object is changing direction whilst staying at the same speed. An object moving in a circle at a constant speed has a constantly changing velocity, as the direction is always changing (e.g. a car going around a roundabout).

3) Objects rarely travel at a constant speed. E.g. when you walk, run or travel in a car, your speed is always changing. Generally the speed referred to is the average (mean) speed.

Whoever left their cat on this top tip please pick it up...

Important things to know in life: how to correctly pronounce 'scone' and the difference between scalars and vectors.

Q1 Describe the difference between scalar and vector quantities. Give an example of each. [2 marks]

Calculating Speed

Are you ready for a super speedy page? Get set... goooooooooo!!

Speed, Distance and Time — the Formula

You really ought to get pretty slick with this equation, it pops up a lot...

$$\text{average speed (m/s)} = \text{distance (m)} \div \text{time (s)}$$

> The equation for calculating velocity is: velocity (m/s) = displacement (m) ÷ time (s).

EXAMPLE: A cat skulks 20 m in 50 s. Find: a) its average speed, b) how long it takes to skulk 32 m.

1) Use the equation above to calculate the average speed.
2) Now rearrange the equation for time.
3) Stick in the value you calculated for average speed and the distance you've been given.

average speed = distance ÷ time
= 20 ÷ 50 = 0.4 m/s

time = distance ÷ average speed
= 32 ÷ 0.4 = 80 s

You Need to be Able to Convert Between Units

1) When using any equation, it's important to have your quantities in the right units.
E.g. in the speed equation above, the speed must be in m/s (metres per second),
the distance must be in m (metres) and the time must be in s (seconds).

2) You may need to convert between units, and you need to understand prefixes — see page 227.

> To convert 8 h (hours) into s:
> Multiply 8 by 60 to find the number of minutes — 8 × 60 = 480 minutes.
> Then multiply 480 minutes by 60 to find the number of seconds — 480 × 60 = 28 800 s.

3) In the real world speeds are often measured in kilometres per hour, (km/h).
Make sure you can convert between km/h and m/s.

> To get from m/s to km/h, divide by 1000 and multiply by 3600.

> Convert km/h into m/s:
> Divide by 3600 (i.e. 60 × 60) to turn h into s.
> Then multiply by 1000 to change from km to m. (Or just divide by 3.6).
> So 48 km/h = 48 ÷ 3.6 = 13.33... ~ 13 m/s (to 2 s.f.).

> The ~ symbol just means it's an approximate value (or answer).

4) Some speeds (and other quantities) that you're given may be in standard form. It's a way of
writing very big or very small numbers. Numbers in standard form always look like this:

A is always a number between 1 and 10.

$$A \times 10^n$$

n is the number of places the decimal point would move if you wrote the number out fully. It's negative for numbers less than 1, and positive for numbers greater than 1.

Learn these Typical Speeds

> If you know a speed in mph, to get (roughly) to m/s, halve it. So 60 mph is about 30 m/s.

You also need to know the usual speeds of some everyday objects. This is handy when you make estimates.

1) Walking — 1.4 m/s (5 km/h)
2) Running — 3 m/s (11 km/h)
3) Cycling — 5.5 m/s (20 km/h)
4) Average wind speed — 7 m/s (25 km/h)
5) Cars in a built-up area — 13 m/s (47 km/h or 30 mph)
6) Cars on a motorway — 31 m/s (112 km/h or 70 mph)
7) Trains — up to 55 m/s (200 km/h)
8) Speed of sound in air — 340 m/s (1220 km/h)

I feel the need, the need for calculating speed...

This stuff is pretty dull, but it's important for the next few pages, so make sure you know it all.

Q1   Calculate the average speed of a cyclist who cycles 660 m in 2.0 minutes.   [3 marks]

Q2   Find the distance travelled in 24 s by a car with a constant speed of 54 km/hr.   [3 marks]

Acceleration

Acceleration is all about speeding up and slowing down. So let's pick up the pace, and dive straight in.

Acceleration is How Quickly You're Speeding Up

1) Acceleration is the change in velocity of an object in a certain amount of time.

2) In most everyday situations, this change in velocity is a change of speed but not a change in direction. This means you can simplify acceleration to be the change of speed of an object in a given time.

3) If an object speeds up, it must be accelerating.

4) If an object slows down, it's decelerating (deceleration is just negative acceleration).

5) You can find the average acceleration of an object using:

$$\text{acceleration (m/s}^2) = \text{change in speed (m/s)} \div \text{time taken (s)}$$

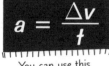
$$a = \frac{\Delta v}{t}$$

6) You might have to estimate the acceleration (or deceleration) of an object. To do this, you might need to use the typical speeds from p.187 or estimate a time:

> You can use this equation with velocities, as long as they're in the same direction.

EXAMPLE: A woman begins cycling from rest. Estimate her acceleration.

1) First estimate the cyclist's typical speed. — typical speed ~ 5.5 m/s
2) Find the change in speed. — change in speed = 5.5 − 0 = 5.5 m/s
3) Make an estimate of how long it would take a cyclist to get from rest to a typical cycling speed. — estimated time ~ 5 s
4) Then substitute this into the acceleration equation. — acceleration = change in speed ÷ time taken
   $= 5.5 \div 5 = 1.1$ m/s^2

There's a Useful Equation for Constant Acceleration

For any object that is travelling with constant acceleration (which you might sometimes be called uniform acceleration), you can use the following equation:

> This equation is really handy, so make sure you're comfortable with rearranging it and using it.

$$\text{(final speed)}^2 - \text{(initial speed)}^2 = 2 \times \text{acceleration} \times \text{distance}$$
$$\text{(m/s)}^2 \qquad \text{(m/s)}^2 \qquad \text{(m/s}^2) \qquad \text{(m)}$$

It might help you to remember the equation in symbols, as $v^2 - u^2 = 2 \times a \times s$.

Objects in free fall near the Earth's surface are common examples of objects that have a constant acceleration — they undergo an acceleration due to gravity of roughly 10 m/s^2 (the same value as g, p.185).

These Equations Can be Used to Form a Computational Model

The equations on this page, and on page 187, can be used to form a simple computational model — a computer based model that can be used to predict the motion of an object. The computer does lots of calculations, and can be used to work out, e.g. the position or speed of an object after a certain amount of time. This can be done for objects travelling at a constant speed or with a constant acceleration.

CAUTION! Accelerating through pages means you miss key info...

Get those equations firmly stuck in your head and make sure you're totally happy rearranging and using them.

Q1   A ball is dropped from a height, h, above the ground.
     The speed of the ball just before it hits the ground is 5.00 m/s.
     Calculate the height the ball is dropped from. (Acceleration due to gravity ≈ 10 m/s^2.)   [3 marks]

Investigating Motion

Here's a simple <u>experiment</u> you can try out to investigate the relation between <u>distance</u>, <u>speed</u> and <u>acceleration</u>.

You can Investigate the Motion of a Trolley on a Ramp

1) Set up your <u>apparatus</u> as shown in the diagram below, and mark a <u>line</u> on the ramp just before the <u>first light gate</u> — this is to make sure the trolley starts from the <u>same point</u> each time.

2) Measure the <u>distances</u> between light gates 1 and 2, and 2 and 3.

3) Hold the trolley <u>still</u> at the start line, and then <u>let go</u> of it so that it starts to roll down the slope.

4) As it rolls down the <u>ramp</u> it will <u>accelerate</u>. When it reaches the <u>runway</u>, it will travel at a <u>constant speed</u> (ignoring any friction).

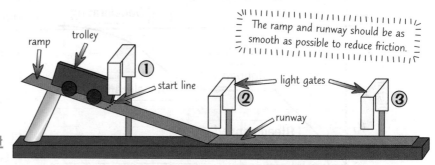

The ramp and runway should be as smooth as possible to reduce friction.

5) Each <u>light gate</u> will record the <u>time</u> when the trolley passes through it. (See page 240 for more on light gates.)

6) The time it takes to travel between <u>gates 1 and 2</u> can be used to find the <u>average speed</u> on the ramp, and between <u>gates 2 and 3</u> gives the <u>speed</u> on the <u>runway</u> (using <u>speed = distance ÷ time</u>, p.187).

7) The <u>acceleration</u> of the trolley on the ramp can be found using <u>acceleration = change in speed ÷ time</u> (p.188) with the following values:

You can also measure speed at a point using one light gate.

- the <u>initial speed</u> of the trolley (= 0 m/s),
- the <u>final speed</u> of the trolley, which equals the speed of the trolley on the <u>runway</u> (ignoring <u>friction</u>),
- the <u>time</u> it takes the trolley to travel between light gates 1 and 2.

The trolley's <u>acceleration</u> on the ramp and its final <u>speed</u> on the runway will <u>increase</u> when the <u>angle</u> of the ramp increases, or the amount of <u>friction</u> between the ramp and the trolley <u>decreases</u>. Increasing the <u>distance</u> between the <u>bottom</u> of the ramp and where the <u>trolley</u> is <u>released</u> will also increase the final speed of the trolley.

Try varying these things in your experiment to see the results for yourself.

You can use Different Equipment to Measure Distance and Time

Generally, you measure <u>speed</u> by <u>measuring distance</u> and <u>time</u>, and then <u>calculating</u> speed. You might need to use <u>different methods</u> for measuring distance and time depending on what you're investigating.

1) If possible, your <u>measuring instrument</u> should always be <u>longer</u> than the <u>distance</u> you're measuring with it — e.g. you shouldn't use a 30 cm ruler to measure something that's 45 cm long.

2) For experiments in the lab like the one above, the distances involved will generally be <u>less than a metre</u>, so you'll be able to measure them with a <u>ruler</u> or a <u>metre stick</u>.

3) If you're investigating e.g. how fast someone <u>walks</u>, you'll want to measure their speed over <u>many metres</u>, so you'll need a <u>long tape measure</u>, or a <u>rolling tape measure</u> (one of those clicky wheel things).

4) To measure time intervals longer than about <u>5 seconds</u>, you can use a <u>stopwatch</u>.

5) To measure <u>short intervals</u>, like in the experiment above it's best to use <u>light gates</u> connected to a <u>computer</u>. Using a stopwatch involves <u>human error</u> (p.224) due to, for example, <u>reaction times</u>. This is more of a problem the shorter the interval you're timing, as the reaction time makes up a <u>larger proportion</u> of the interval.

If you want to investigate motion you'll need to invest in gates...

Think about it this way — say you were measuring the height of an elephant, you wouldn't use a 30 cm ruler, that would be daft. You'd be there forever. What experiment are you doing with an elephant anyway?

Q1   Explain how the speed of an object can be found using two light gates.   [3 marks]

Q2   Explain why using light gates to measure short time intervals is more accurate than a stopwatch.   [2 marks]

Distance-Time Graphs

A <u>graph</u> speaks a thousand words, so they make life a lot easier on your vocal cords...

Distance-Time Graphs Tell You How Far Something has Travelled

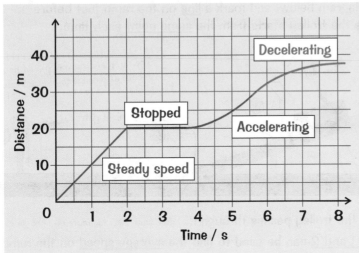

The different parts of a <u>distance-time graph</u> describe the <u>motion</u> of an object:

- The <u>slope</u> (<u>gradient</u>) at <u>any</u> point gives the <u>average speed</u> of the object.
- A <u>steeper</u> graph means it's going <u>faster</u>.
- <u>Flat</u> sections are where it's <u>stopped</u>.
- <u>Straight uphill</u> sections mean it is travelling at a <u>steady speed</u>.
- <u>Curves</u> represent <u>acceleration</u>.
- A <u>steepening</u> curve means it's <u>speeding up</u> (increasing gradient).
- A <u>levelling off</u> curve means it's <u>slowing down</u>.

The Average Speed of an Object can be Found From a Distance-Time Graph

1) The <u>gradient</u> of a distance-time graph at any point is equal to the <u>average speed</u> of the object at that time.

2) If the graph is a <u>straight line</u>, the gradient at any point along the line is equal to $\dfrac{\text{change in the vertical}}{\text{change in the horizontal}}$.

> <u>Example:</u> In the graph above, the average speed at any time between 0 s and 2 s is:
>
> Average speed = gradient = $\dfrac{\text{change in the vertical}}{\text{change in the horizontal}} = \dfrac{20}{2} = \underline{10 \text{ m/s}}$

3) If the graph is <u>curved</u>, to find the average speed at a certain time you need to draw a <u>tangent</u> to the curve at that point, and then find the <u>gradient</u> of the <u>tangent</u>.

A tangent is a line that is parallel to the curve at that point.

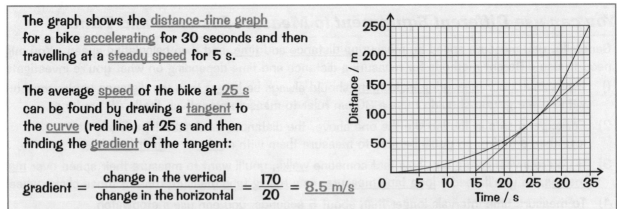

The graph shows the <u>distance-time graph</u> for a bike <u>accelerating</u> for 30 seconds and then travelling at a <u>steady speed</u> for 5 s.

The average <u>speed</u> of the bike at <u>25 s</u> can be found by drawing a <u>tangent</u> to the <u>curve</u> (red line) at 25 s and then finding the <u>gradient</u> of the tangent:

gradient = $\dfrac{\text{change in the vertical}}{\text{change in the horizontal}} = \dfrac{170}{20} = \underline{8.5 \text{ m/s}}$

You can also use distance-time graphs to calculate the <u>average acceleration</u> between two points. First, find the <u>speed</u> at <u>both points</u> (draw a tangent or find the gradient of the line) then <u>divide</u> the <u>difference in speed</u> by the <u>time taken</u> to accelerate.

For example, the average acceleration after <u>25 s</u> can be calculated as:

average acceleration = $\dfrac{\text{difference in speed}}{\text{time taken to accelerate}} = \dfrac{(8.5 - 0)}{25} = \underline{0.34 \text{ m/s}^2}$

Tangent — a man who's just come back from holiday...

For practice, try sketching distance-time graphs for different scenarios. Like cycling up a hill or running from a bear.

Q1   Sketch a distance-time graph for an object that first accelerates, then travels at a constant speed.   [2 marks]

Velocity-Time Graphs

Huzzah, more graphs. And they're velocity-time graphs too, you lucky thing. And just like distance-time graphs, these beauties are also brilliant ways to describe the motion of an object.

Velocity-Time Graphs can Be Used to Find Average Acceleration

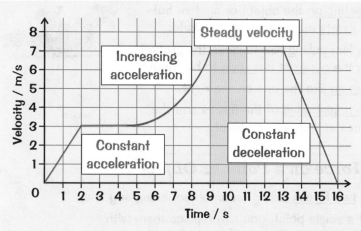

- Gradient = average acceleration.
- Flat sections represent steady velocity.
- The steeper the graph, the greater the average acceleration or deceleration.
- Uphill sections (/) are acceleration.
- Downhill sections (\) are deceleration.
- A straight line means constant acceleration.
- A curve means changing acceleration.
- You can calculate the average acceleration at a point by finding the gradient of a tangent at that point.

- The area under any section of the graph is equal to the distance travelled in that time interval.
- If the graph is a straight line, you can calculate the distance travelled using geometry — e.g. the distance travelled between 9 s and 11 s is equal to the area of the shaded rectangle.
- If the graph is curved, you may have to use other methods to calculate the area beneath it, see below.
- Velocity-time graphs are sometimes called speed-time graphs if the object's moving in a straight line. You can find the average acceleration of the object by finding the gradient of a speed-time graph. And the distance travelled is the area under the graph — just like for velocity-time graphs.

You can Use the Counting Squares Method To Find the Area Under the Graph

1) If an object has an increasing or decreasing acceleration, the graph is curved. You can estimate the distance travelled from the area under the graph by counting squares.

2) First you need to find out how much distance one square of the graph paper represents (in metres). To do this, multiply the width of square (in seconds) by the height of one square (in metres per second).

3) Then you just multiply this by the number of squares under the graph. If there are squares that are partly under the graph, you can add them together to make whole squares (see below).

The graph below is a velocity-time graph. You can estimate the distance travelled in the first 10 s by counting the number of squares under the graph (shown by the shaded area).

Total number of shaded squares = 32

Distance represented by one square
= width of square × height of square
= 1 s × 0.2 m/s = 0.2 m

So total distance travelled in 10 s
= 32 × 0.2 = 6.4 m

These two partially shaded squares add up to make one square.

As you go through and count the squares, it helps to put a dot in the square once it's been counted. That way you don't lose track of what's been counted and what hasn't.

Anyone up for a game of squares?

Remember — the acceleration of an object on a velocity-time graph is the gradient of the curve at that time.

Q1   Sketch a velocity-time graph for a car that initially travels at a steady speed and then decelerates constantly to a stop. It is then stationary for a short time before accelerating with increasing acceleration.   [3 marks]

Free Body Diagrams and Forces

A <u>free body diagram</u> is really useful to understanding how and why a object is moving or not moving.

Free Body Diagrams Show All the Forces Acting on an Object

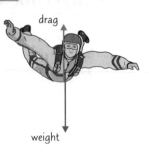

drag

weight

1) You need to be able to <u>describe</u> all the <u>forces</u> acting on an <u>isolated object</u> or a <u>system</u> (p.162) — i.e. <u>every</u> force <u>acting on</u> the object or system but <u>none</u> of the forces the object or system <u>exerts</u> on the rest of the world.

2) For example, a skydiver's <u>weight</u> acts on him pulling him towards the ground. <u>Drag</u> (air resistance) also acts on him, in the <u>opposite direction</u> to his motion.

3) This can be shown using a <u>free body diagram</u> like the one on the right.

4) The <u>sizes</u> of the arrows show the <u>relative magnitudes</u> of the forces and the <u>directions</u> show the directions of the forces acting on the object.

A Resultant Force is the Overall Force on a Point or Object

1) In most <u>real</u> situations there are at least <u>two forces</u> acting on an object along any line.

2) If you have a <u>number of forces</u> acting at a single point, you can replace them with a <u>single force</u> that takes into account the <u>sizes</u> and <u>directions</u> of all of the forces. The single force has the <u>same effect</u> as all the individual forces <u>added together</u>.

3) This single force is called the <u>resultant force</u>.

4) If the forces all act along the <u>same line</u> (they're all parallel), the <u>overall effect</u> is found by <u>adding</u> those going in the <u>same</u> direction and <u>subtracting</u> any going in the opposite direction.

5) If you have two forces that are <u>perpendicular</u> (at 90°) to each other, the resultant force can be found using <u>scale drawings</u> (see next page).

EXAMPLE: For the following force diagram, calculate the resultant force acting on the van.

1) Consider the <u>horizontal</u> and <u>vertical</u> directions <u>separately</u>.

2) State the <u>size</u> and <u>direction</u> of the <u>resultant</u> force.

Vertical: 1500 − 1500 = 0 N
Horizontal: 1200 − 1000 N = 200 N

The resultant force is 200 N to the left.

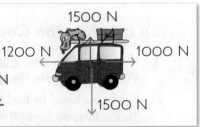

1500 N

1200 N   1000 N

1500 N

The diagram shows an apple sat on a table.

The <u>force</u> due to <u>gravity</u> (its <u>weight</u>, see p.185) is acting <u>downwards</u>. The <u>normal contact force</u> from the table top is pushing <u>up</u> on the apple.

These two forces are equal in size and act in opposite directions. This is a special case where the forces are balanced and cause a <u>zero resultant force</u>. The object is said to be in <u>equilibrium</u> (p.193).

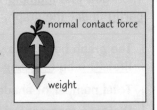

normal contact force

weight

There are <u>four</u> forces acting on an <u>accelerating</u> block.

The <u>weight</u> and <u>normal contact force</u> are equal in size and act in the opposite direction, so the resultant <u>vertical</u> force is <u>zero</u> (like the apple above).

The <u>pushing force</u> on the block is <u>larger</u> than the <u>friction</u>, so there <u>is</u> a <u>resultant horizontal force</u>. This force is equal to the <u>pushing force minus the friction</u>.

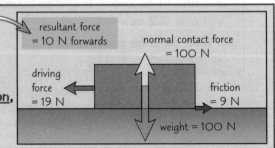

resultant force = 10 N forwards

normal contact force = 100 N

driving force = 19 N

friction = 9 N

weight = 100 N

Consolidate all your forces into one easy-to-manage force...

Free body diagrams make most force questions easier, so start by sketching one. Then get to work.

Q1 Draw a free body diagram for a book resting on a table. [2 marks]

Forces and Scale Drawings

Scale drawings are useful things — they can help you work out the resultant force.

Use Scale Drawings to Find Resultant Forces

1) Draw all the forces acting on an object, to scale, 'tip-to-tail'.

2) Then draw a straight line from the start of the first force to the end of the last force — this is the resultant force.

3) Measure the length of the resultant force on the diagram to find the magnitude and measure the angle to find the direction of the force.

EXAMPLE: A man is on an electric bicycle that has a driving force of 4 N north. However, the wind produces a force of 3 N east. Find the magnitude and direction of the resultant force.

1) Start by drawing a scale drawing of the forces acting.

2) Make sure you choose a sensible scale (e.g. 1 cm = 1 N).

3) Draw the resultant from the tail of the first arrow to the tip of the last arrow.

4) Measure the length of the resultant with a ruler and use the scale to find the force in N.

5) Use a protractor to measure the direction as a bearing.

A bearing is an angle measured clockwise from north, given as a 3 digit number, e.g. 10° = 010°.

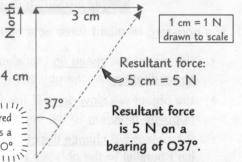

1 cm = 1 N drawn to scale

Resultant force: 5 cm = 5 N

Resultant force is 5 N on a bearing of 037°.

4) Putting forces tip-to-tail to find the resultant force works for any number of forces. So don't worry if you have more than one force acting in the same direction, just draw them all.

An Object is in Equilibrium if the Forces Acting on it are Balanced

1) If all of the forces acting on an object combine to give a resultant force of zero, the object is in equilibrium.

2) On a scale diagram, this means that the tip of the last force you draw should end where the tail of the first force you drew begins. E.g. for the four forces below, the scale drawing will form a square.

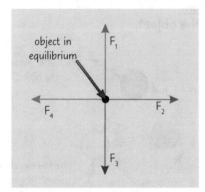

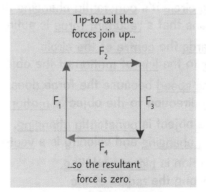

3) You might be given forces acting on an object and told to find a missing force, given that the object is in equilibrium. To do this, draw out the forces you do know (to scale and tip-to-tail), then join the end of the last force to the start of the first force. This line is the missing force, so you can measure its size and direction.

Make sure you draw the last force in the right direction. It's in the opposite direction to how you'd draw a resultant force.

Don't blow things out of proportion — it's only scale drawings...

Keep those pencils sharp and those scale drawings accurate — or you'll end up with the wrong answer.

Q1 A toy boat crosses a stream. The motor provides a 12 N driving force to the north. The river's current causes a force of 5 N west to act on the boat. Find the magnitude of the resultant force. [2 marks]

Newton's First Law and Circular Motion

You met <u>Newton's third law</u> on page 184, and now it's time for the <u>first</u> of Newton's incredibly useful laws.

Newton's First Law — A Force is Needed to Change Motion

1) <u>Newton's first law says</u> that a <u>resultant force</u> is needed to <u>change the motion</u> of an object.

2) So for an object travelling in a <u>straight line</u>, <u>Newton's first law says</u>:

> If the <u>resultant force</u> on a moving object is <u>zero</u>, it will just carry on moving at a constant speed in a straight line.

And for <u>stationary objects</u>:

> If the resultant force on a <u>stationary</u> object is <u>zero</u>, the object will <u>remain stationary</u>.

3) If a <u>non-zero</u> resultant force acts on an object, <u>three</u> things can happen:

- the object will <u>speed up</u> (accelerate) if the force is in the <u>same direction</u> as the object's motion (see page 188).

- the object will <u>slow down</u> if the force is in the <u>opposite direction</u> to the object's motion.

- the object will <u>change direction</u> if the force <u>isn't parallel</u> to the object's motion (i.e. the force doesn't act <u>entirely</u> along the <u>line of motion</u> of the object). This usually leads to a <u>change of speed</u> as well.

If there's a non-zero resultant force on an object, it will have unequal arrows on its free body diagram, p.192.

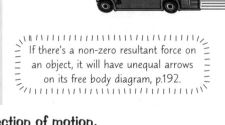

4) If a non-zero force acts at 90° (<u>perpendicular</u>) to an object's direction of motion, then the object will <u>travel in a circle</u> at a <u>constant speed</u>. There's more on this below.

Objects in Circular Motion have Constant Speed but Changing Velocity

1) If an object is <u>travelling in a circle</u> it's <u>constantly changing direction</u>. As you saw above, this means that a <u>resultant force</u> is acting on the object.

2) This force always acts <u>towards</u> the <u>centre of the circle</u> and is always <u>perpendicular</u> to the <u>line of motion</u> of the object.

3) So the object <u>never changes speed</u> because the force doesn't act in the <u>same</u> or <u>opposite</u> direction to the object's <u>motion</u>.

4) However, the <u>velocity</u> of the object is <u>constantly changing</u>, as its <u>direction</u> is <u>constantly changing</u> and velocity is a <u>vector</u>.

5) A good example of this in action is <u>planets orbiting</u> the <u>Sun</u>. The force acting along the <u>radius of the orbit</u> is provided by <u>gravity</u> and it acts at <u>right angles</u> to the path the planet takes around the Sun.

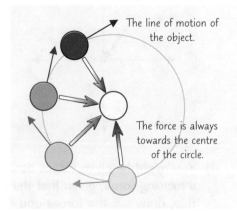

The line of motion of the object.

The force is always towards the centre of the circle.

Now you've started revising, you won't need a push to keep going...

Newton's first law means that an object at a steady speed doesn't need a net force to keep moving. Remember that.

Q1   A car is moving at a constant velocity. State the resultant force acting on it.   [1 mark]

Q2   A student attaches a stone to the end of a piece of string. She swings it around her head in a circular motion at a constant speed. Describe the resultant force acting on the stone.   [2 marks]

Momentum and Newton's Second Law

All moving objects have momentum. Like this book when I throw it across the room.

Momentum = Mass × Velocity

The greater the mass of an object and the greater its velocity, the more momentum the object has. They're linked by this equation:

> momentum (kg m/s) = mass (kg) × velocity (m/s)   or $p = m \times v$

Momentum is a vector — it has size and direction.

 **EXAMPLE:** A 65 kg kangaroo is moving in a straight line at 12 m/s. Calculate its momentum.

momentum = mass × velocity = 65 × 12 = **780 kg m/s**

Forces Cause Changes of Momentum

1) When a resultant force acts on an object, it causes a change in the object's velocity (see previous page). As momentum = mass × velocity, this means that the resultant force also causes a change of momentum in the direction of the force.

2) Newton's second law says that this change of momentum is proportional to the size of the resultant force and the time over which the force acts on the object.

3) Newton's second law in terms of momentum can be written as:

> change of momentum (kg m/s) = resultant force (N) × time for which it acts (s)

4) You can also write Newton's second law as: $\Delta p = F \times t$

EXAMPLE: A rock of mass 1.0 kg is travelling through space at 15 m/s. A comet hits the rock, applying a force of 2500 N for 0.60 seconds. Calculate:
a) the rock's initial momentum
b) the rock's change of momentum resulting from the impact.

a) Substitute into the equation for momentum. momentum = mass × velocity = 1.0 × 15 = **15 kg m/s**

b) Use the equation for force and momentum to find what happens when the comet hits the rock. change of momentum = resultant force × time for which it acts = 2500 × 0.60 = **1500 kg m/s**

5) The slower a given change of momentum happens, the smaller the average force causing the change must be (i.e. if t gets bigger in the equation above, F gets smaller).

6) Similarly, the faster a change of momentum happens, the larger the average force must be.

7) So if someone's momentum changes very quickly, like in a car crash, the forces on the body will be very large, and more likely to cause injury. There's more about this on page 200.

8) Newton's second law can also be expressed in terms of force, mass and acceleration. There's more on this on page 197.

Learn this stuff — it'll only take a moment... um.

Make sure you remember that momentum equation at the top of the page and practise using both equations.

Q1 Calculate the momentum of a 220 000 kg aeroplane that is travelling at 250 m/s. [2 marks]

Q2 Calculate the force a golf club needs to apply to a 45 g golf ball to accelerate it from rest to 36 m/s in 10.8 ms. [5 marks]

Conservation of Momentum

Momentum is always <u>conserved</u>. Easy peasy. Go squeeze some lemons.

Momentum Before = Momentum After

Make sure you learn the <u>law of conservation of momentum</u>:

> In a collision when no other external forces act, <u>momentum is conserved</u>
> — i.e. the total momentum <u>after</u> a collision is the <u>same</u> as it was <u>before</u> it.

- Imagine a <u>white</u> snooker ball rolls towards a <u>stationary yellow</u> snooker ball with the <u>same mass</u>. At the point of collision, the <u>yellow ball</u> has a momentum of <u>0</u>, and the <u>white ball</u> has a momentum equal to <u>its mass × its velocity</u> (p.195).
- If after the collision, the white ball <u>stops</u> and the yellow ball <u>moves off</u>, then the yellow ball will have the <u>same velocity</u> as the original velocity of the white ball (assuming there's no friction).
- This is because the <u>white ball</u> will now have a momentum of <u>0</u>, so by conservation of momentum, the <u>yellow ball's momentum</u> must <u>equal</u> the momentum of the white ball <u>before</u> the collision. Since the <u>mass</u> of the balls are the <u>same</u>, the yellow ball must now move with the <u>same velocity</u> as the white ball moved at when it hit the yellow ball.

You can use the idea of conservation of momentum to find the <u>velocity</u> of an object <u>after</u> a <u>collision</u>:

 **EXAMPLE:** Ball A (mass, m_A = 0.08 kg) is moving with an initial velocity (u_A) of 9 m/s towards ball B (mass, m_B = 0.36 kg). Ball B is moving at an initial velocity (u_B) of 3 m/s in the same direction as ball A. The two balls collide. After the collision, ball A is stationary (v_A = 0 m/s) and ball B moves away with a velocity of v_B. Calculate the velocity of ball B after the collision.

Before

 A
u_A = 9 m/s

 B
u_B = 3 m/s

After

 A   B
v_A = 0 m/s v_B = ? m/s

1) First, calculate the <u>total momentum</u> before the collision.

total momentum before = ball A's momentum + ball B's momentum
$$= (m_A \times u_A) + (m_B \times u_B)$$
$$= (0.08 \times 9) + (0.36 \times 3) = 1.8 \text{ kg m/s}$$

2) The total momentum <u>before</u> the collision is <u>equal</u> to the total momentum <u>after</u> the collision.

total momentum before = total momentum after = 1.8 kg m/s

3) Write out the equation for the total momentum <u>after</u> the collision, and substitute in the values you know.

total momentum after = $(m_A \times v_A) + (m_B \times v_B)$
$$1.8 = (0.08 \times 0) + (0.36 \times v_B)$$
$$1.8 = 0 + (0.36 \times v_B)$$

4) Rearrange and <u>solve</u> the equation.

$v_B = 1.8 \div 0.36 = 5 \text{ m/s}$

If two objects collide and <u>join together</u>, then the total momentum of <u>both</u> objects <u>before</u> the collision is equal to the momentum of the <u>combined</u> objects <u>after</u> the collision. So in the example above, if the balls had <u>joined together</u> and moved away at a <u>steady speed</u>, you would have ended up with <u>total momentum after = (mass of A + mass of B) × velocity of the combined balls</u>.

Homework this week — play pool to investigate momentum...

sigh if only. It's probably best to practise questions instead. Much less fun, but definitely useful for your exams.

Q1 A 2.0 kg trolley travelling at 1.5 m/s collides with a 3.0 kg stationary trolley. They then stick together and move off together at a constant speed. Calculate the final velocity of the two trolleys. [4 marks]

Q2 A 20 kg object is travelling to the right at 3 m/s. It hits another 20 kg object travelling to the left at 2 m/s. Following the collision the two objects bounce off each other, and one object moves at a speed of 1 m/s to the left. Calculate the velocity of the other object, assuming that momentum is conserved. [4 marks]

Newton's Second Law and Inertia

In the interests of keeping things moving, this page is on <u>inertia</u>...

Inertial Mass Can be Used in Newton's Second Law

1) When Newton was coming up with his laws of motion, he wrote about how a <u>force applied</u> to an object over a given time affects its <u>amount of motion</u>. He was referring to what we now call <u>momentum</u>.

2) Newton's second law in terms of momentum is:
   <u>change of momentum = resultant force × time for which it acts</u> (p.195).
   But you can also express it in terms of <u>acceleration</u>:

   - (Resultant) force = change of momentum ÷ time (for which the force acts).
   - You know that <u>momentum = mass × velocity</u> from page 195.
   - Substituting this into Newton's 2nd law, you get force = (mass × change in velocity) ÷ time.
   - <u>Acceleration</u> is the <u>change of velocity ÷ time</u>, so you can write this as <u>force = mass × acceleration</u>.

   > *You need to be able to show how to get from one version of Newton's second law to the other.*

3) So <u>Newton's second law</u> in terms of <u>acceleration</u> is:

   | force (N) = mass (kg) × acceleration (m/s²) | or | $F = m \times a$ |

Inertia Explains Why it's Harder to Move a Hammer Than a Feather

1) <u>Inertia</u> is the tendency for an object's <u>motion</u> to <u>remain unchanged</u> — i.e. <u>stationary</u> objects tend to <u>remain stationary</u> and <u>moving</u> objects tend to <u>keep moving</u>.

2) You learnt that an object's <u>mass</u> is the <u>amount of matter</u> in an object on p.185. But you can <u>also</u> define mass in terms of <u>inertia</u>.

3) The <u>inertial mass</u> of an object is the <u>measure</u> of <u>how difficult</u> it is to <u>change the velocity</u> of the object.

4) You can define inertial mass using Newton's second law. <u>Inertial mass = force ÷ acceleration</u>, i.e. inertial mass is the <u>ratio</u> of the applied <u>force</u> to the <u>acceleration it causes</u>.

> Imagine that a <u>bowling ball</u> and a <u>golf ball</u> roll towards you with the <u>same velocity</u>. You would find it <u>more difficult</u> to stop the <u>bowling ball</u> than the <u>golf ball</u> — a <u>larger force</u> would be required to <u>stop</u> the bowling ball in a <u>given time</u>.
>
> This is because the bowling ball has a <u>larger inertial mass</u> than the golf ball, so it is <u>more difficult</u> to change its motion (velocity).

Newton's Three Laws Required Creativity

So now you've met all of Newton's laws of motion. They're some of the most important laws in physics and are brilliant <u>examples</u> of needing lots of <u>imagination</u> to come up with a <u>scientific explanation</u> to observations. Newton expressed the laws in a way that meant they could be applied to <u>any</u> scenario, which meant that they could be <u>tested</u> over many years.

> *Some people think that Newton's creation of the laws of motion was one of the major intellectual advances in our understanding of the world.*

Over the years, <u>observations</u> and <u>discussions</u> have <u>agreed</u> with Newton's three laws of motion. His three laws are considered <u>scientific knowledge</u> (p.221).

Accelerate your learning — force yourself to revise...

A lot to get your head around on this page, but the physics is dead useful. $F = ma$ crops up all over the place.

Q1 A full shopping trolley and an empty one are moving at the same speed. Explain why it is easier to stop the empty trolley than the full trolley over the same amount of time. [2 marks]

Reaction Times

Go long! You need fast <u>reaction times</u> to avoid getting hit in the face when playing catch.

You can Measure Reaction Times with the Ruler Drop Test

<u>Everyone's</u> reaction time is different and many different <u>factors</u> affect it (see next page).
<u>Typical</u> human reaction times are between <u>0.2 s and 0.6 s</u>.
You can do a <u>simple experiment</u> to investigate your reaction time.
As reaction times are <u>so short</u>, you haven't got a chance of measuring one with a <u>stopwatch</u>.
One way of measuring reaction times is to use a <u>computer-based test</u> (e.g. <u>clicking a mouse</u> when the screen changes colour). Another is the <u>ruler drop test</u>:

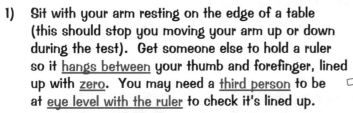

1) Sit with your arm resting on the edge of a table (this should stop you moving your arm up or down during the test). Get someone else to hold a ruler so it <u>hangs between</u> your thumb and forefinger, lined up with <u>zero</u>. You may need a <u>third person</u> to be at <u>eye level with the ruler</u> to check it's lined up.

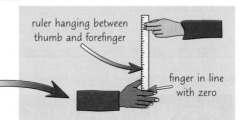

ruler hanging between thumb and forefinger

finger in line with zero

2) Without giving any warning, the person holding the ruler should <u>drop it</u>. Close your thumb and finger to try to <u>catch the ruler as quickly as possible</u>.

3) The measurement on the ruler at the point where it is caught is <u>how far</u> the ruler fell in the time it took for you to react.

4) The <u>longer</u> the <u>distance</u>, the <u>longer</u> your <u>reaction time</u>.

5) You can calculate <u>how long</u> the ruler falls for (your <u>reaction</u> time) because <u>acceleration due to gravity is constant</u> (roughly 10 m/s^2).

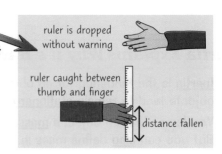

ruler is dropped without warning

ruler caught between thumb and finger

distance fallen

> E.g. say you catch the ruler at 20 cm. From p.188 you know:
>
> (final speed)^2 – (initial speed)^2 = 2 × acceleration × distance
>
> Initial speed = 0, acceleration = 10 m/s^2 and distance = 0.2 m, so:
>
> final speed = $\sqrt{2 \times \text{acceleration} \times \text{distance} + (\text{initial speed})^2}$ = $\sqrt{2 \times 10 \times 0.2 + 0}$ = <u>2 m/s</u>
>
> As initial speed is zero, final speed is equal to the <u>change in speed</u> of the ruler.
>
> From page 188 you also know: acceleration = change in speed ÷ time, so
>
> time = change in speed ÷ acceleration = 2 ÷ 10 = <u>0.2 s</u>.
>
> This gives your <u>reaction time</u>.

6) It's <u>pretty hard</u> to do this experiment <u>accurately</u>, so you should do a lot of <u>repeats</u>. The results will be better if the ruler falls <u>straight down</u> — you might want to add a <u>blob of modelling clay</u> to the bottom to stop it from waving about.

7) Make sure it's a <u>fair test</u> — use the <u>same ruler</u> for each repeat and have the <u>same person</u> dropping it.

8) You could try to investigate some factors affecting reaction time, e.g. you could introduce <u>distractions</u> by having some <u>music</u> playing or by having someone <u>talk to you</u> while the test takes place.

Test a friend's reaction time by throwing this book at them...

Not really. Instead re-read this page and make sure you can describe the experiment. Much more fun.

Q1 Briefly describe one method other than the ruler drop test that can be used to investigate reaction times. [2 marks]

Q2 Mark's reaction time is tested using the ruler drop test. He catches the ruler after it has fallen a distance of 16.2 cm. Calculate Mark's reaction time. [4 marks]

Stopping Distances

Knowing what affects stopping distances is useful for everyday life, as well as the exam.

Stopping Distance = Reaction Distance + Braking Distance

1) In an emergency (e.g. a hazard ahead in the road), a vehicle driver may perform an emergency stop.

2) This is where maximum force is applied by the brakes in order to stop the vehicle in the shortest possible distance. The longer it takes to perform an emergency stop, the higher the risk of crashing.

3) The distance it takes to stop a vehicle in an emergency (its stopping distance) is the sum of the reaction distance and the braking distance, i.e. stopping distance = reaction distance + braking distance.

The reaction distance is the distance the vehicle travels in the driver's reaction time (the time between noticing the hazard and applying the brakes). It's affected by two main factors:

- Your reaction time — the longer your reaction time, the longer your reaction distance. It is affected by tiredness, alcohol, drugs and distractions.

- Your speed — the faster you're going, the further you'll travel during your reaction time.

The braking distance is the distance taken to stop once the brakes have been applied. It's affected by:

- Your speed — the faster you're going, the further it takes to stop (see below).

- The mass of the vehicle — a vehicle full of people and luggage won't stop as quickly as an empty one.

- The condition of the brakes — worn or faulty brakes won't be able to brake with as much force.

- How good the grip of your tyres is — you're more likely to skid when the road is dirty or if it's icy or wet. If the tyres are bald (they don't have any tread left) this can lead to them skidding on top of the water.

4) You need to be able to describe the factors affecting a vehicle's stopping distance and how this affects safety — especially in an emergency.

5) E.g. icy conditions increase the chance of skidding (and so increase the stopping distance) so driving too close to other cars in icy conditions is unsafe. The longer your stopping distance, the more space you need to leave in front in order to stop safely.

Braking Relies on Friction Between the Brakes and Wheels

1) When the brake pedal is pushed, this causes brake pads to be pressed onto the wheels.

2) This contact causes friction, which causes work to be done.

3) The work done (p.162) between the brakes and the wheels transfers energy away from the kinetic energy stores (p.202) of the wheels.

4) You can write this as work done by the brakes = energy transferred away from kinetic energy store, or:
braking force × braking distance = 0.5 × mass of vehicle × (speed of vehicle)^2.

5) So the faster a vehicle is going, the more energy it has in its kinetic energy stores, and the more work needs to be done to stop it.

6) In an emergency stop, where the maximum braking force is applied, this means that the faster the vehicle is going before the emergency stop, the longer its braking distance.

7) As speed increases, reaction distance increases at the same rate as the speed. The driver's reaction time will stay fairly constant, but the higher the speed, the further you go in that time (p.187).

8) However, because of that (speed)^2 in the equation for energy in kinetic energy stores, braking distance and speed have a squared relationship — e.g. if speed doubles, braking distance increases 4-fold (2^2).

Stop right there — and learn this page...

Bad visibility also causes accidents — if it's foggy, it's harder to notice a hazard, so there's less room to stop.

Q1   A 1000 kg car travelling at 25 m/s makes an emergency stop. It brakes with a force of 5000 N.
Estimate the braking distance of the car, using ideas about energy in the car's kinetic store.   [5 marks]

Vehicle Safety

You need to know about <u>large decelerations</u> and how they can be reduced to <u>prevent injuries</u>.

Large Decelerations can be Dangerous

1) The <u>faster</u> an object is going, the <u>more momentum</u> it has.
   A <u>force</u> is needed to <u>change</u> this momentum (see p.195).

2) The <u>larger</u> the <u>change of momentum</u> or the <u>quicker</u> this change happens
   (i.e. the <u>larger</u> the <u>acceleration</u>), the <u>larger</u> the <u>force</u> on the object.

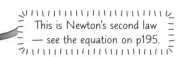
This is Newton's second law
— see the equation on p195.

3) So for events like <u>car crashes</u>, where the momentum changes a lot in a short amount of time, the
   <u>forces</u> acting on the <u>car</u> and its <u>passengers</u> are very <u>large</u>. These <u>large forces</u> can cause <u>injuries</u>.

4) <u>Very large decelerations</u> can also be <u>dangerous</u> because they may cause brakes to <u>overheat</u>.
   This means the brakes won't work as well.

5) Very large decelerations may also cause the vehicle to <u>skid</u>.

Safety Features Reduce Forces in Collisions

<u>Safety features</u> in cars are designed to <u>increase collision times</u>.
This <u>reduces</u> the <u>deceleration</u> and <u>forces</u>, and so reduces the risk of injury.

<u>Seat belts</u>

- In vehicles (e.g. cars), the <u>seat belts</u> are designed to
  <u>stretch</u> slightly when a large force is applied to them.
- This slows passengers down over a <u>longer period of time</u> during a crash.
- This means the <u>forces</u> on the passengers during the crash are
  <u>smaller</u>, so they're <u>less likely</u> to harm the passengers.

<u>Air bags</u>

- <u>Air bags</u> in cars inflate rapidly if there's a collision, so the passengers
  hit the <u>compressible</u> air bag instead of the <u>solid</u> dashboard.
- Like seat belts, this means passengers slow
  down over a <u>longer period of time</u>.

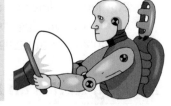

<u>Crumple zones</u>

- <u>Crumple zones</u> are areas at the front and back of a car which <u>crumple up easily</u> in a collision.
- This increases the time taken for the <u>whole car</u> to stop,
  which reduces the forces on the car <u>and</u> the passengers.

<u>Safety helmets</u>

- <u>Motorbike</u> and <u>bicycle helmets</u> contain a <u>crushable layer</u> of foam.
- In a collision, the foam is compressed, which increases the
  <u>time taken</u> for the cyclist's head to stop. This will <u>reduce</u> the
  <u>force</u> on a cyclist's head if they're in an accident.

It's thanks to our understanding of <u>Newton's laws of motion</u> that we have been able to <u>improve</u>
<u>technologies</u> like these, as well as <u>develop new materials</u> that have improved the <u>safety</u> of travelling.

It's enough to put you off learning to drive, isn't it...

So there you go — why not amaze your friends with these fun safety facts next time you're popping a
seat belt on? Make sure you can explain how each safety feature helps reduce the risk of passengers getting hurt.

Q1 Explain why a car braking and undergoing a large deceleration is dangerous. [3 marks]

Q2 Explain how cycle helmets are designed to reduce
    the risk of a cyclist being injured in a collision. [2 marks]

Work Done and Energy Transfers

This page is all about <u>work</u>. But not the kind you're already doing by reading this book.
Oh no, this is all about our old friends <u>energy transfers</u> (have a look over at page 162 for more about these).

Work is Done When a Force Moves an Object

When a <u>FORCE</u> makes an object <u>MOVE</u>, <u>ENERGY IS TRANSFERRED</u> and <u>WORK IS DONE</u>.

1) Whenever something begins to <u>move</u>, or <u>changes</u> how it's moving (e.g. speeds up, slows down or changes direction), something is providing some sort of <u>effort</u> (force) to move it.

2) If a <u>force</u> is exerted <u>on</u> the object, you can say that <u>work is done on the object</u> by the force. Energy is transferred <u>to</u> the object's energy stores.

See Chapter P2 for lots more about energy.

3) Similarly, if the <u>object</u> itself exerts the force (or transfers energy in a different way, see page 162), work is done <u>by the object</u> and energy is transferred <u>from</u> the object's energy stores.

4) Whether this energy is <u>transferred usefully</u> (e.g. by <u>lifting a load</u>) or <u>wasted</u> (e.g. dissipated by <u>heating</u> from <u>friction</u>), you still say that '<u>work is done</u>'. 'Work done' and '<u>energy transferred</u>' are <u>the same</u>.

5) The <u>formula</u> to calculate the <u>amount of work done</u> (energy transferred) when an object is moved through a distance by a force is:

$$\text{work done (Nm or J)} = \text{force (N)} \times \text{distance (m)} \quad \text{or} \quad W = F \times d$$

The <u>distance</u> here is the distance moved <u>along</u> the <u>line of action</u> of the <u>force</u> (i.e. the distance moved in the <u>direction</u> of the force).

6) Work done is sometimes given in newton-metres, <u>Nm</u>, but it's the same as joules, <u>J</u>. <u>1 Nm = 1 J</u>. You need to be able to <u>convert</u> between the two, e.g. 5 Nm = 5 J.

They said joule, Dave.

Energy is Always Conserved

1) You saw back on page 163 that for <u>any</u> event or process, <u>energy is always conserved</u>.

2) So if in the process you're looking at, the <u>energy before doesn't equal the energy after</u>, you know that process <u>can't happen</u>.

3) If a process <u>can</u> happen, the formulas for <u>work done</u> (above) and the <u>energy</u> in certain <u>stores</u> (the next page) can be used to <u>calculate what will happen</u>. But they <u>cannot</u> explain <u>why</u> a process happens.

4) In situations where there are <u>no frictional forces</u> acting (i.e. no <u>friction</u>, no <u>air resistance</u> etc.), the <u>work done</u> on an object will be <u>equal</u> to the energy transferred to <u>useful energy stores</u>.

> If a force does work on an object and <u>increases</u> its <u>velocity</u> (along the line of action of the force), <u>energy is transferred</u> to the object's <u>kinetic energy store</u> (p.202). <u>If there's no friction</u>, the energy in the kinetic energy store will <u>equal</u> the <u>work done</u> on the object by the force.

5) In most processes in the <u>real world</u>, some work must be done <u>against</u> resistive forces.

6) This causes some energy to be <u>dissipated</u> (p.163), usually through <u>heating</u>.

7) So if there are <u>frictional forces</u> and work is done <u>to</u> an object, the <u>energy transferred</u> to the object's <u>useful</u> energy store (p.164) <u>won't equal</u> the <u>work done</u> to cause the energy transfer.

> <u>Work is done</u> on an object to <u>increase</u> its <u>velocity</u>. <u>Frictional forces</u> act on the object. The energy in the <u>kinetic</u> energy store of the object will be <u>less than</u> the <u>work done</u> by the <u>force applied to move the object</u>. <u>Some</u> energy will be transferred to <u>thermal stores</u>. The <u>work done</u> to move the object will <u>equal</u> the energy in the objects <u>kinetic energy store</u> + the energy in thermal energy stores.

8) If work is done <u>by</u> the object, work done = energy transferred <u>from</u> the object's <u>useful energy store</u>.

Energy transfers can be a lot of work...

Work done is just energy transferred. Make sure you remember how work done is related to motion and forces.

Q1 A book sliding across a table has 1.25 J of energy in its kinetic energy store. Friction from the table provides a constant force of 5.0 N. Calculate the distance travelled by the book before it stops. [3 marks]

Kinetic and Potential Energy Stores

This page covers two types of <u>energy stores</u> (p.162) and how to calculate <u>how much</u> energy is in them.

An Object at a Height has Energy in its Gravitational Potential Energy Store

1) When an object is at any <u>height</u> above the Earth's surface,
   it will have <u>energy</u> in its <u>gravitational potential energy (g.p.e.) store</u>.

2) When an object is <u>raised</u>, energy is <u>transferred to</u> its gravitational potential energy store.

3) When it is <u>lowered</u>, or <u>falls</u>, energy is <u>transferred away</u> from its gravitational potential energy store.

4) You need to be able to <u>describe</u> the energy transfers in terms of <u>work done</u> when these things happen.

> When an object is <u>lifted above the ground</u>, work is done <u>by the lifting force</u> (against gravity)
> to move the object. Energy is transferred to the object's <u>gravitational potential energy store</u>.
> Assuming there's <u>no friction</u> or <u>air resistance</u>, when the object stops moving, the <u>work done</u> to
> lift the object will be <u>equal</u> to the energy transferred to its <u>gravitational potential energy store</u>.

5) You can <u>calculate</u> the <u>amount</u> of <u>energy</u> in the
   gravitational potential energy store using the equation:

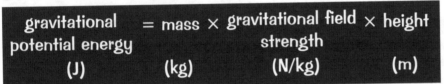

$$\text{gravitational potential energy (J)} = \text{mass (kg)} \times \text{gravitational field strength (N/kg)} \times \text{height (m)}$$

or

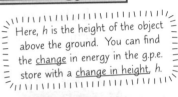

$$GPE = m \times g \times h$$

> *Here, h is the height of the object above the ground. You can find the <u>change</u> in energy in the g.p.e. store with a <u>change in height, h</u>.*

A Moving Object has Energy in its Kinetic Energy Store

1) When an object is <u>moving</u>, it has <u>energy</u> in its <u>kinetic energy store</u>.

2) This <u>energy</u> depends on both the object's <u>mass</u> and <u>speed</u>.

3) The <u>greater its mass</u> and the <u>faster it's going</u>, the <u>more</u> energy it has in its kinetic energy store.

4) You need to remember and know how to use the <u>formula</u>:

$$\text{kinetic energy (J)} = 0.5 \times \text{mass (kg)} \times (\text{speed})^2 \ (\text{m/s})^2$$

or

$$KE = \tfrac{1}{2} \times m \times v^2$$

EXAMPLE: A car of mass 1450 kg is travelling at 28 m/s. Calculate the
energy in its kinetic energy store, giving your answer to 2 s.f.

kinetic energy = 0.5 × mass × (speed)²
        = 0.5 × 1450 × 28²
        = 568 400 = 570 000 J (to 2 s.f.)

> *Watch out for the (speed)², that's where people tend to make mistakes and lose marks.*

5) You need to be able to use <u>this equation</u> and the one above to <u>calculate</u>
   energy transfers in a given process or event (e.g. a falling object).

6) Remember, <u>energy is always conserved</u>. So if you <u>assume</u> there are no frictional forces,
   <u>energy lost/gained by the kinetic store = energy gained/lost by the gravitational potential store</u>.

There's potential for a joke here somewhere...

More equations to learn here. Look on the bright side, at least you don't have to learn something like
$G_{\mu\nu} = 8\pi G(T_{\mu\nu} + \rho_\Lambda g_{\mu\nu})$. And we all know what that equation is — altogether now, it's... erm...*

Q1   Calculate the energy in the gravitational potential energy store
of a 0.80 kg ball at a height of 1.5 m above the Earth's surface.   [2 mark]

Q2   An otter is swimming with a speed of 2.0 m/s. It has a mass of 4.9 kg.
Calculate the energy in the otter's kinetic energy store.   [2 mark]

*don't panic, you <u>really</u> don't need to know what this is.

Energy Transfers and Power

Whenever I think of <u>power</u>, I have to stop myself from plotting world domination whilst stroking a cat.

You Might Need to Describe How Energy is Transferred

<u>Transfers of energy</u> result in a change in the <u>system</u> (p.162). If you understand a few different <u>examples</u>, it'll be easier to think through whatever they ask you about in the exam.

<u>A BALL THROWN UPWARDS OR:</u> energy is transferred <u>mechanically</u> from the <u>kinetic energy store</u>
<u>ROLLING UP A SLOPE</u> of the ball to its <u>gravitational potential energy store</u>.

<u>A BAT HITTING A (STATIONARY) BALL:</u> some energy in the <u>kinetic energy store</u> of the bat is transferred <u>mechanically</u> to the <u>thermal energy stores</u> of the bat, the ball and their surroundings. Some energy is transferred <u>mechanically</u> from the <u>kinetic energy store</u> of the bat to the <u>kinetic energy store</u> of the ball. The <u>rest</u> of the energy is carried away by <u>sound</u>.

<u>A CAR SLOWING DOWN:</u> when you apply the brakes in a car, <u>work is done</u> and energy is transferred <u>mechanically</u> from the <u>kinetic</u> energy store of the <u>car</u> to the <u>thermal</u> energy stores of the <u>brakes</u>. Energy is also transferred <u>by heating</u> to the <u>thermal</u> energy store of the <u>environment</u> and some energy is carried away by <u>sound</u>.

<u>A SKYDIVER FALLING TO EARTH:</u> energy is transferred <u>mechanically</u> from the <u>gravitational potential energy</u> store of the skydiver to his <u>kinetic energy store</u>. The rest of the energy would be <u>dissipated</u> through <u>heating</u> and <u>sound</u> due to air resistance.

Power is the 'Rate of Energy Transfer' — i.e. How Much per Second

<u>Power</u> is the <u>rate</u> at which <u>energy is transferred</u> (or work is done) in a system.

1) The proper unit of power is the <u>watt</u> (<u>W</u>). <u>1 W = 1 J of energy transferred per second</u> (J/s).

2) So, the power of a <u>machine</u> is the <u>rate</u> at which it <u>transfers energy</u>. For example, if an <u>electric drill</u> has a power of <u>700 W</u> this means it can transfer <u>700 J</u> of energy (or do 700 J of work) <u>every second</u>.

3) This is the <u>very easy formula</u> for power:

power (W) = energy transferred (J) ÷ time (s) or $P = E \div t$

EXAMPLE: A motor transfers 4.8 kJ of useful energy in 2 minutes. Find its power output.

1) <u>Convert</u> the values to the <u>correct units</u> first. 4.8 kJ = 4800 J and 2 mins = 120 s

2) <u>Substitute</u> the values into the power equation. power = energy transferred ÷ time
= 4800 ÷ 120 = **40 W**

4) Electrical appliances are <u>useful</u> because they have <u>high powers</u>. If you <u>calculate</u> how much work is done to, e.g. <u>lift</u> a <u>heavy crate</u> or even just to <u>climb</u> a bunch of <u>stairs</u>, you'll see that it requires a <u>lot</u> of energy.

5) Machines can often transfer energy <u>much quicker</u> than people — their <u>power output</u> is much larger than a person's. This makes them dead handy as it <u>reduces</u> the <u>time</u> taken to do loads of <u>everyday tasks</u>.

Watt's power? Power's watts...

Phew, you've reached the end of the chapter. Well done — do these questions then have a break. You've earned it.

Q1 Describe the energy transfers for a falling ball landing on the ground without bouncing. [3 marks]

Q2 Calculate the energy transferred by a 12 W power supply in 5.0 minutes. [3 marks]

Revision Questions for Chapter P4

Phew! It's the end of Chapter P4. Now it's time to see what you've got in the bag and what needs work.

- Try these questions and tick off each one when you get it right.
- When you've done all the questions for a topic and are completely happy with it, tick off the topic.

Forces (p.184-186) ☑

1) What is the definition of an interaction pair? ☑
2) What is Newton's third law of motion? Give an example of it in action. ☑
3) What is the difference between mass and weight? How can weight be calculated? ☑
4) True or false? Velocity is a scalar quantity. ☑

Speed and Acceleration (p.187-191) ☑

5) What is the equation for calculating the average speed of an object? ☑
6) Define acceleration. ☑
7) Describe an experiment to investigate the acceleration of a trolley down a ramp. ☑
8) How is the average speed of an object found from its distance-time graph? ☑
9) What does a flat section on a velocity-time graph represent? ☑
10) How is the distance travelled by an object found from its velocity-time graph? ☑

Newton's First and Second Laws (p.192-197) ☑

11) Draw a free body diagram of a remote-controlled car travelling at a constant speed. ☑
12) Explain how to use a scale drawing to find the resultant force on an object. ☑
13) What is Newton's first law of motion? ☑
14) Give the equation for momentum in terms of mass and velocity. ☑
15) Give the equation for Newton's second law in terms of momentum. ☑
16) True or false? The total momentum before a collision always equals the total momentum after it. ☑
17) What is inertial mass? ☑
18) Give the equation for Newton's second law in terms of acceleration. ☑

Reaction Times and Stopping Distances (p.198-200) ☑

19) Describe the ruler drop test which is used to measure reaction times. ☑
20) What is meant by a driver's reaction time? ☑
21) State two factors which affect the braking distance of a vehicle. ☑
22) True or false? If the speed of a car trebles, its braking distance increases by a factor of 9. ☑
23) Explain how crumple zones reduce the risk of injury in a crash. ☑

Energy Transfers (p.201-203) ☑

24) Give the equation for the work done on an object when it's moved a certain distance by a force. ☑
25) How does the energy in an object's gravitational potential energy store vary with height? ☑
26) Give the equation for the energy in the kinetic energy store of a moving object. ☑
27) What is meant by power? How is power calculated? ☑

Developing the Model of the Atom

All this started with a Greek fella called Democritus in the 5th Century BC. He thought that all matter, whatever it was, was made up of identical lumps called "atomos". And that's as far as it got until the 1800s...

Rutherford Came up with the Nuclear Model...

1) In 1804 John Dalton agreed with Democritus that matter was made up of tiny spheres ("atoms") that couldn't be broken up, but he reckoned that each element was made up of a different type of "atom".

2) Nearly 100 years later, J. J. Thomson discovered particles called electrons that could be removed from atoms. So Dalton's theory wasn't quite right. This led scientists to believe that atoms were spheres of positive matter with tiny negative electrons stuck in them like currants in a cake.

3) That theory didn't last long though. The Rutherford-Geiger-Marsden alpha particle scattering experiment fired a beam of alpha particles (see p.206) at thin gold foil. It was expected that the particles would pass straight through the gold sheet, or only be slightly deflected. But although most of the particles did go straight through the sheet, some were deflected more than expected, and a few were deflected back the way they had come — something the original model couldn't explain.

4) These results provided evidence that the gold atom was mostly empty space — most of the alpha particles weren't deflected. It also provided evidence that the atom had a central, tiny nucleus containing most of the atom's mass (as most alpha particles passed straight through, but some were deflected by large angles) which was positively charged (because it repelled positively-charged alpha particles). This led to the first nuclear model of the atom in 1910. (All models with a nucleus are called nuclear models.)

...Which Developed into the Modern Nuclear Model of the Atom

1) Rutherford, Geiger and Marsden's nuclear model described the atom as a positively charged nucleus orbited by a cloud of negative electrons.

2) Scientists realised that electrons in a 'cloud' around the nucleus of an atom like this would be attracted to the nucleus, causing the atom to collapse. Niels Bohr got round this by adapting the initial model to show that electrons orbiting the nucleus can only do so at certain distances.

3) This means that electrons can move within (or sometimes leave) the atom.

Take a look at p.156 for more on electrons around the nucleus and how they can move within the atom.

The Modern Model of the Atom

Each atom has a tiny nucleus at its centre that makes up almost all of the mass of the atom. It contains protons (which are positively charged — they have a +1 relative charge) and neutrons (which are neutral, with a relative charge of 0) — which gives it an overall positive charge. It is about 100 000 times smaller than the diameter of the atom.

The rest of the atom is mostly empty space. Negative electrons (relative charge −1) whizz round the outside of the nucleus really fast. They give the atom its overall size — the diameter of an atom is about 1×10^{-10} m (which is also quite tiny).

Atoms can join together to form molecules. Small molecules are roughly the same size as an atom (1×10^{-10} m).

The number of protons = the number of electrons, as protons and electrons have an equal but opposite charge and atoms have no overall charge. If atoms lose or gain electrons and become charged, they become ions (p.156).

Our current nuclear model of the atom has evolved over time. At every stage, scientists had to use logic and reasoning to create a model which would be able to explain all the available evidence. Old models were rejected, and either old models were modified or new ones created or adapted to explain all the evidence.

These models don't have anything on my miniature trains...

That's a whole lot of history, considering this is a book about physics. It's all good, educational fun though.

Q1   a) Describe the modern model of the atom.   [4 marks]
       b) State the diameter of an atom and describe how this compares to the size of its nucleus.   [2 marks]

Isotopes and Radioactive Decay

Understanding what <u>isotopes</u> are is important for learning about <u>radioactive decay</u>. So let's get cracking.

Isotopes are Different Forms of the Same Element

1) The <u>atomic or proton number</u> is the <u>number of protons</u> in an atom's <u>nucleus</u>.

2) This can also be thought of as the <u>charge</u> of the nucleus, as all protons have the <u>same positive charge</u> ($+1$) and all neutrons are <u>neutral</u>.

> Remember, electrons have a charge of −1. They are sometimes written as $_{-1}^{0}e$ — see p.207.

3) The <u>identity</u> of an <u>element</u> is <u>defined</u> by the <u>number of protons</u> in the atom. <u>Nuclei</u> of an element <u>always</u> have the <u>same number of protons</u>, (e.g. a carbon atom <u>always</u> has <u>6 protons</u>) but they can have <u>different amounts</u> of <u>neutrons</u>.

4) This means that the nucleus of <u>each element</u> has a <u>particular</u> positive <u>charge</u> (e.g. carbon <u>always</u> has a charge of $+6$).

5) The <u>mass number</u> is the <u>number of protons</u> plus the <u>number of neutrons</u> in an atom. It tells you the <u>mass</u> of the <u>nucleus</u> (the <u>nuclear mass</u>).

6) You can <u>represent</u> atoms using this <u>notation</u>:

Mass number —— **A** — Chemical symbol
Atomic number —— **Z** **X**

7) <u>Isotopes</u> of an element are atoms that have the <u>same</u> number of <u>protons</u> as each other but a <u>different</u> number of <u>neutrons</u>. E.g. $_{6}^{12}C$, $_{6}^{13}C$ and $_{6}^{14}C$ are all <u>isotopes of carbon</u>. So different isotopes of an element have <u>different nuclear masses</u> but the <u>same nuclear charge</u>.

8) <u>Most elements</u> have different isotopes, but there are usually only one or two <u>stable</u> ones.

9) The nuclei of other <u>unstable isotopes</u> tend to <u>decay</u> into <u>other elements</u> and give out <u>radiation</u> as they try to become more stable. This process is called <u>radioactive decay</u>.

10) Substances containing unstable isotopes are <u>radioactive</u> — they <u>always</u> emit one or more types of <u>ionising radiation</u> from their <u>nucleus</u> — <u>alpha particles</u>, <u>beta particles</u>, <u>gamma rays</u> or <u>neutrons</u>.

11) <u>Ionising radiation</u> is radiation that knocks <u>electrons</u> off atoms, creating <u>positive ions</u>. The ionising <u>power</u> of radiation is how <u>easily</u> it can do this.

You Need to Know These Four Types of Ionising Radiation

- An <u>alpha</u> particle (α) is <u>two neutrons</u> and <u>two protons</u> — the same as a <u>helium nucleus</u>. They have a <u>relative mass of 4</u> and a <u>relative charge of +2</u>.
- They are relatively <u>big</u>, <u>heavy</u> and <u>slow moving</u>.

- A <u>beta</u> particle (β) is identical to an <u>electron</u>, with <u>virtually no mass</u> and a <u>relative charge of −1</u>.
- <u>Beta particles</u> move <u>quite</u> fast and are <u>quite</u> small.
- For every <u>beta particle</u> emitted, a <u>neutron</u> turns into a <u>proton</u> in the nucleus.

- <u>After</u> spitting out an alpha or beta particle, the nucleus might need to get rid of some <u>extra energy</u>. It does this by emitting a <u>gamma ray</u> — a type of <u>electromagnetic radiation</u> with a <u>high frequency</u>.
- Gamma rays (γ) have <u>no mass</u> and <u>no charge</u>. They <u>just transfer energy</u>, so they <u>don't</u> change the element of the nucleus that emits them.

- If a nucleus contains <u>a lot</u> of <u>neutrons</u>, it may just <u>throw out</u> a neutron.
- The <u>number of protons</u> stays the <u>same</u>, but it now has a <u>different nuclear mass</u>, so it becomes a <u>different isotope</u> of the <u>same element</u>.

Isotopes of an outfit — same dress, different accessories...

I'd learn those alpha, beta, gamma and neutron radiations if I were you. They'll be coming up again, mark my words.

Q1 An oxygen atom has 8 protons and 8 neutrons.
    Which one of the following represents an isotope of this oxygen atom?

    A: $_{9}^{17}O$ B: $_{7}^{16}O$ C: $_{8}^{17}O$ D: $_{9}^{16}O$ [1 mark]

Penetration Properties and Decay Equations

Time to learn a bit <u>more</u> about some of the types of radiation before putting them in <u>equations</u>. How thrilling.

Different Types of Radiation Have Different Penetration Properties

1) How <u>far</u> radiation can travel through a material before it's <u>absorbed</u> (how far it can <u>penetrate</u> a material) depends on the <u>ionising power</u> of the radiation and <u>material</u> it's travelling through.

2) <u>Alpha particles</u> have the <u>highest</u> ionising power — this means that they <u>can't</u> travel <u>very far</u> through a substance without hitting an atom and <u>ionising</u> it. <u>Gamma radiation</u> has the <u>lowest</u> ionising power — it can penetrate <u>far</u> into materials before it is <u>stopped</u>.

- <u>Alpha particles</u> are blocked by e.g. <u>paper</u>.
- <u>Beta particles</u> are blocked by e.g. thin <u>aluminium</u>.
- <u>Gamma rays</u> are blocked by e.g. <u>thick lead</u>.

The alpha and beta particles would also be blocked by the lead, and the alpha particles would also be blocked by the aluminium.

Sheet of paper stops alpha   Thin aluminium stops beta   Thick lead stops gamma

You Need to be Able to Balance Nuclear Equations

You can write nuclear decays as <u>nuclear equations</u>. You need to be able to <u>balance</u> these equations for <u>alpha</u>, <u>beta</u>, <u>gamma</u> and <u>neutron</u> decays by balancing the total <u>masses (mass numbers)</u> and <u>charges</u> (atomic numbers) on each side.

Emitting an Alpha Particle

- The <u>mass decreases by 4</u> — it <u>loses</u> two protons and two neutrons.
- The <u>charge decreases by 2</u> — because it has <u>two less</u> protons.

Radium decaying to radon: $^{226}_{88}\text{Ra} \rightarrow \,^{222}_{86}\text{Rn} + \,^{4}_{2}\text{He}$

| mass number: | 226 | $\rightarrow$ | 222 | + | 4 (= 226) |
| atomic number: | 88 | $\rightarrow$ | 86 | + | 2 (= 88) |

You can also write the alpha particle as $^{4}_{2}\alpha$ and the beta particle as $^{0}_{-1}\beta$ in equations.

Emitting a Beta Particle

A neutron changes into a proton, so:

- The <u>mass doesn't change</u> — as it has <u>lost</u> a neutron but <u>gained</u> a proton.
- The <u>nuclear charge increases by 1</u> — because it has <u>one more</u> proton.

Carbon decaying to nitrogen: $^{14}_{6}\text{C} \rightarrow \,^{14}_{7}\text{N} + \,^{0}_{-1}\text{e}$

| mass number: | 14 | $\rightarrow$ | 14 | + | 0 | (= 14) |
| atomic number: | 6 | $\rightarrow$ | 7 | + | (–1) | (= 6) |

In both alpha and beta emissions, a new element will be formed, as the number of protons changes.

Emitting a Gamma Ray

- The <u>mass doesn't change</u>.
- And the charge <u>doesn't change</u>.

Iodine decaying to a more stable atom of iodine: $^{130}_{53}\text{I} \rightarrow \,^{130}_{53}\text{I} + \,^{0}_{0}\gamma$

Emitting a Neutron

- The <u>mass decreases by 1</u> — because it has one less neutron.
- The <u>nuclear charge doesn't change</u>.

Helium decaying to a different isotope of helium: $^{5}_{2}\text{He} \rightarrow \,^{4}_{2}\text{He} + \,^{1}_{0}\text{n}$

I think balancing equations is more fun than anything ever...

Right? Right?? *cough* I can't see your face, but I'm going to take a wild guess and say you don't believe me.

Q1   A uranium nucleus (U), with an atomic number of 238 and a mass number of 92, decays into a thorium (Th) atom by emitting an alpha particle. Write a balanced equation to show this decay.   [3 marks]

Activity and Half-life

Radioactive decay is <u>totally random</u>, so how can we know how an isotope will decay? I give you, <u>half-lives</u>.

The Radioactivity of a Sample Always Decreases Over Time

1) <u>Radioactive decay</u> is a <u>random process</u> — you <u>can't predict</u> exactly <u>which</u> nucleus in a sample will decay next, or <u>when</u> any one of them will decay.

2) But each <u>nucleus</u> of a given <u>isotope</u> has a <u>fixed chance</u> of decaying. You can use this to work out the <u>time</u> it takes for the <u>amount of radiation</u> emitted by a source to <u>halve</u> — known as the <u>half-life</u>. It can be used to make <u>predictions</u> about radioactive sources, even though their decays are <u>random</u>.

3) The <u>number of unstable nuclei</u> that <u>decay</u> in a given time is called the <u>activity</u> and is measured in <u>becquerels (Bq)</u> — the number of nuclei that decay each second. So you can define half-life as:

> The half-life of a source is the average time taken for its activity to halve.

4) It's also the <u>average time taken</u> for <u>half</u> of the remaining <u>unstable nuclei</u> of a given <u>isotope</u> to <u>decay</u>.

5) Each time a radioactive nucleus <u>decays</u> to become a <u>stable nucleus</u>, the activity of the sample will <u>decrease</u>. So over time, the activity <u>always decreases</u>.

6) A <u>short half-life</u> means the <u>activity falls quickly</u>, because <u>lots</u> of the nuclei decay in a <u>short time</u>. A <u>long half-life</u> means the activity <u>falls more slowly</u> because <u>most</u> of the nuclei don't decay <u>for a long time</u>.

7) A <u>Geiger-Muller tube</u> can detect <u>radiation</u> that has been emitted from a decaying nucleus. It measures the <u>count rate</u> — the number of radiation counts that reach a Geiger-Muller tube in a <u>given time</u>.

Half-life can be Calculated from Numbers or from a Graph

You could be asked to <u>calculate</u> how you'd expect the <u>activity</u> of a source to <u>change over time</u>:

A <u>sample</u> of a radioactive isotope has an <u>activity of 1000 Bq</u> and a <u>half-life of 5 years</u>:

- After <u>1 half-life</u> (<u>5 years</u>) the activity will be 1000 ÷ 2 = <u>500 Bq</u>.
- After <u>2 half-lives</u> (<u>10 years</u>) the activity will be 500 ÷ 2 = <u>250 Bq</u>.

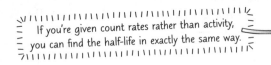
If you're given count rates rather than activity, you can find the half-life in exactly the same way.

You also need to be able to find the half-life of a sample from a <u>graph</u>...

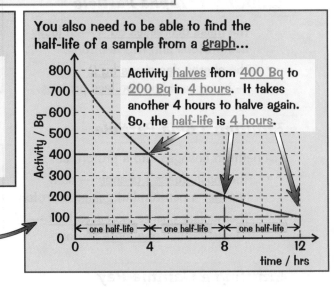

Activity <u>halves</u> from <u>400 Bq</u> to <u>200 Bq</u> in <u>4 hours</u>. It takes another 4 hours to halve again. So, the <u>half-life</u> is <u>4 hours</u>.

EXAMPLE: The half-life of a radioactive sample is 30 minutes. Calculate how long it will take for the activity of the radioactive sample to fall to one quarter of its initial value, A

1) Find how many <u>half-lives</u> it will take for the activity to fall to <u>one quarter</u> of its <u>initial value</u>.

2) Calculate <u>how long</u> this is using the value for the half-life.

Initially: after 1 half-life: after 2 half-lives:

A $(÷2) →$ $\frac{A}{2}$ $(÷2) →$ $\frac{A}{4}$

2 × 30 minutes = **60 minutes (or 1 hour)**

Half-life of a box of chocolates — about five minutes...

To measure half-life, you time how long it takes for the activity to halve. This can be in seconds, days, years...

Q1 The half-life of a radioactive source is 60 hours. The initial activity of the sample is 2000 Bq. Calculate the activity of the radioactive source after 10 days. [2 marks]

Dangers of Radioactivity

Time to find out about the hazards of <u>ionising radiation</u> — it <u>damages</u> living cells when it ionises atoms in them.

Ionising Radiation Harms Living Cells

1) Ionising radiation can <u>enter living cells</u> and <u>interact with molecules</u>.

2) These interactions cause <u>ionisation</u> (see p.156).

3) <u>Lower doses</u> of ionising radiation <u>damage living cells</u> by causing <u>mutations</u> in the <u>DNA</u>. This can cause the cell to <u>divide uncontrollably</u> — which is <u>cancer</u>.

4) <u>Higher doses</u> tend to <u>kill cells completely</u>, which causes <u>radiation sickness</u> if a lot of cells <u>all get blasted at once</u>.

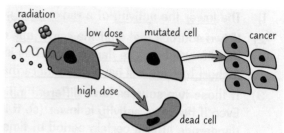

radiation · low dose · mutated cell · cancer · high dose · dead cell

All Radioactive Sources Have Irradiation and Contamination Risks

1) Whenever your body is <u>exposed</u> to radiation, there is a risk that your cells will be <u>damaged</u>.

2) If <u>radiation</u> from a <u>radioactive source</u> reaches your body, you are being <u>irradiated</u>.

3) As the <u>distance</u> between you and the source <u>increases</u>, the amount of radiation reaching your body decreases. So standing <u>far</u> from a source is one way to <u>reduce irradiation</u>. Other ways to reduce irradation are to <u>not point</u> sources <u>directly at people</u> and to store them in <u>lead-lined boxes</u> when not in use.

4) If a radioactive source ends up <u>on</u> or <u>inside</u> your body, your body is <u>contaminated</u>.

5) How <u>likely</u> you are to be contaminated <u>depends on the source</u>. If it's a <u>solid</u>, but you <u>don't touch</u> it, there's <u>very little</u> chance of contamination. However, radioactive <u>gases</u> can spread and be <u>inhaled</u>, so contamination is much more <u>likely</u>.

6) Wearing <u>gloves</u> or using <u>tongs</u> reduces the chance of particles getting stuck to you or under your nails and so <u>reduce</u> the chance of <u>contamination</u>.

7) <u>Irradiation is temporary</u> — if the source is <u>taken away</u>, any irradiation it's causing stops, and it no longer poses a risk to your health.

8) <u>Contamination lasts longer</u> — if the <u>original source</u> is taken away, the contaminating atoms are <u>left behind</u>.

9) So contamination by a <u>given</u> source poses a <u>higher risk</u> of harm than irradiation as cells in the body will be <u>exposed</u> to ionising radiation until the source <u>leaves the body</u>.

The Hazards Depend on the Type of Radiation

1) <u>Outside</u> the body, <u>beta</u> and <u>gamma</u> sources are the most dangerous.

2) This is because <u>beta particles</u> and <u>gamma rays</u> can both <u>penetrate the body</u> and get to delicate <u>organs</u>. <u>Gamma rays</u> can <u>penetrate further</u>, so they are <u>more dangerous</u> than beta particles.

3) Alpha particles are the <u>least dangerous</u> because they <u>can't penetrate the skin</u> and are easily blocked by a <u>small air gap</u>.

4) <u>Inside the body</u>, <u>alpha</u> particles are the <u>most</u> dangerous, because they do all their damage in a <u>very localised area</u>.

5) <u>Beta</u> particles are <u>less damaging</u> inside the body, as radiation is absorbed over a <u>wider area</u>, and some <u>passes out</u> of the body altogether.

6) <u>Gamma</u> rays are the <u>least dangerous</u> inside the body, as they mostly <u>pass straight out</u> without doing any damage — they have the <u>lowest ionising power</u>.

Top tip number 364 — if something is radioactive, don't lick it...

If you're working with radioactive sources, read about the safety risks and make experiments as safe as possible.

Q1   Give two effects that ionisation caused by radiation can have on living cells.   [2 marks]

Half-life and Uses of Radiation

Ionising radiation is very <u>dangerous</u> stuff, but used in the <u>right way</u> it can be so useful that it <u>saves lives</u>.

The Hazards Associated with a Radioactive Source Depend on its Half-Life

1) The <u>lower</u> the <u>activity</u> of a <u>radioactive source</u>, the <u>safer</u> it is to be around.

2) If two sources that emit the <u>same type</u> of radiation start off with the <u>same activity</u>, the one with the <u>longer</u> half-life will be <u>more dangerous</u>. This is because, after <u>any period</u> of time, the activity of the source with a <u>short half-life</u> will have <u>fallen more</u> than the activity of the source with a <u>long half-life</u>.

3) If those two sources have <u>different initial activities</u>, the danger associated with them changes over time. Even if its <u>initial activity</u> is lower (so it is <u>initially safer</u>), the source with the <u>longer half-life</u> will be <u>more dangerous</u> after a certain period of time because its <u>activity</u> falls <u>more slowly</u>.

4) The <u>half-life</u> can be used to work out <u>how long</u> it is before a radioactive source becomes <u>relatively safe</u>.

Tracers in Medicine — Short Half-life Gamma Emitters

1) Certain <u>radioactive isotopes</u> that emit <u>gamma</u> radiation are used as <u>tracers</u> in the body.

2) They can be <u>injected</u> or <u>ingested</u> (<u>drunk</u> or <u>eaten</u>) to see how parts of the body, e.g. organs, are <u>working</u>.

3) They <u>spread</u> through the body and their progress is followed on the outside using a <u>radiation detector</u>.

4) They need a relatively <u>short half-life</u> — i.e. <u>a few hours</u>, so that the source becomes relatively safe <u>quite quickly</u>, but long enough that it still emits <u>enough radiation</u> by the time it reaches the correct place.

5) <u>Medical tracers</u> are <u>GAMMA</u> (never alpha) sources. Gamma radiation <u>penetrates tissue</u>, so can <u>pass out the body</u> and be <u>detected</u>. Alpha and beta <u>can't</u> and cause more damage <u>in the body</u> compared to gamma.

Radiotherapy — the Treatment of Cancer Using Radiation

1) Since high doses of radiation will <u>kill living cells</u>, they can be used to <u>treat cancers</u>.

2) The radiation is <u>directed carefully</u> and at a specific <u>dosage</u> (depending on the <u>size</u> and <u>type of tumour</u>, and <u>size and age of patient</u>), so it kills the <u>cancer cells</u> without damaging too many <u>normal cells</u>.

3) Radiation can be used to <u>remove</u> tumours completely or to <u>control</u> and <u>stop</u> them <u>spreading further</u>.

4) However, a <u>fair bit of damage</u> is often done to <u>normal cells</u>, which makes the patient feel <u>very ill</u>.

5) Before ionising radiation is used as part of any medical treatment, both the <u>patient</u> and <u>doctor</u> need to make an <u>informed decision</u> on whether the <u>benefits outweigh the risks</u>.

<u>To treat cancer externally</u> (using <u>gamma rays</u>):
- The gamma rays are <u>focused</u> on the tumour using a <u>wide beam</u>.
- The patient stays <u>still</u> and the beam is <u>rotated</u> round them with the tumour at the centre.
- This <u>minimises</u> the exposure of <u>normal cells</u> to radiation so the <u>damage</u> to <u>healthy tissue</u> is <u>limited</u>.
- The treatment is given in doses with <u>time between</u> for the healthy cells to be <u>repaired or replaced</u>.

Source rotated outside the body.

γ rays focused on tumour

<u>To treat cancer internally</u>:
- <u>Implants</u> containing <u>beta-emitters</u> are placed <u>next to</u> or <u>inside</u> the tumour. The beta particles damage the cells in the tumour, but have a <u>short enough range</u> that the <u>damage</u> to <u>healthy tissue</u> is <u>limited</u>.
- An implant with a <u>long half-life</u> should be <u>removed</u> to stop the radiation killing healthy cells once the cancerous cells have been killed. If the half-life is <u>short</u> enough, the implant can be <u>left in</u>.
- <u>Alpha-emitters</u> can be injected into a tumour. Alpha particles are <u>strongly ionising</u>, so they do lots of damage to the cancer cells. But as they have a <u>short range</u>, damage to normal tissue is <u>limited</u>.

healthy cells
implant emitting radiation
tumour

So radiation is pretty handy in medicine...

Try making lists of when and why the different types of radiation are used in medicine to see what you've learnt.

Q1   Explain why radioactive sources that emit gamma radiation are used as medical tracers.   [2 marks]

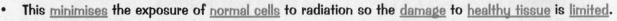

Revision Questions for Chapter P5

So that's it for Chapter P5 — not long, but full of really important information.

- Try these questions and tick off each one when you get it right.
- When you've done all the questions for a topic and are completely happy with it, tick off the topic.

The Model of the Atom (p.205) ☑

1) Briefly explain how the model of the atom has changed over time. ☑
2) True or false? Atoms have no overall charge. ☑
3) What happens to an atom if it loses one or more of its electrons? ☑

Isotopes, Radioactive Decay and Half-life (p.206-208) ☑

4) What is the atomic number of an atom equal to: the nuclear charge or the nuclear mass? ☑
5) What number is equal to the number of protons + the number of neutrons in the nucleus? ☑
6) What defines the identity of an element: the nuclear charge or the nuclear mass? ☑
7) What is an isotope? Are they usually stable? ☑
8) True or false? Gamma radiation can be stopped by a thin sheet of aluminium. ☑
9) Draw the symbols for both alpha and beta radiation in nuclear equations. ☑
10) What type of radioactive decay doesn't change the mass or charge of the nucleus? ☑
11) What is the activity of a source? What are its units? ☑
12) Define half-life. ☑
13) True or false? A short half-life means a small proportion of unstable nuclei are decaying per second. ☑
14) Explain how you would find the half-life of a source, given a graph of its activity over time. ☑

Dangers and Uses of Radiation (p.209-210) ☑

15) Explain how exposure to radiation can lead to cancer. ☑
16) What is meant by irradiation? ☑
17) What is meant by contamination? ☑
18) Compare the hazards of being irradiated and contaminated by:
   a) an alpha source,   b) a gamma source. ☑
19) Give one example of how to protect against: a) contamination,   b) irradiation. ☑
20) Explain the dangers of a radioactive source with a long half-life. ☑
21) Explain what sort of half-life a source must have in order to be used as a medical tracer. ☑
22) Apart from medical tracers, give one other way that radiation is used in medicine. ☑

Density

Time for some <u>maths</u> I'm afraid. But at least it comes with a fun experiment, so it's not all bad...

Density is Mass per Unit Volume

<u>Density</u> is a measure of the '<u>compactness</u>' (for want of a better word) of a substance.
<u>Mass</u> (the <u>amount of matter</u> in a substance) depends on the <u>density</u> of the substance,
and its <u>volume</u> (the amount of <u>space</u> it takes up).

Density is <u>defined</u> by:

$$\text{density (kg/m}^3\text{)} = \frac{\text{mass (kg)}}{\text{volume (m}^3\text{)}}$$

$$\frac{m}{\rho \times V}$$

The symbol for density is a Greek letter, rho (ρ) — it looks like a p but it isn't.

The <u>units</u> of density are g/cm³ or kg/m³.
The density of an object depends on what it's <u>made</u> of. Density <u>doesn't vary</u> with <u>size</u> or <u>shape</u>.

You Can Measure the Density of Solids and Liquids

1) To <u>measure</u> the density of a substance, measure the <u>mass</u> and <u>volume</u>
   of a sample of the substance and use the formula above.

2) You can measure the <u>mass</u> of a solid or liquid using a <u>mass balance</u> (see page 233).

3) To measure the volume of a <u>liquid</u>, you can just pour it into a <u>measuring cylinder</u>.

4) <u>1 ml = 1 cm³</u>. If you need to convert a volume into other units, e.g. m³, you get the
   <u>scaling factor</u> by <u>cubing</u> the scaling factor that you'd use for converting the <u>distance</u> units.
   For example, to convert 50 cm³ into m³, you need to divide by 100³ = 1 000 000
   (as there are 100 cm in 1 m). So <u>50 cm³</u> = 50 ÷ 1 000 000 = <u>5 × 10⁻⁵ m³</u>.

5) If you want to measure the volume of a <u>solid cuboid</u>, measure its <u>length</u>, <u>width</u>, and <u>height</u>,
   then <u>multiply</u> them together. The volume of <u>any prism</u> is the <u>area</u> of its <u>base</u> multiplied by its <u>height</u>.

6) An object <u>submerged</u> in water will displace a volume of water <u>equal</u> to its <u>own volume</u>.
   You can use this to find the volume of <u>any object</u>. It is particularly useful in finding
   the volume of objects with <u>irregular shapes</u> which can't be easily calculated mathematically.
   You can do this, for example, using a <u>eureka</u> (Archimedes) <u>can</u>:

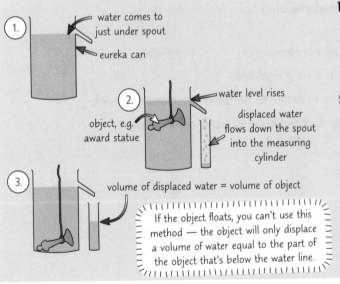

1. water comes to just under spout
    eureka can

2. water level rises
    object, e.g. award statue
    displaced water flows down the spout into the measuring cylinder

3. volume of displaced water = volume of object

If the object floats, you can't use this method — the object will only displace a volume of water equal to the part of the object that's below the water line.

PRACTICAL

1) You need the eureka can
   to be filled so that the water
   level is <u>just under</u> the spout.
   The best way to do this is to <u>slightly over-fill</u>
   the can then let the extra water <u>drain away</u>.

2) Place a measuring cylinder under the spout,
   then <u>gently lower</u> your object in the can, using
   a <u>thin</u>, <u>strong thread</u>. The displaced water will
   start to <u>come out</u> of the spout.

3) Wait for the spout to <u>stop dripping</u>, then
   measure the <u>volume</u> of water collected in
   the <u>cylinder</u>. This is the volume of water
   displaced by the object, which is equal to
   the <u>volume of the object</u>.

4) Repeat three times and calculate a <u>mean</u>.

I'm feeling a bit dense after that lot...

Converting between volume units catches people out all the time, so be careful.

Q1   Describe an experiment to calculate the density of an irregular solid object.   [4 marks]

Q2   An object has a mass of 4.5 × 10⁻² kg and a volume of 75 cm³. Calculate its density in kg/m³.   [3 marks]

The Particle Model of Matter

According to the particle model, everything's made of <u>tiny little balls</u>. The table, this book, your Gran...

The Particle Model is a Way of Modelling Matter

The <u>particle model of matter</u> explains how the particles (atoms and molecules) that make up <u>matter behave</u>.

1) In the <u>particle model</u>, matter is made up of <u>tiny particles</u>. You can <u>think</u> of them as <u>tiny balls</u>.
2) There's <u>nothing</u> in between the tiny balls — they make up <u>all matter</u>
    (e.g. <u>air</u> is made up of <u>tiny particles</u>, and <u>in between</u> there is <u>nothing</u>).
3) A <u>substance</u> is made up of <u>identical particles</u>, and particles of any <u>other</u> substance have <u>different</u> masses.
4) There are <u>attractive</u> forces between the particles. The size of the force <u>differs</u> for different substances.
5) The particles are always <u>moving</u> — <u>how much</u> they can move depends on what <u>state</u> they are in.

The particle model is a key example of how scientists use <u>models</u> to explain observations (see page 221).

The Particle Model Explains the Properties of the States of Matter...

The <u>three states of matter</u> are <u>solid</u> (e.g. ice), <u>liquid</u> (e.g. water) and <u>gas</u> (e.g. water vapour). The <u>particles</u> of a substance in each state are the same — only the <u>arrangement</u> and <u>energy</u> of the particles are different.

SOLIDS — <u>strong</u> forces of attraction hold the particles <u>close together</u> in a <u>fixed</u>, <u>regular</u> arrangement. The particles don't have much <u>energy</u> so they can only <u>vibrate</u> about their fixed positions and can't <u>move away</u> from neighbouring particles. The <u>density</u> is generally <u>highest</u> in this state as the particles are <u>closest together</u>.

LIQUIDS — there are <u>weaker</u> forces of attraction between the particles. The particles are <u>close</u> together, but can <u>slide past</u> each other, and form <u>irregular arrangements</u>. They have <u>more</u> energy than the particles in a solid — they can <u>vibrate</u> and <u>jostle</u> around in <u>random</u> directions at <u>low speeds</u>. Liquids are generally <u>less dense</u> than solids.

GASES — there are <u>no noticeable</u> forces of attraction between the particles. The particles have <u>more energy</u> than in liquids and solids — they're <u>free to move</u> and travel in <u>random directions</u> at <u>high speeds</u>. Gases are generally <u>less dense</u> than liquids — they have <u>low</u> densities.

...and the Effects of Heating a System

1) The particles in a system <u>vibrate</u> or <u>move around</u> — they have energy in their <u>kinetic energy stores</u>.
2) They also have energy in their <u>potential energy stores</u> due to their <u>positions</u>.
3) The <u>energy stored</u> in a system is stored by its <u>particles</u>. The <u>internal energy</u> of a system is the <u>total energy</u> that its particles have in their <u>kinetic</u> and <u>potential</u> energy stores.
4) <u>Experiments</u> combined with <u>mathematical analysis</u> have shown a link between the <u>temperature</u> of a substance and the amount of <u>energy</u> in the <u>kinetic energy stores</u> of its particles — the <u>higher</u> the temperature, the <u>higher</u> the average energy. The <u>particle model</u> can explain this.
5) <u>Heating</u> the system <u>transfers</u> energy to its particles, increasing the <u>internal energy</u>.
6) As the substance is heated, the particles <u>gain</u> energy in their <u>kinetic stores</u> and move <u>faster</u>. The <u>hotter</u> a substance is, the <u>more</u> its particles can <u>move around</u>.
7) If the system is <u>heated</u> to a <u>high enough temperature</u>, the substance will <u>change state</u> (see page 214). During a change in state, energy is transferred by <u>heating</u> to the particles' <u>potential energy stores</u> instead of their <u>kinetic energy stores</u>.
8) So <u>heating</u> a system will either lead to a <u>change in temperature</u> or a <u>change in state</u>.

Particles can't be trusted — they make everything up...

The particle model explains a lot of what's coming up, so make sure you know it inside out.

Q1   Describe how the density of solids, liquids and gases generally varies and explain why this is.   [3 marks]

More on the Particle Model of Matter

The particle model explains all sorts... so why stop after just one page? Read on for more particle model fun...

In a Change of State, Mass is Conserved But Density Changes

1) When you heat a liquid, it boils (or evaporates) and becomes a gas. When you heat a solid, it melts and becomes a liquid. These are both changes of state.

2) The state can also change due to cooling.

3) The changes of state are:

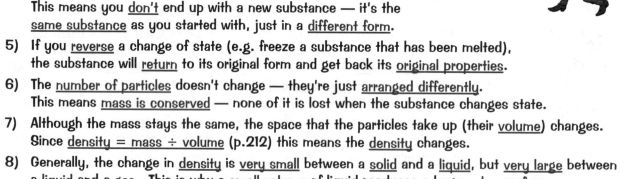

SOLID   freezing   LIQUID   condensing   GAS

melting   evaporating

sublimating

4) A change of state is a physical change (rather than a chemical change). This means you don't end up with a new substance — it's the same substance as you started with, just in a different form.

5) If you reverse a change of state (e.g. freeze a substance that has been melted), the substance will return to its original form and get back its original properties.

6) The number of particles doesn't change — they're just arranged differently. This means mass is conserved — none of it is lost when the substance changes state.

7) Although the mass stays the same, the space that the particles take up (their volume) changes. Since density = mass ÷ volume (p.212) this means the density changes.

8) Generally, the change in density is very small between a solid and a liquid, but very large between a liquid and a gas. This is why a small volume of liquid produces a large volume of gas.

The Particle Model Explains Gas Pressure Too

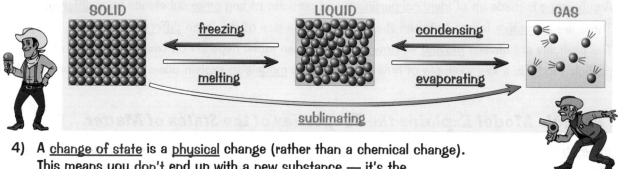

particles collide with the container

net force at right angles to surface

1) As gas particles move about, they randomly bang into each other and whatever else gets in the way, like the walls of their container.

2) Particles are light, but they still have a mass and so a momentum (p.195).

3) When the particles collide with something they change direction, and so change momentum. This exerts a force on the thing they collided with.

4) All these collisions cause a net force at right angles to the inside surface of the container.

5) The force per unit area is the pressure, so the gas exerts a pressure on its container.

6) As you know from the previous page, increasing the temperature of a substance makes its particles move faster. Faster particles exert a larger net force on their container for two reasons:

- As the particles are travelling faster, they hit the sides of the container more often in a given amount of time.

- Faster particles also have a larger momentum. This means the change in momentum, and so the force exerted, is larger when they collide with the container.

7) A larger force means a larger pressure, so as temperature goes up, so does pressure. Temperature and pressure for a gas at a constant volume are proportional to each other.

Gas particles need to watch where they're going...

Remember, the higher the temperature of a gas, the faster the particles travel, and the higher the pressure. Simple.

Q1   Explain what happens to the pressure of a gas in a sealed container with a fixed volume when the particles move slower due to a decrease in temperature.

[3 marks]

Specific Heat Capacity

The energy needed to change the temperature is different for every material...

Heating and Mechanical Work Done are the Same as 'Energy Transferred'

1) In the 18th and 19th centuries, a number of scientists noticed that heating and mechanical work done were both forms of energy transfer. Joule devised experiments that showed that the same amount of mechanical work would always produce the same increase in temperature in a given substance.

> In an electric kettle, energy is transferred electrically from the mains to the thermal energy store of the kettle's heating element. It is then transferred by heating to the thermal energy store of the water (the kinetic energy stores of the particles) — the water's temperature rises.

> When an object slows down, there is a resultant force on it (see page 194). Energy is transferred mechanically (work is done by the force) from the kinetic energy stores of the object to its thermal energy store. This causes a rise in the temperature of the object. Similarly, if an object hits an obstacle, the object (and the obstacle) heats up (p.203).

2) An increase in temperature of a substance is always caused by energy being transferred. It can be transferred by burning a fuel, using an electric heater, or doing mechanical work on the substance. The size of the temperature rise depends on the mass and material of the substance and the energy supplied.

3) It takes more energy to increase the temperature of some materials than others. These materials also release more energy when they cool down. They store more energy for a given temperature change.

4) The energy stored by 1 kg of a material for a 1 °C temperature rise is its specific heat capacity.

$$\text{Change in Internal Energy (J)} = \text{Mass (kg)} \times \text{Specific Heat Capacity (J/kg°C)} \times \text{Change in Temperature (°C)}$$

5) You could be asked to find the energy transferred to or from a system that's changed temperature using this equation. The energy transferred will be equal to the change in the internal energy of the system.

This equation can only be used if there's no change of state.

You can Find the Specific Heat Capacity of a Substance

PRACTICAL

You can use this experiment to find the specific heat capacity of a liquid or a solid.

The joulemeter measures the energy supplied.

1) Use a mass balance to measure the mass of your substance.

2) Set up the experiment shown below. Make sure the joulemeter reads zero.

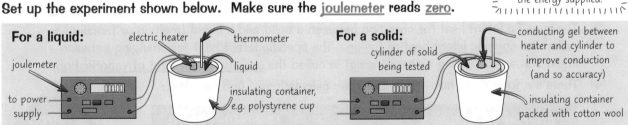

For a liquid: electric heater, thermometer, joulemeter, liquid, insulating container, e.g. polystyrene cup, to power supply

For a solid: cylinder of solid being tested, conducting gel between heater and cylinder to improve conduction (and so accuracy), insulating container packed with cotton wool

3) Make sure that the apparatus is set up correctly and used safely — e.g. make sure not to burn yourself when handling the heater and that there is no chance of the liquid spilling out of the polystyrene cup.

4) Measure the temperature of the substance you're investigating, then turn on the power. Keep an eye on the thermometer. When the temperature has increased by e.g. ten degrees, stop the experiment and record the energy on the joulemeter and the increase in temperature.

You could also use a voltmeter and ammeter instead of a joulemeter — time how long the heater is on for, then calculate the energy supplied (see p.174).

5) Use your results to calculate the specific heat capacity of your substance. Repeat the whole experiment at least three times, then calculate an average specific heat capacity (see p.225).

I wish I had a high specific fact capacity...

Make sure you fully understand that equation — it's a bit of a tricky one.

Q1   If a metal has a specific heat capacity of 420 J/kg°C, calculate how much the temperature of a 0.20 kg block of the metal will increase by if 1680 J of energy are supplied to it. [3 marks]

Specific Latent Heat

If you heat up a pan of water on the stove, the water never gets any hotter than 100 °C. You can carry on heating it up, but the temperature won't rise. How come, you say? It's all to do with latent heat...

You Need to Put In Energy to Break Intermolecular Bonds

1) Remember, when you heat a solid or liquid and the temperature rises, you're transferring energy to the kinetic energy stores of the particles in the substance, making the particles vibrate or move faster.

2) If you heat a substance enough, it will reach its melting or boiling point, and start to change state.

3) When a substance is melting or boiling, energy is transferred to the potential energy stores of the particles as the energy is used to break intermolecular bonds and move the molecules further apart. So the temperature doesn't change but the internal energy increases.

4) There are flat spots on the heating graph at the melting and boiling points where energy is being transferred but the temperature does not change.

5) When a substance is condensing or freezing, bonds are forming between particles, which releases energy. This means the internal energy decreases but the temperature doesn't go down until all the substance has turned into a liquid (condensing) or a solid (freezing).

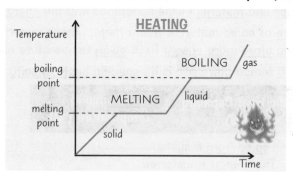
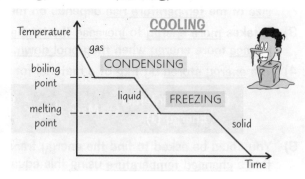

Specific Latent Heat is the Energy Needed to Change State

1) The specific latent heat of a change of state for a substance is the change of energy when 1 kg of the substance changes state without changing its temperature (i.e. the substance has got to be at the right temperature already).

Be careful not to get this confused with specific heat capacity (p.215).

2) Specific latent heat is different for different materials, and for different changes of state.

3) The specific latent heat for changing between a solid and a liquid (melting or freezing) is called the specific latent heat of fusion. The specific latent heat for changing between a liquid and a gas (boiling or condensing) is called the specific latent heat of vaporisation.

4) There's a formula to help you with all the calculations. And here it is:

| Energy to cause a Change of State (J) | = Mass (kg) × | Specific Latent Heat (J/kg) |

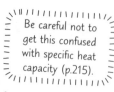

this is specific latent heat

$$\frac{Energy}{Mass \times SLH}$$

EXAMPLE: The specific latent heat of vaporisation for water is 2.26×10^6 J/kg. 2.825×10^6 J of energy is used to boil dry a pan of water at 100 °C. What was the mass of water in the pan?

Energy to cause a change of state = mass × specific latent heat,
so mass = energy to cause a change of state ÷ specific latent heat
= $2.825 \times 10^6 \div 2.26 \times 10^6 = 1.25$ kg

You came across standard form on page 187, e.g. $2.26 \times 10^6 = 2\,260\,000$.

Breaking Bonds — Blofeld never quite manages it...

Remember, whilst there's a change of state, there's no change in temperature.

Q1   Sketch a graph showing how the temperature of a sample of water will change over time as it is constantly heated from −5 °C to 105 °C.   [3 marks]

Forces and Elasticity

Elasticity involves lots of physics and pinging elastic bands at people. Ok, maybe not that last one.

A Deformation can be Elastic or Plastic

1) When you apply forces to an object it can be stretched, compressed or twisted — this is deformation.

2) To deform an object, you need at least two forces. Think of a spring — if you just pull one end of it, and there's no force at the other end, you'll just pull the spring along rather than stretching it.

3) If an object returns to its original shape after the forces are removed, you can say the object is elastic and it has been elastically deformed. If the object doesn't return to its original shape when you remove the forces, the forces were too large. The object has become plastic, and has been plastically deformed.

4) You can explain both elastic and plastic deformation with the particle model of matter (see p.213). Woo.

5) Solids are held in fixed shapes due to the forces between their particles. During elastic deformation the separation between particles changes so the forces between them also change. However, once the applied force has been removed, the particles return to their original positions within the substance.

6) In plastic deformation, the separation and forces between particles change. However, the applied forces are too large, so when they're removed the particles don't return to their original positions. The object is permanently deformed.

The Relationship Between Extension and Force can be Linear or Non-Linear

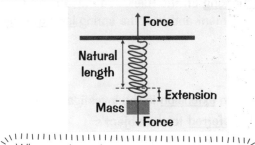

1) If a material is supported at the top and a mass is attached to the bottom, it stretches.

2) In some cases, e.g. a spring, this relationship is linear. The extension (or compression) of the stretched material is directly proportional to the load or force applied.

3) The relationship between the extension of a material and the force is called Hooke's law:

| force exerted by a spring (N) | = | extension (m) | × | spring constant (N/m) |

When a spring and mass are in equilibrium (i.e. the spring isn't stretching any further), the force applied on the spring (the weight of the mass) is equal to the force exerted by the spring upwards on the mass.

$$F = x \times k$$

4) The spring constant depends on the material that you are stretching — a stiffer spring has a greater spring constant.

5) Hooke's law also works for compression (the difference between the natural and compressed lengths).

6) In other cases, the relationship is non-linear, e.g. rubber bands. Force is not proportional to extension.

7) Most objects behave linearly up to a point, and then start to behave non-linearly.

8) The graph shows force against extension for an object being stretched.

9) Up to point P, the graph is a straight line and Hooke's law applies.

10) The gradient of the straight line is equal to the spring constant of the object — the larger the spring constant, the steeper the gradient.

11) Beyond point P, the object no longer obeys Hooke's law. The relationship between force and extension has become non-linear, so the force-extension graph curves and the spring stretches more for each unit increase in force.

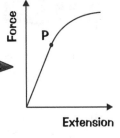

It's important to remember that being 'elastic' doesn't mean an object obeys Hooke's law. Rubber bands are elastic objects. They return to their original shape when released. But they DON'T obey Hooke's Law.

I hope this stuff isn't stretching you too much...

The gradient of a force-extension graph for a material obeying Hooke's law is equal to its spring constant.

Q1 A spring has a natural length of 0.16 m. When a force of 3.0 N is applied to the spring, it stretches linearly and its length becomes 0.20 m. Calculate the spring constant of the spring. [3 marks]

Investigating Hooke's Law

More springs here, but now you actually get to do some experiments with them. Hip hip hooray.

You can Investigate the Extension of a Spring

PRACTICAL

1) Hang your spring from a clamp stand, as shown in the diagram (without the masses, but with the hook the masses hang from), then measure the spring's length using the ruler — this is the spring's original length.
2) Weigh your masses and add them one at a time to the hook hanging from the spring, so the force on the spring increases.
3) After each mass is added, measure the new length of the spring, then calculate the extension: extension = new length – original length
4) Plot a graph of force (weight) against extension using your results and draw a line of best fit.
5) A straight line of best fit is where the spring obeys Hooke's law and the gradient = spring constant (see page 217). If you've loaded the spring with enough masses, the graph will start to curve.
6) Make sure you carry out the experiment safely. You should be standing up so you can get out of the way quickly if the masses fall, and wearing safety goggles to protect your eyes in case the spring snaps.

Spring
Clamp and clamp stand
Hook
Pointer (to help measure the length of the spring)
Masses
Ruler

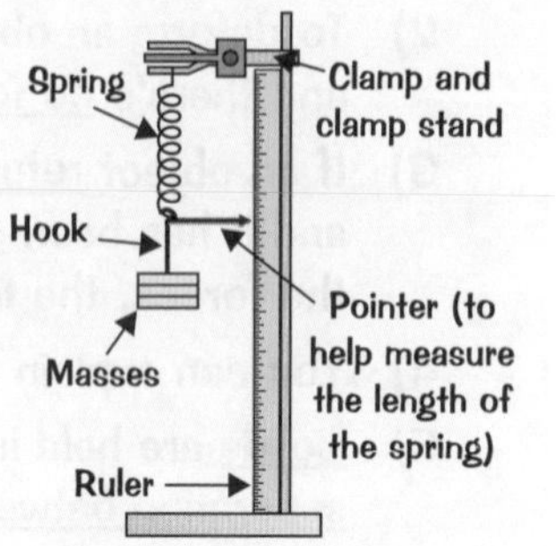

When measuring the length of the spring, you should move yourself so the pointer on the hook is at eye level. Otherwise it could look like it is next to a different marking on the ruler. You also need to make sure the ruler is exactly vertical to get an accurate measurement and that the spring isn't moving.

You Can Find the Work Done in Stretching a Spring

1) You can also find the work done in stretching the spring by a certain extension in the investigation above.
2) When a force deforms an object, work is done and energy is transferred to the object's elastic potential energy store. This energy can be recovered when the forces are removed.
3) For linear relationships, all the energy transferred is stored by the object, so work done = energy stored.
4) The equation for the energy stored in a stretched spring (if it obeys Hooke's Law) is:

energy stored in a stretched spring (J) = ½ × spring constant (N/m) × (extension)² (m)²

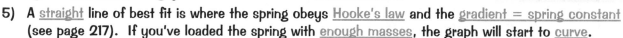

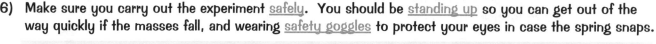

5) This also works for objects obeying Hooke's law that are being compressed. Just use the compression in place of the extension in the equation.

$$E = \frac{1}{2} \times k \times x^2$$

EXAMPLE: A spring has a spring constant of 32 N/m. Calculate the work done on the spring if it is stretched linearly from 0.40 m to 0.45 m.

extension = new length – original length = 0.45 – 0.40 = 0.05 m

energy stored in a stretched spring = 0.5 × spring constant × (extension)² = 0.5 × 32 × 0.05² = **0.04 J**

Remember: work done = energy transferred.

6) You can also find the work done or energy transferred when an object is deformed linearly from its force-extension graph. The work done is equal to the area under the graph up to its current extension.
7) You can find this area by calculating the area of the triangle or by counting squares (p.191).

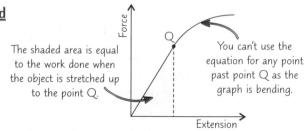

Force
Q
Extension
The shaded area is equal to the work done when the object is stretched up to the point Q.
You can't use the equation for any point past point Q as the graph is bending.

Tell your parents you need to buy a trampoline for your revision...

More energy transfers — you'd better get used to them, there's more of them coming up later on in the book.

Q1 A 1.2 m long spring (k = 54 N/m) extends linearly to 1.3 m. Calculate the work done. [3 marks]

Revision Questions for Chapter P6

Well, that wraps up <u>Chapter P6</u> — now lets see if you know it better than the back of your hand.

*   Try these questions and <u>tick off each one</u> when you <u>get it right</u>.
*   When you've done <u>all the questions</u> for a topic and are <u>completely happy</u> with it, tick off the topic.

<u>Density, Particles, Heating and Cooling (p.212-216)</u> ☑

1) Define 'density'? ☑
2) True or false? According to the particle model, the forces between all particles of any substance are the same. ☑
3) Describe solids, liquids and gases in terms of the movements of their particles. ☑
4) What is the relationship between the temperature of a substance and the average energy in the kinetic energy stores of its particles? ☑
5) Describe and explain the general change in density when a liquid is: a) boiled   b) frozen ☑
6) Explain how the pressure of a gas at constant volume changes with a temperature rise? ☑
7) What is the specific heat capacity of a substance? ☑
8) Describe an experiment to find the specific heat capacity of water. ☑
9) Explain why the temperature of a substance doesn't change when it is melting. ☑
10) What is meant by the specific latent heat of fusion? ☑

<u>Elasticity and Hooke's Law (p.217-218)</u> ☑

11) What is the difference between elastic deformation and plastic deformation? ☑
12) Give the equation that relates the force exerted by a spring with its extension and spring constant. ☑
13) Give an example of an object that doesn't obey Hooke's law. ☑
14) What value can be found by calculating the gradient of a force-extension graph for a material obeying Hooke's law? ☑
15) Describe a simple experiment to investigate Hooke's law. ☑

The Scientific Method

This section isn't about how to 'do' science — but it does show you the way most scientists work...

Scientists Come Up With Hypotheses — Then Test Them

1) Scientists try to explain things. Not only that — they try to explain things really well. There isn't a single scientific method that all scientists use to do this, but scientists do follow certain conventions and scientific principles.

2) They usually start by observing or thinking about a natural phenomenon that they don't understand. They then try to come up with a hypothesis:

Developing scientific explanations involves a cycle of making a hypothesis, collecting data, analysing this data and then adjusting the hypothesis, collecting more data and so on until scientists are convinced the explanation is valid.

- A hypothesis isn't just a summary of their observations (e.g. iron can displace copper from salts).

- It's a tentative explanation (e.g. iron can displace copper from salts because it's more reactive than copper).

- Observations made by scientists are just that — observations. They don't tell you why something happens. In order to come up with a decent explanation for their observations, scientists need to use their imaginations.

- A good hypothesis should account for all of the observations made and any other available data (i.e. what's already been observed). If it doesn't, it's not really a very good explanation.

3) The next step is to test whether the hypothesis might be right or not. This involves making a prediction based on the hypothesis, e.g. that changing a particular factor will affect the outcome of a situation. The prediction is then tested by gathering evidence (i.e. data) from investigations.

Investigations must be designed so data can be collected in a safe, repeatable, accurate way — see pages 223-224.

> For example, a scientist might predict that an increase in temperature will increase the rate of a reaction. This prediction could be written as a statement, or it could be presented visually as a diagram or sketch graph.

4) If evidence from well-conducted experiments backs up a prediction, it increases confidence in the hypothesis — in other words, people are more likely to believe that the hypothesis is true. It doesn't prove a hypothesis is correct though — evidence could still be found that disagrees with it.

5) If the experimental evidence doesn't fit with the hypothesis, then either those results or the hypothesis must be wrong — this decreases confidence in the hypothesis.

Data is collected by measuring scientific quantities such as mass, moles or volume.

6) Sometimes a hypothesis will account for all the data and still turn out to be wrong — that's why every hypothesis needs to be tested further (see next page).

Different Scientists Can Come Up With Different Explanations

1) Different scientists can make the same observations and come up with different explanations for them — and both these explanations might be perfectly good ones. It's the same with data — two scientists can look at the same data and explain it differently.

2) This is because you need to interpret the thing you're observing (or your data) to come up with an explanation for it — and different people often interpret things in different ways.

3) Sometimes a scientist's personal background, experience or interests will influence the way he or she thinks. For example, a trained geneticist might lean towards a genetic explanation for a particular disease, but someone else might think it's more about the environment.

4) In these situations, it's important to test the explanations as much as possible — to see which one is most likely to be true (or whether it's a combination of both or a totally different one).

5) Our ability to test explanations has improved as technology has developed. That's because technology allows us to make new observations and find new evidence. For example, microscopes that have an extremely high magnification have allowed us to understand the structure of nanoparticles (see p.123-124).

6) New data can cause scientists to modify their ideas and hypotheses to fit. E.g.

> When Ernest Rutherford carried out his alpha scattering experiment, he expected the particles to pass straight through a thin sheet of gold foil. The results didn't match his prediction, showing that the plum pudding model of the atom was incorrect, and leading to the development of the nuclear model (see page 89).

The Scientific Method

Several Scientists Will Test a Hypothesis

1) Traditionally, new scientific explanations are announced in peer-reviewed journals, or at scientific conferences.

> A peer-reviewed journal is one where other scientists check results and scientific explanations before the journal is published. They check that people have been 'scientific' about what they're saying (e.g. that experiments have been done in a sensible way). But this doesn't mean that the findings are correct, just that they're not wrong in any obvious kind of way.

2) Once other scientists have found out about a hypothesis, they'll start to base their own predictions on it and carry out their own experiments.

3) When other scientists test the new hypothesis they will also try to reproduce the earlier results. When other scientists can't reproduce a set of results, confidence in those results tends to drop and the scientific community is sceptical about them.

4) When testing a hypothesis, a scientist might get some unexpected results. While these could lead to a change in the hypothesis, they tend to be treated with scepticism until they've been repeated (by the same scientist) and reproduced (by other scientists).

If Evidence Supports a Hypothesis, It's Accepted — for Now

1) If a hypothesis is backed up by evidence from loads of experiments, scientists start to have a lot of confidence in it and accept it as a scientific theory — a widely accepted explanation that can be applied to lots of situations. Our current theories have been tested many times over the years and survived.

2) Once scientists have gone through this process and accepted a theory, they take a lot of persuading to drop it — even if some new data appears that can't be explained using the existing theory.

3) Until a better, more plausible explanation is found (one that can explain both the old and new data), the tried and tested theory is likely to stick around — because it already explains loads of other observations really well. And remember, scientists are always sceptical about new data until it's been proved to be repeatable and reproducible (see page 224).

Theories Can Involve Different Types of Models

Models are used to explain ideas and so help with understanding scientific concepts. They pick out the key features of a system or process, and the rules that determine how the different features work together. This means they can be used to make predictions and solve problems. There are different types of models:

- Representational models are simplified descriptions or pictures of what's going on in real life. E.g. the Bohr model of an atom is a simplified way of showing the arrangement of electrons in an atom (see p.89). It can be used to explain trends down groups in the periodic table.

- Spatial models represent physical space and the position of objects within it. They can be used to predict things like the path that will be taken by a storm.

- Descriptive models are used to describe how things work. For example, describing sound waves as a series of compressions and rarefactions (p.151) explains how sound can travel through materials.

- Mathematical models use patterns found in data from past events to predict what might happen in the future. They require lots of calculations, but modern computers can do these very quickly, which is why many mathematical models are now computational.

- Computational models are mathematical models that use computers. They often involve simulations of complex real-life processes, e.g. climate change.

Models sometimes allow scientists to investigate real-life situations more quickly than they could using experiments (which may also have ethical or practical limitations). However, all models have limitations on what they can explain or predict. For example, climate change models have several limitations — it's hard to take into account all the biological and chemical processes that influence a climate. It can also be difficult to include regional variations in climate.

I'm off to the zoo to test my hippo-thesis...

There's an awful lot to take in here. Make sure you understand it all before moving on as it's really important stuff.

Designing Investigations

Dig out your lab coat and dust down your badly-scratched safety glasses... it's investigation time.

Investigations Produce Evidence to Support or Disprove a Hypothesis

1) Scientists observe things and come up with hypotheses to explain them (see p.220).
You need to be able to do the same. For example:

> Observation: People have big feet and spots.
>
> Hypothesis: People get spots because they have big feet.

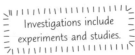
Investigations include experiments and studies.

2) To determine whether or not a hypothesis is right, you need to do an investigation to gather evidence.
To do this, you need to use your hypothesis to make a prediction — something you think will happen
that you can test. E.g. people who have bigger feet will have more spots.

3) Investigations are used to see if there are patterns or relationships between two variables,
e.g. to see if there's a pattern or relationship between the variables 'number of spots' and
'size of feet'. You can also carry out investigations to check someone else's data.

Evidence Needs to be Repeatable, Reproducible and Valid

1) Repeatable means that if the same person does an experiment again using
the same methods and equipment, they'll get similar results.

You'll need to know all the scientific terms on this page, so make sure you understand and learn them.

2) Reproducible means that if someone else does the experiment, or a different
method or piece of equipment is used, the results will still be similar.

3) If data is repeatable and reproducible, it's reliable and scientists are more likely to have confidence in it.

4) Valid results are both repeatable and reproducible AND they answer the original question.
They come from experiments that were designed to be a fair test.

To Make an Investigation a Fair Test You Have to Control the Variables

1) In a lab experiment you usually change one variable and measure how it affects another variable.

2) To make it a fair test, everything else that could affect the results should stay the same
— otherwise you can't tell if the thing you're changing is causing the results or not.

3) The variable you change is called the INDEPENDENT VARIABLE.

4) The variable you measure is the DEPENDENT VARIABLE.

5) Variables that you keep the same are called CONTROL VARIABLES.

> You could find how temperature affects reaction rate by measuring the volume of gas formed over time.
> • The independent variable is the temperature.
> • The dependent variable is the volume of gas produced.
> • Control variables include the concentration and amounts of
>   reactants, the time period you measure, etc.

6) You need to be able to suggest ways to control variables in experiments. For example, you could use
a stop watch to make sure you measure over the same time period, and a measuring cylinder and mass
balance to make sure the amounts of your reactants are always the same.

7) Because you can't always control all the variables, you often need to use a control experiment. This is
an experiment that's kept under the same conditions as the rest of the investigation, but doesn't have
anything done to it. This is so that you can see what happens when you don't change anything at all.

You Can Devise Procedures to Produce or Characterise Substances

You also need to know how to carry out experiments where you produce or characterise a substance.
There's lots more information on these in previous chapters. For example, when you carry out a reaction to
form a salt (see p.142-143), you're producing a substance (the salt). And when you test a gas to work out
its identity (see p.86), you're characterising a substance.

Chapter BCP7 — Ideas About Science

Designing Investigations

Investigations Can be Hazardous

1) A <u>hazard</u> is something that can <u>potentially cause harm</u>. Hazards include:

- <u>Microorganisms</u>, e.g. some bacteria can make you ill.
- <u>Chemicals</u>, e.g. sulfuric acid can burn your skin and alcohols catch fire easily.
- <u>Fire</u>, e.g. an unattended Bunsen burner is a fire hazard.
- <u>Electricity</u>, e.g. faulty electrical equipment could give you a shock.

Hmm... Where did my bacteria sample go?

2) Part of planning an investigation is making sure that it's <u>safe</u>.

3) You should always make sure that you <u>identify</u> all the hazards that you might encounter. Then you should think of ways of <u>reducing the risks</u> from the hazards you've identified. For example:

- If you're working with <u>sulfuric acid</u>, always wear safety goggles to reduce the risk of the acid coming into contact with your eyes. Also, use the lowest concentration possible.
- If you're working with a <u>Bunsen burner</u>, keep it on the safety flame when you're not using it. This will reduce the risk of accidently putting something flammable in the flame, like your clothes.

You can find out about potential hazards by looking in textbooks, doing some internet research or asking your teacher.

The Bigger the Sample Size the Better

Sometimes, your investigation might involve sampling a population — in which case you'll need to <u>decide how big</u> your sample size is going to be. There are a couple of things you need to bear in mind:

1) Data based on <u>small samples</u> isn't as good as data based on large samples. A sample should <u>represent</u> the <u>whole population</u> (i.e. it should share as many of the characteristics in the population as possible) — a small sample can't do that as well. It's also harder to spot <u>outliers</u> (see next page) if your sample size is too small.

2) The <u>bigger</u> the sample size the <u>better</u>, but scientists (and you) have to be <u>realistic</u> when choosing how big. For example, if a scientist was studying the effects of living near a nuclear power plant, it'd be great to study <u>everyone</u> who lived near a nuclear power plant (a huge sample), but it'd take ages and cost loads. It's more realistic to study a thousand people, with a mixture of ages, gender, and race.

Trial Runs Help Figure out the Range and Interval of Variable Values

1) It's a good idea to do a <u>trial run</u> first — a <u>quick version</u> of your experiment. Trial runs are used to figure out the <u>range</u> of variable values used in the proper experiment (the upper and lower limits).

2) If you <u>don't</u> get a <u>change</u> in the dependent variable at the upper values in the trial run, you might <u>narrow</u> the range in the proper experiment. But if you still get a <u>big change</u> at the upper values you might <u>increase</u> the range.

3) And trial runs can be used to figure out the <u>interval</u> (gaps) between the values too. The intervals <u>can't be too small</u> (otherwise the experiment would take ages), or <u>too big</u> (otherwise you might miss something).

For example, if you were investigating how <u>temperature</u> affects the <u>rate of a reaction</u>...
- You might do a trial run with a range of 10-50 °C. If there was no observable reaction at the lower end (e.g. 10-20 °C), you might <u>narrow the range</u> to 20-50 °C for the proper experiment.
- If using 10 °C intervals gives you a big change in the rate of reaction, you might decide to use 5 °C intervals, e.g. 20, 25, 30, 35 °C...

This is no high street survey — it's a designer investigation...

Not only do you need to be able to plan your own investigations, you should also be able to look at someone else's plan and decide whether or not it needs improving. Those examiners aren't half demanding.

Collecting Data

You've designed the perfect investigation — now it's time to get your hands mucky and <u>collect some data</u>.

Your Data Should be Repeatable, Reproducible, Accurate and Precise

1) To <u>check repeatability</u> you need to <u>repeat</u> the readings and check that the results are similar. You need to repeat each reading at least <u>three times</u>.

2) To make sure your results are <u>reproducible</u> you can cross check them by taking a <u>second set of readings</u> with <u>another instrument</u> (or a <u>different observer</u>).

3) Your data also needs to be ACCURATE. Really accurate results are those that are <u>really close</u> to the <u>true answer</u>. The accuracy of your results usually depends on your <u>method</u> — you need to make sure you're measuring the right thing and that you don't <u>miss anything</u> that should be included in the measurements. E.g. estimating the <u>amount of gas</u> released from a reaction by <u>counting the bubbles</u> isn't very accurate because you might <u>miss</u> some of the bubbles and they might have different <u>volumes</u>. It's <u>more accurate</u> to measure the volume of gas released using a <u>gas syringe</u> (see p.234).

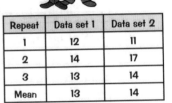
Brian's result was a curate.

Repeat	Data set 1	Data set 2
1	12	11
2	14	17
3	13	14
Mean	13	14

Data set 1 is more precise than data set 2.

4) Your data also needs to be PRECISE. Precise results are ones where the data is <u>all really close</u> to the <u>mean</u> (average) of your repeated results (i.e. not spread out).

Your Equipment has to be Right for the Job

1) The measuring equipment you use has to be <u>sensitive enough</u> to measure the changes you're looking for. For example, if you need to measure changes of 1 cm³ you need to use a measuring cylinder that can measure in 1 cm³ steps — it'd be no good trying with one that only measures in 10 cm³ steps.

2) The <u>smallest change</u> a measuring instrument can <u>detect</u> is called its RESOLUTION. E.g. some mass balances have a resolution of 1 g, some have a resolution of 0.1 g, and some are even more sensitive.

3) Also, equipment needs to be <u>calibrated</u> by measuring a known value. If there's a <u>difference</u> between the <u>measured</u> and <u>known value</u>, you can use this to <u>correct</u> the inaccuracy of the equipment.

You Need to Look out for Errors and Outliers

Random errors and errors in making observations mean that data can never be completely relied on.

1) The results of your experiment will always <u>vary a bit</u> because of RANDOM ERRORS — unpredictable differences caused by things like <u>human errors</u> in measuring. E.g. the errors you make when reading from a measuring cylinder are random. You have to estimate or round the level when it's between two marks — so sometimes your figure will be a bit above the real one, and sometimes it will be a bit below.

2) You can <u>reduce</u> the effect of random errors by taking <u>repeat readings</u> and finding the <u>mean</u>. This will make your results <u>more accurate</u>.

If there's no systematic error, then doing repeats and calculating a mean can make your results more accurate.

3) If a measurement is wrong by the <u>same amount every time</u>, it's called a SYSTEMATIC ERROR. For example, if you measured from the very end of your ruler instead of from the 0 cm mark every time, all your measurements would be a bit small. Repeating the experiment in the exact same way and calculating a mean <u>won't</u> correct a systematic error.

4) Just to make things more complicated, if a systematic error is caused by using <u>equipment</u> that <u>isn't zeroed properly</u>, it's called a ZERO ERROR. For example, if a mass balance always reads 1 gram before you put anything on it, all your measurements will be 1 gram too heavy.

5) You can <u>compensate</u> for some systematic errors if you know about them though, e.g. if your mass balance always reads 1 gram before you put anything on it you can subtract 1 gram from all your results.

6) Sometimes you get a result that <u>doesn't fit in</u> with the rest at all. This is called an OUTLIER. You should investigate it and try to <u>work out what happened</u>. If you can work out what happened (e.g. you <u>measured</u> or <u>recorded</u> something <u>wrong</u>) you can <u>ignore</u> it when processing your results — otherwise you should treat it as real <u>data</u>.

Watch what you say to that mass balance — it's very sensitive...

Weirdly, data can be really precise but not very accurate. For example, a fancy piece of lab equipment might give results that are really precise, but if it's not been calibrated properly those results won't be accurate.

Processing and Presenting Data

Once you've got your <u>data</u>, you need to <u>interpret</u> it. This means doing a bit of <u>maths</u> to make it <u>more useful</u>.

Data Needs to be Organised and Processed

1) Tables are dead useful for <u>recording results</u> and <u>organising data</u>. When you draw a table <u>use a ruler</u> and make sure <u>each column</u> has a <u>heading</u> (including the <u>units</u>).

2) When you've done repeats of an experiment you should always calculate the <u>mean</u> (a type of average that gives the best estimate of a value from your results). To do this, <u>add together</u> all the data values and <u>divide by</u> the total number of values in the sample. ← *Ignore outliers when calculating these.*

3) You might also need to calculate the <u>range</u>. This tells you how spread out the data is. To do this, find the <u>largest</u> number and <u>subtract</u> the <u>smallest</u> number from it. The bigger the range, the less precise the data (and so the less confidence you can have in it).

EXAMPLE: The results of an experiment to find the mass of gas lost from a reaction are shown below. Calculate the mean and the range for the mass of gas lost in the reaction.

Test tube	Repeat 1 (g)	Repeat 2 (g)	Repeat 3 (g)
A	30	34	32

mean = (30 + 34 + 32) ÷ 3
= 32 g
range = 34 − 30 = 4 g

You should also be able to calculate the median and mode (two more types of average).

If Your Data Comes in Categories, Present It in a Bar Chart

You should be able to draw charts and plot graphs from results in a table.

1) Once you've recorded and processed your results, you should <u>present</u> them in a nice <u>chart</u> or <u>graph</u> to help you <u>spot any patterns</u> in your data.

2) If the independent variable is <u>categoric</u> (comes in distinct categories, e.g. colour, state) you should use a <u>bar chart</u> to <u>display</u> the data. You also use them if the independent variable is <u>discrete</u> (the data can be counted in chunks, where there's no in-between value, e.g. number of bacteria is discrete because you can't have half a bacterium). Here are the <u>rules</u> you need to follow for <u>drawing</u> bar charts:

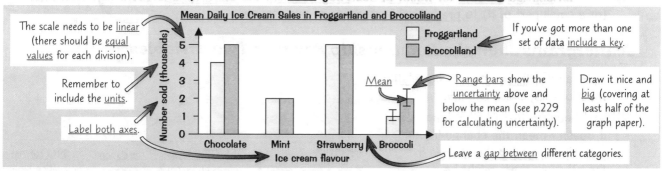

The scale needs to be <u>linear</u> (there should be <u>equal values</u> for each division).

Remember to include the <u>units</u>.

<u>Label both axes</u>.

If you've got more than one set of data <u>include a key</u>.

Range bars show the <u>uncertainty</u> above and below the mean (see p.229 for calculating uncertainty).

Draw it nice and <u>big</u> (covering at least half of the graph paper).

Leave a <u>gap between</u> different categories.

If Your Data is Continuous, Plot a Graph

If both variables are <u>continuous</u> (numerical data that can have any value within a range, e.g. length, volume, temperature) you should use a <u>graph</u> to display the data. Here are the rules for plotting points on a graph:

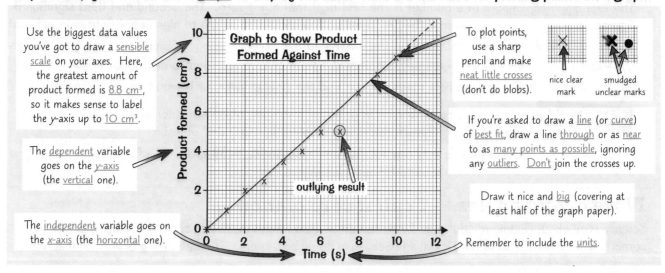

Use the biggest data values you've got to draw a <u>sensible scale</u> on your axes. Here, the greatest amount of product formed is <u>8.8 cm³</u>, so it makes sense to label the y-axis up to <u>10 cm³</u>.

The <u>dependent</u> variable goes on the <u>y-axis</u> (the <u>vertical</u> one).

The <u>independent</u> variable goes on the <u>x-axis</u> (the <u>horizontal</u> one).

To plot points, use a sharp pencil and make <u>neat little crosses</u> (don't do blobs). *nice clear mark / smudged unclear marks*

If you're asked to draw a <u>line</u> (or <u>curve</u>) of <u>best fit</u>, draw a line <u>through</u> or as <u>near</u> to as <u>many points as possible</u>, ignoring any <u>outliers</u>. <u>Don't</u> join the crosses up.

Draw it nice and <u>big</u> (covering at least half of the graph paper).

Remember to include the <u>units</u>.

Processing and Presenting Data

Graphs Can Give You a Lot of Information About Your Data

1) The <u>gradient</u> (slope) of a graph tells you how quickly the <u>dependent variable</u> changes if you change the <u>independent variable.</u>

$$\text{gradient} = \frac{\text{change in } y}{\text{change in } x}$$

You can use this method to calculate any rates from a graph, not just the rate of a reaction. Just remember that a rate is how much something changes over time, so x needs to be the time.

This <u>graph</u> shows the <u>volume of gas</u> produced in a reaction against <u>time</u>. The graph is <u>linear</u> (it's a straight line graph), so you can simply calculate the <u>gradient</u> of the line to find out the <u>rate of reaction</u>.

1) To calculate the gradient, pick <u>two points</u> on the line that are easy to read and a <u>good distance</u> apart.

2) <u>Draw a line down</u> from one of the points and a <u>line across</u> from the other to make a <u>triangle</u>. The line drawn down the side of the triangle is the <u>change in y</u> and the line across the bottom is the <u>change in x</u>.

Change in y = 6.8 – 2.0 = 4.8 cm³   Change in x = 5.2 – 1.6 = 3.6 s

$$\text{Rate = gradient} = \frac{\text{change in } y}{\text{change in } x} = \frac{4.8 \text{ cm}^3}{3.6 \text{ s}} = \underline{1.3 \text{ cm}^3/\text{s}} \text{ or } \underline{1.3 \text{ cm}^3 \text{ s}^{-1}}$$

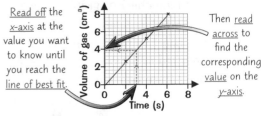

The units of the gradient are (units of y)/(units of x). cm³/s can also be written as cm³ s⁻¹.

2) The <u>intercept</u> of a graph is where the line of best fit crosses one of the <u>axes</u>. The <u>x-intercept</u> is where the line of best fit crosses the x-axis and the <u>y-intercept</u> is where it crosses the <u>y-axis</u>.

3) You can use the line of best fit to <u>interpolate data</u> — this means you can find approximate values <u>in between</u> the values you <u>recorded</u>. E.g. if you recorded the volume of gas produced at 2 second intervals and you wanted to work out how much was produced after 3 seconds, you could use your graph to work it out.

Read off the <u>x-axis</u> at the value you want to know until you reach the <u>line of best fit</u>.

Then <u>read</u> <u>across</u> to find the corresponding <u>value</u> on the <u>y-axis</u>.

4) You can <u>extrapolate data</u> by <u>extending</u> the <u>line of best fit</u> (or a small part of it) to <u>predict</u> values outside of your range.

Scattergrams Show the Relationship Between Two Variables

1) You can get <u>three</u> types of <u>correlation</u> (relationship) between variables:

2) Just because there's correlation, it doesn't mean the change in one variable is <u>causing</u> the change in the other — there might be <u>other factors</u> involved (see page 228).

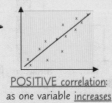

<u>POSITIVE</u> correlation: as one variable <u>increases</u> the other <u>increases</u>.

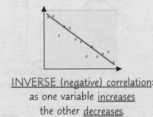

<u>INVERSE</u> (negative) correlation: as one variable <u>increases</u> the other <u>decreases</u>.

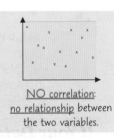

<u>NO</u> correlation: <u>no relationship</u> between the two variables.

When Doing a Calculation, Round to the Lowest Number of Significant Figures

The <u>first significant figure</u> of a number is the first digit that's <u>not zero</u>. The second and third significant figures come <u>straight after</u> (even if they're zeros). You should be aware of significant figures in calculations.

1) In <u>any</u> calculation, you should round the answer to the <u>lowest number of significant figures</u> (s.f.) given.

2) Remember to write down <u>how many</u> significant figures you've rounded to after your answer.

3) If your calculation has multiple steps, <u>only</u> round the <u>final</u> answer, or it won't be as accurate.

 What is the concentration in g/dm³ of a solution of lithium chloride where 17.6 g of lithium chloride is dissolved in 0.30 dm³ of water?

Concentration = 17.6 g ÷ 0.30 dm³ = 58.6666... = **59 g/dm³ (2 s.f.)** — Final answer should be rounded to 2 s.f.

　　　　　　　　　　3 s.f.　　　2 s.f.

I love eating apples — I call it core elation...

Science is all about finding relationships between things. And I don't mean that chemists gather together in corners to discuss whether or not Devini and Sebastian might be a couple... though they probably do that too.

Units and Equations

Graphs and maths skills are all very well, but the numbers don't mean much if you can't get the units right.

S.I. Units Are Used All Round the World

1) It wouldn't be all that useful if I defined volume in terms of bath tubs, you defined it in terms of egg-cups and my pal Sarwat defined it in terms of balloons — we'd never be able to compare our data.

2) To stop this happening, scientists have come up with a set of standard units, called S.I. units, that all scientists use to measure their data. Here are some S.I. units you'll see in GCSE science:

Quantity	S.I. Base Unit
mass	kilogram, kg
length	metre, m
time	second, s
amount of a substance	mole, mol

Scaling Prefixes Can Be Used for Large and Small Quantities

1) Quantities come in a huge range of sizes. For example, the volume of a swimming pool might be around 2 000 000 000 cm^3, while the volume of a cup is around 250 cm^3.

2) To make the size of numbers more manageable, larger or smaller units are used. These are the S.I. base unit (e.g. metres) with a prefix in front:

prefix	tera (T)	giga (G)	mega (M)	kilo (k)	deci (d)	centi (c)	milli (m)	micro (µ)	nano (n)
multiple of unit	10^{12}	10^9	1 000 000 (10^6)	1000	0.1	0.01	0.001	0.000001 (10^{-6})	10^{-9}

3) These prefixes tell you how much bigger or smaller a unit is than the base unit. So one kilometre is one thousand metres.

The conversion factor is the number of times the smaller unit goes into the larger unit.

4) To swap from one unit to another, all you need to know is what number you have to divide or multiply by to get from the original unit to the new unit — this is called the conversion factor.

- To go from a bigger unit (like m) to a smaller unit (like cm), you multiply by the conversion factor.
- To go from a smaller unit (like g) to a bigger unit (like kg), you divide by the conversion factor.

5) Here are some conversions that'll be useful for GCSE science:

Mass can have units of kg and g.
kg ×1000→ g, ÷1000

Energy can have units of J and kJ.
kJ ×1000→ J, ÷1000

Volume can have units of m^3, dm^3 and cm^3.
m^3 ×1000→ dm^3 ×1000→ cm^3, ÷1000 ÷1000

Length can have lots of units, including mm, µm and nm.
mm ×1000→ µm ×1000→ nm, ÷1000 ÷1000

Always Check The Values Used in Equations Have the Right Units

1) Formulas and equations show relationships between variables.

2) To rearrange an equation, make sure that whatever you do to one side of the equation you also do to the other side.

You can find the number of moles of something using the equation: moles = mass ÷ molar mass. You can rearrange this equation to find the mass by multiplying each side by molar mass to give: mass = moles × molar mass.

3) To use a formula, you need to know the values of all but one of the variables. Substitute the values you do know into the formula, and do the calculation to work out the final variable.

4) Always make sure the values you put into an equation or formula have the right units. For example, you might have done a titration experiment to work out the concentration of a solution. The volume of the solution will probably have been measured in cm^3, but the equation to find concentration uses volume in dm^3. So you'll have to convert your volume from cm^3 to dm^3 before you put it into the equation.

5) To make sure your units are correct, it can help to write down the units on each line of your calculation.

I wasn't sure I liked units, but now I'm converted...

It's easy to get in a muddle when converting between units, but there's a handy way to check you've done it right. If you're moving from a smaller unit to a larger unit (e.g. g to kg) the number should get smaller, and vice versa.

Drawing Conclusions

Congratulations — you're nearly at the end of a gruelling investigation, time to <u>draw conclusions</u>.

You Can Only Conclude What the Data Shows and NO MORE

1) Drawing conclusions might seem pretty straightforward — you just <u>look at your data</u> and <u>say what pattern or relationship you see</u> between the dependent and independent variables.

	Catalyst	Rate of reaction (cm³/s)	
The table on the right shows the rate of a reaction in the presence of two <u>different</u> catalysts:	A	13.5	
	B	19.5	
	No catalyst	5.5	

The table on the right shows the rate of a reaction in the presence of two <u>different</u> catalysts:

<u>CONCLUSION</u>:
Catalyst <u>B</u> makes <u>this reaction</u> go faster than catalyst A.

2) But you've got to be really careful that your conclusion <u>matches the data</u> you've got and <u>doesn't go any further</u>.

> You <u>can't</u> conclude that catalyst B increases the rate of <u>any other reaction</u> more than catalyst A — the results might be completely different.

3) You also need to be able to <u>use your results</u> to <u>justify your conclusion</u> (i.e. back up your conclusion with some specific data).

> Catalyst B made the rate of reaction on average <u>6.5 cm³/s</u> faster than catalyst A.

4) When writing a conclusion you need to <u>refer back</u> to the original hypothesis and say whether the data <u>supports it</u> or not. You might remember from page 220 that if data backs up a prediction it <u>increases confidence</u> in the hypothesis (although it doesn't prove the hypothesis is correct). If the data doesn't support the prediction, it can <u>decrease confidence</u> in it.

> The hypothesis for this experiment might have been that catalyst B would make the reaction go <u>quicker</u> than catalyst A. If so, the data <u>supports</u> the hypothesis.

5) You could also make more <u>predictions</u> based on your conclusion, then <u>further experiments</u> could be carried out to test them.

> The extent to which data might affect the confidence in a hypothesis depends on the quality of the data. That includes factors such as whether representative samples have been used (see p.223) as well as how accurate or precise the data is (see p.224).

Don't Forget, Correlation DOES NOT Mean Cause

Just because there's a <u>correlation</u> (relationship) between a factor and an outcome, it <u>doesn't mean</u> that the factor <u>causes</u> the outcome. There are several reasons for this...

1) Sometimes two things can show a correlation purely due to <u>chance</u>. This is why an <u>individual case</u> (e.g. a correlation between people's hair colour and how good they are at frisbee in a particular school) <u>isn't enough</u> to <u>convince scientists</u> that a factor is causing an outcome. <u>Repeatable</u>, <u>reproducible</u> data must be collected first.

2) A lot of the time it may look as if a factor is causing an outcome but it isn't — <u>another</u>, hidden <u>factor</u> links them both.

> E.g. there's a correlation between <u>water temperature</u> and <u>shark attacks</u>. This isn't because warmer water makes sharks crazy. They're linked by a third variable — the <u>number of people swimming</u> (more people swim when the water's hotter, and with more people in the water you get more shark attacks).

3) Sometimes a correlation is just when a factor makes an outcome <u>more likely</u>, but <u>not inevitable</u>.

> E.g. if you eat a diet high in saturated fat, it increases your risk of heart disease, but it doesn't mean you will get it. That's because there are <u>lots of different factors interacting</u> to influence the outcome.

4) Scientists don't usually accept that a factor causes an outcome (there is a <u>cause-effect link</u>) unless they can work out a <u>plausible mechanism</u> that <u>links</u> the <u>two things</u>.

> E.g. there's a correlation between <u>increased carbon dioxide</u> levels in the atmosphere and <u>global warming</u>. Carbon dioxide can absorb thermal radiation and re-emit it back towards Earth — this is the mechanism.

I conclude that this page is a bit dull...

...although, just because I find it dull doesn't mean that I can conclude it's dull. In the exam you could be given a conclusion and asked whether the data supports it — you need to make sure the data fully justifies the conclusion.

Uncertainties and Evaluations

You can never be certain that your data is 100% correct. You need to decide how confident you are in it...

Uncertainty is the Amount of Error Your Measurements Might Have

1) When you repeat a measurement, you often get a slightly different figure each time you do it due to random error. This means that each result has some uncertainty to it.

2) The measurements you make will also have some uncertainty in them due to limits in the resolution of the equipment you use and human errors (see p.224).

The range is the largest value minus the smallest value (p.225).

3) This all means that the mean of a set of results will also have some uncertainty to it. You can calculate the uncertainty of a mean result using the equation:

$$\text{uncertainty} = \frac{\text{range}}{2}$$

4) The larger the range, the less precise your results are and the more uncertainty there will be in your results. Uncertainties are shown using the '±' symbol.

EXAMPLE: The table below shows the results of a respiration experiment to determine the volume of carbon dioxide produced. Calculate the uncertainty of the mean.

Repeat	1	2	3	mean
Volume of CO_2 produced (cm^3)	20.2	19.8	20.0	20.0

1) First work out the range:

Range = 20.2 − 19.8
= 0.4 cm^3

2) Use the range to find the uncertainty:

Uncertainty = range ÷ 2 = 0.4 ÷ 2 = 0.2 cm^3. So the uncertainty of the mean = 20.0 ± 0.2 cm^3

5) Measuring a greater amount of something helps to reduce uncertainty. For example, in a rate of reaction experiment, measuring the amount of product formed over a longer period compared to a shorter period will reduce the percentage uncertainty in your results.

You Need to Evaluate Your Data

Before you make any conclusions based on your data, you need perform an evaluation.
An evaluation is a critical analysis of the whole investigation, including the data you obtained.

1) You should comment on the method — was it valid? Did you control all the other variables to make it a fair test?

I'd value this E somewhere in the region of 250-300k

2) Comment on the quality of the results — were the results repeatable, reproducible, accurate and precise? Were there sources of random or systematic error?

3) Were there any outliers? If there were none then say so. If there were any, try to explain them — were they caused by errors in measurement? You should comment on the level of uncertainty in your results too.

4) All this analysis will allow you to say how confident you are that your results are good.

5) Then you can suggest any changes to the method that would improve the quality of the results, so that you could have more confidence in your data. For example, you might suggest changing the way you controlled a variable, carrying out further repeats or increasing the number of measurements you took. Taking more measurements at narrower intervals could give you a more accurate result. For example:

Enzymes have an optimum temperature (a temperature at which they work best). Say you do an experiment to find an enzyme's optimum temperature and take measurements at 10 °C, 20 °C, 30 °C, 40 °C and 50 °C. The results of this experiment tell you the optimum is 40 °C. You could then repeat the experiment, taking more measurements around 40 °C to a get a more accurate value for the optimum.

When suggesting improvements to the investigation, always make sure that you say why you think this would make the results better.

Evaluation — next time, I'll make sure I don't burn the lab down...

By now you should have realised how important trustworthy evidence is (even more important than a good supply of spot cream). Evaluations are a good way to assess evidence and see how things can be improved in the future.

New Technologies and Risk

By reading this page you are agreeing to the risk of a paper cut or severe drowsiness...

Scientific Technology Usually Has Benefits and Negative Impacts

Scientists have created loads of new technologies that could improve our lives. For example, by developing processes that are more sustainable, or in the following developments in nanoscience:

- Developing new sun creams which are better at protecting the skin from UV radiation.
- Using nanotubes to cage drug molecules so that they are released in specific parts of the body.
- Developing new catalysts which increase the rate of reactions more effectively than bulk materials.

However, it's not all good news. Sometimes new technology can have unintended or undesired impacts on our quality of life or the environment. For example:

- Nanoparticles are very small so could get into our cells. As they react differently to the bulk materials, they could cause side effects that haven't been discovered.
- Nanoparticles are so small that they might not get filtered out of waste water when they get washed away. This could mean they might end up in rivers, where they could impact plants or animals.

When developing new technologies, scientists try and come up with ways to reduce these impacts, but...

Nothing is Completely Risk-Free

Risks can affect an individual or a whole group of people.

1) Everything we do has a risk attached to it — this is the chance that it will cause harm.

2) The risks of some things seem pretty obvious, or we've known about them for a while, like the risk of causing acid rain by polluting the atmosphere, or of having a car accident when you're travelling in a car.

3) New technology arising from scientific advances can bring new risks, e.g. carbon capture is very useful for reducing the carbon dioxide emissions that contribute to global warming but it can also pose its own risks. For example, a large leak in the system could be harmful to humans, as well as causing environmental issues in soil, water and plants through acidification. These risks needs to be considered alongside the benefits of reducing CO_2 emissions (see p.86).

4) When deciding whether to develop a new technology, scientists or governments need to consider how great the benefit is, compared to the number of people who will be put at risk, and how great that risk might be.

5) You can estimate the size of a risk based on how many times something happens in a big sample (e.g. 100 000 people) over a given period (e.g. a year). For example, you could assess the risk of a driver crashing by recording how many people in a group of 100 000 drivers crashed their cars over a year.

6) To make decisions about activities that involve hazards, we need to take into account the chance of the hazard causing harm, and how serious the consequences would be if it did. If an activity involves a hazard that's very likely to cause harm, with serious consequences if it does, it's considered high risk.

People Make Their Own Decisions About Risk

1) Not all risks have the same consequences, e.g. if you chop veg with a sharp knife you risk cutting your finger, but if you go scuba-diving you risk death. You're much more likely to cut your finger during half an hour of chopping than to die during half an hour of scuba-diving. But most people are happier to accept a higher probability of an accident if the consequences are short-lived and fairly minor.

2) People tend to be more willing to accept a risk if they choose to do something (e.g. go scuba diving), compared to having the risk imposed on them (e.g. having a nuclear power station built next door).

3) People's perception of risk (how risky they think something is) isn't always accurate. There is sometimes a big difference between perceived risk and calculated risk. People tend to view familiar activities as low-risk and unfamiliar activities as high-risk — even if that's not the case. For example, cycling on roads is often high-risk, but many people are happy to do it because it's a familiar activity. Air travel is actually pretty safe, but a lot of people perceive it as high-risk. People may also over-estimate the risk of unfamiliar things that have long-term or invisible effects, e.g. ionising radiation.

Not revising — an unacceptable exam risk...

All activities pose some sort of risk, it's just a question of deciding whether that risk is worth it in the long run.

Communication and Issues Created by Science

Scientific developments can be great, but they can sometimes <u>raise more questions</u> than they answer...

It's Important to Communicate Scientific Discoveries

Scientists need to be able to <u>communicate their findings</u> to <u>other scientists</u>, and groups like the <u>public</u> and <u>politicians</u>, in a way everyone can understand. This means that people can make <u>informed choices</u>. For example:

> <u>New technologies</u> are being developed to generate <u>renewable energy</u>. Information about these new methods to generate power need to be communicated to <u>politicians</u> who <u>decide</u> whether to allow their development, and to the <u>public</u>, who will be <u>affected</u> by the schemes.

1) One way discoveries can be communicated to the public is through the <u>media</u>. However, <u>reports</u> about scientific discoveries in the <u>media</u> (e.g. newspapers or television) <u>aren't</u> peer-reviewed.

2) This means that, even though news stories are often <u>based</u> on data that has been peer-reviewed, the data might be <u>presented</u> in a way that is <u>over-simplified</u> or <u>inaccurate</u>, making it open to <u>misinterpretation</u>.

3) People who want to make a point can sometimes <u>present data</u> in a <u>biased way</u>. (Sometimes <u>without knowing</u> they're doing it.) For example, a scientist might overemphasise a relationship in the data, or a newspaper article might describe details of data <u>supporting</u> an idea without giving any evidence <u>against</u> it.

Scientific Developments are Great, but they can Raise Issues

Scientific <u>knowledge is increased</u> by doing experiments. And this knowledge leads to <u>scientific developments</u>, e.g. new technologies or new advice. These developments can create <u>issues</u> though. For example:

<u>Economic issues:</u> Society <u>can't</u> always <u>afford</u> to do things scientists recommend (e.g. investing in alternative energy sources) without <u>cutting back elsewhere</u>.

<u>Personal issues:</u> Some decisions will affect <u>individuals</u>. For example, someone might support <u>alternative energy</u>, but object if a <u>wind farm</u> is built next to their house.

<u>Social issues:</u> Decisions based on scientific evidence affect <u>people</u> — e.g. should fossil fuels be taxed more highly? <u>Would the effect on people's lifestyles be acceptable?</u>

<u>Environmental issues:</u> <u>Human activity</u> often affects the <u>natural environment</u>. For example, building a <u>dam</u> to produce electricity will change the <u>local habitat</u> so some species might be displaced. But it will also reduce our need for <u>fossil fuels</u>, so will help to reduce <u>climate change</u>.

Science Can't Answer Every Question — Especially Ethical Ones

1) We don't <u>understand everything</u>. We're always finding out <u>more</u>, but we'll never know <u>all</u> the answers.

2) In order to answer scientific questions, scientists need <u>data</u> to provide <u>evidence</u> for their hypotheses.

3) Some questions can't be answered <u>yet</u> because the data <u>can't</u> currently be <u>collected</u>, or because there's <u>not enough</u> data to <u>support</u> a theory. <u>Eventually</u>, as we get <u>more evidence</u>, we'll answer some of the questions that <u>currently</u> can't be answered, e.g. what the impact of global warming on sea levels will be.

4) But there will always be the "<u>Should we be doing this at all?</u>"-type questions that experiments <u>can't</u> help us to answer...

> Think about <u>new drugs which can be taken to boost your 'brain power'</u>.
> - Some people think they're <u>good</u> as they could improve concentration or memory. New drugs could let people think in ways beyond the powers of normal brains.
> - Other people say they're <u>bad</u> — they could give you an <u>unfair advantage</u> in exams. And people might be <u>pressured</u> into taking them so that they could work more <u>effectively</u>, and for <u>longer hours</u>.

THE GAZETTE
BRAIN-BOOSTING DRUGS MAKE A MOCKERY OF EXAMS

THE POST
GENIUS PILLS TO BECOME THE NEW COFFEE

5) When making decisions that involve <u>ethical dilemmas</u> like this, a commonly used argument is that the <u>right decision</u> is the one that brings the <u>greatest benefit</u> to the <u>most people</u>.

Tea to milk or milk to tea? — Totally unanswerable by science...

Science can't tell you whether or not you should do something. That's for you and society to decide. But there are tons of questions science might be able to answer, like where life came from and where my superhero socks are.

Revision Questions for Chapter BCP7

That's all for Chapter BCP7 — time to conclude and evaluate what you've learnt.

- Try these questions and tick off each one when you get it right.
- When you've done all the questions under a heading and are completely happy, tick it off.

The Scientific Method (p.220-221) ☑

1) What is a hypothesis? ☑
2) Give two reasons why scientists may come up with different explanations for the same observation. ☑
3) Briefly explain how the peer-review process works. ☑
4) True or false? "Scientific theories are explanations that still need to be accepted." ☑
5) Give one advantage of using models. ☑

Designing Investigations and Collecting Data (p.221-224) ☑

6) What is meant by the term 'valid result'? ☑
7) How could a scientist try to make their investigation a fair test? ☑
8) Why is a control experiment important in an investigation? ☑
9) Give a potential hazard in an experiment where a Bunsen burner is used
   and explain what you would do to reduce the risk. ☑
10) Give one reason why it is better to have a large sample size than a small sample size in an investigation. ☑
11) Suggest how you would work out the range of variable values to use in your experiment. ☑
12) What are precise results? ☑
13) What type of error is caused if a measurement is wrong by the same amount every time? ☑

Processing and Presenting Data, Units and Equations (p.225-227) ☑

14) How would you calculate: a) the mean of a set of results, b) the range of results? ☑
15) What type of data would you present on a bar chart? ☑
16) What is the intercept of a graph? ☑
17) Sketch a graph showing: a) a positive correlation, b) a negative correlation. ☑
18) Which of the following prefixes signifies a smaller unit: nano or micro? ☑
19) How would you convert a value that has units of J so that it has units of kJ? ☑

Uncertainties, Evaluations and Conclusions (p.228-229) ☑

20) Describe the effect data has on people's view of the hypothesis if the data backs up the prediction. ☑
21) What do scientists need to find to accept a cause-effect link between a factor and an outcome? ☑
22) How can you calculate the uncertainty of a mean result? ☑
23) Give four things you should consider when evaluating the quality of data. ☑

New Technologies and Risk (p.230) ☑

24) How might someone calculate risk? ☑
25) True or false? "If a situation is unfamiliar, people are more likely
    to perceive it as high-risk than if it's familiar." ☑

Communication and Issues Created by Science (p.231) ☑

26) Give an example of how information could be presented in a biased way. ☑
27) State four types of issues that might be created by new scientific developments. ☑

Measuring Techniques

- <u>Chapter BCP8</u> covers <u>practical skills</u> you'll need to know about for the course (including at least 15% of your exams).

- You're required to do experiments to cover at least <u>16 Practical Activity Groups</u>. These are covered in <u>Chapters B1-B6</u>, <u>C1-C6</u> and <u>P1-P6</u> earlier in the book and they're <u>highlighted</u> with <u>practical stamps</u> like this one.

  PRACTICAL

- The following pages of this topic cover some <u>extra bits and bobs</u> you need to know about practical work. First up, some <u>measuring techniques</u>...

Mass Should Be Measured Using a Balance

1) To measure mass, start by putting the <u>container</u> you're measuring the substance <u>into</u> on the <u>balance</u>.

2) Set the balance to exactly <u>zero</u> and then start adding your substance.

3) It's <u>no good</u> carefully measuring out your substance if it's not all transferred to your reaction vessel — the amount in the <u>reaction vessel</u> won't be the same as your measurement. Here are a couple of methods you can use to make sure that none gets left in your weighing container...

- If you're <u>dissolving</u> a mass of a solid in a solvent to make a <u>solution</u>, you could <u>wash</u> any remaining solid into the new container using the <u>solvent</u>. This way you know that <u>all</u> the solid you weighed has been transferred.

- You could <u>reweigh</u> the weighing container <u>after</u> you've transferred the substance. This means you can work out <u>exactly</u> how much you added to your experiment.

Three Ways to Measure Liquids

There are a few methods you might use to measure the volume of a liquid. Whichever method you use, always read the volume from the <u>bottom of the meniscus</u> (the curved upper surface of the liquid) when it's at <u>eye level</u>.

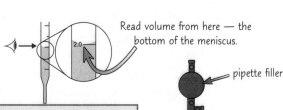

Read volume from here — the bottom of the meniscus.

pipette filler

<u>Pipettes</u> are long, narrow tubes that are used to suck up an <u>accurate</u> volume of liquid and <u>transfer</u> it to another container. A <u>pipette filler</u> attached to the end of the pipette is used so that you can <u>safely control</u> the amount of liquid you're drawing up. Pipettes are often <u>calibrated</u> to allow for the fact that the last drop of liquid stays in the pipette when the liquid is ejected. This reduces <u>transfer errors</u>.

<u>Burettes</u> measure from top to bottom (so when they're filled to the top of the scale, the scale reads zero). They have a tap at the bottom which you can use to release the liquid into another container (you can even release it drop by drop). To use a burette, take an <u>initial reading</u>, and once you've released as much liquid as you want, take a <u>final reading</u>. The <u>difference</u> between the readings tells you <u>how much</u> liquid you used.

Burettes are used a lot for titrations. There's loads more about titrations on p.137-138.

<u>Measuring cylinders</u> are the most common way to measure out a liquid. They come in all different <u>sizes</u>. Make sure you choose one that's the right size for the measurement you want to make. It's no good using a huge 1000 cm³ cylinder to measure out 2 cm³ of a liquid — the graduations will be too big, and you'll end up with <u>massive errors</u>. It'd be much better to use one that measures up to 10 cm³.

If you only want a couple of drops of liquid, and don't need it to be accurately measured, you can use a dropping pipette to transfer it. For example, this is how you'd add a couple of drops of indicator into a mixture.

Measuring Techniques

Gas Syringes Measure Gas Volumes

1) Gases can be measured with a gas syringe. They should be measured at <u>room temperature and pressure</u> as the <u>volume</u> of a gas <u>changes</u> with temperature and pressure. You should also use a gas syringe that's the <u>right size</u> for the measurement you're making. Before you use the syringe, you should make sure it's <u>completely sealed</u> and that the plunger moves <u>smoothly</u>.

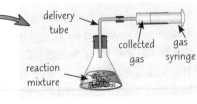

delivery tube

collected gas

gas syringe

reaction mixture

2) Alternatively, you can use an <u>upturned measuring cylinder</u> filled with <u>water</u>. The gas will <u>displace</u> the water so you can <u>read the volume</u> off the <u>scale</u> — see page 238.

3) Another method to measure the amount of gas is to <u>count the bubbles</u>. This method is <u>less accurate</u>, but will give you <u>relative</u> amounts of gas to <u>compare results</u>.

4) When you're measuring a gas, you need to make sure that the equipment is set up so that none of the gas can <u>escape</u>, otherwise your results won't be <u>accurate</u>.

Eureka Cans Measure the Volumes of Solids

1) <u>Eureka cans</u> are used in <u>combination</u> with <u>measuring cylinders</u> to find the volumes of <u>irregular solids</u> (p.212).

2) They're essentially a <u>beaker with a spout</u>. To use them, fill them with water so the water level is <u>above the spout</u>.

3) Let the water <u>drain</u> from the spout, leaving the water level <u>just below</u> the start of the spout (so <u>all</u> the water displaced by an object goes into the measuring cylinder and gives you the <u>correct volume</u>).

4) Place a <u>measuring cylinder</u> below the end of the spout. When you place a solid in the beaker, it causes the water level to <u>rise</u> and water to flow out of the spout.

5) Make sure you wait until the spout has <u>stopped dripping</u> before you measure the volume of the water in the measuring cylinder. And eureka! You know the object's volume.

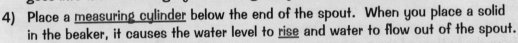

eureka can

measuring cylinder

object, e.g. award statue

Measure Most Lengths with a Ruler

1) In most cases a bog-standard <u>centimetre ruler</u> can be used to measure <u>length</u>. It depends on what you're measuring though — <u>metre rulers</u> are handy for <u>large</u> distances, while <u>micrometers</u> are used for measuring tiny things like the <u>diameter of a wire</u>.

2) The ruler should always be <u>parallel to</u> what you want to measure.

3) If you're dealing with something where it's <u>tricky</u> to measure just <u>one</u> accurately (e.g. water ripples, p.152), you can measure the length of <u>ten</u> of them and then <u>divide</u> to find the <u>length of one</u>.

4) If you're taking <u>multiple measurements</u> of the <u>same</u> object (e.g. to measure changes in length) then make sure you always measure from the <u>same point</u> on the object. It can help to draw or stick small <u>markers</u> onto the object to line up your ruler against.

ruler   spring

marker

5) Make sure the ruler and the object are always at <u>eye level</u> when you take a reading. This stops <u>parallax</u> affecting your results.

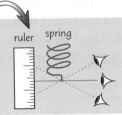

<u>Parallax</u> is where a measurement appears to <u>change</u> based on <u>where you're looking from</u>. The <u>blue line</u> is the measurement taken when the spring is at <u>eye level</u>. It shows the correct length of the spring.

ruler   spring

Measuring Techniques

Measuring the Area of Something

You might need to measure the <u>area</u> of something (e.g. part of a habitat, a living thing). Living things are usually quite <u>complex shapes</u>, but you can make their area easier to work out by comparing them to a <u>simpler shape</u> and working out the area of that (e.g. <u>clear zones</u> in bacterial lawns are roughly <u>circular</u> — see p.15-16). To find the area of something:

1) First, you'll need to take <u>accurate measurements</u> of its dimensions.

> If you want to <u>measure</u> the area of a <u>field</u> that is <u>rectangular</u>, you'll need to use a <u>tape measure</u> or a <u>trundle wheel</u> to measure the <u>length</u> and <u>width</u> of the field. Record your readings in metres.

2) Then you can <u>calculate</u> its <u>area</u>.

> Area of a <u>rectangle</u> = <u>length</u> × <u>width</u>.
> So, if your field is 30 m by 55 m, the <u>area</u> would be 30 × 55 = <u>1650 m²</u>.

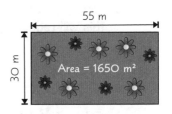

Here are some examples of other area formulas that may come in useful:

- Area of a triangle = ½ × base × height
- Area of a circle = πr^2

Don't forget the units of area are always something squared, e.g. mm².

Use a Protractor to Find Angles

1) First align the <u>vertex</u> (point) of the angle with the mark in the <u>centre</u> of the protractor.

2) Line up the <u>base line</u> of the protractor with one line that forms the <u>angle</u> and then measure the angle of the other line using the scale on the <u>protractor</u>.

3) If the lines creating the angle are very <u>thick</u>, align the protractor and measure the angle from the <u>centre</u> of the lines. Using a <u>sharp pencil</u> to trace light rays or draw diagrams helps to <u>reduce errors</u> when measuring angles.

4) If the lines are <u>too short</u> to measure easily, you may have to <u>extend</u> them. Again, make sure you use a <u>sharp pencil</u> to do this.

Measure Temperature Accurately

You can use a <u>thermometer</u> to measure the temperature of a substance:

1) Make sure the <u>bulb</u> of your thermometer is <u>completely submerged</u> in any mixture you're measuring.

2) If you're taking an initial reading, you should wait for the temperature to <u>stabilise</u> first.

3) Read your measurement off the <u>scale</u> on a thermometer at <u>eye level</u> to make sure it's correct.

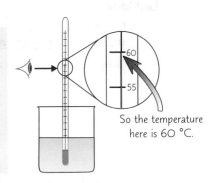

So the temperature here is 60 °C.

Measuring Techniques

You May Have to Measure the Time Taken for a Change

1) You should use a <u>stopwatch</u> to <u>time</u> experiments.
   These measure to the nearest <u>0.1 s</u>, so are <u>sensitive</u>.

2) Always make sure you <u>start</u> and <u>stop</u> the stopwatch at exactly the
   right time. Or alternatively, set an <u>alarm</u> on the stopwatch so you
   know exactly when to stop an experiment or take a reading.

3) You might be able to use a <u>light gate</u> instead (p.240).
   This will <u>reduce the errors</u> in your experiment.

Measure pH to Find Out How Acidic or Alkaline a Solution Is

You need to be able to decide the best method for <u>measuring pH</u>, depending on what your experiment is.

Indicators

• <u>Indicators</u> are dyes that <u>change colour</u> depending on whether they're in an <u>acid</u> or an <u>alkali</u>.
  You use them by adding a couple of drops of the indicator to the solution you're interested in.

• <u>Universal indicator</u> is a <u>mixture</u> of indicators that changes colour
  <u>gradually</u> as pH changes. It doesn't show a <u>sudden</u> colour change.
  It's useful for <u>estimating</u> the pH of a solution based on its colour.

Indicator paper

• Indicators can be soaked into <u>paper</u> and strips of this paper can be used for testing pH.

• If you use a dropping pipette to spot a small amount of a solution onto some indicator
  paper, it will <u>change colour</u> depending on the pH of the solution.

  > <u>Litmus paper</u> turns <u>red</u> in acidic conditions and <u>blue</u> in basic conditions.
  > <u>Universal indicator paper</u> can be used to <u>estimate</u> the pH based on its colour.

• Indicator paper is useful when you <u>don't</u> want to change the colour of <u>all</u> of the substance,
  or if the substance is <u>already</u> coloured so might <u>obscure</u> the colour of the indicator.

• You can also hold a piece of <u>damp indicator paper</u> in a <u>gas sample</u> to test its pH.

pH probes

• <u>pH probes</u> are attached to pH meters which have a <u>digital display</u>
  that gives a <u>numerical</u> value for the pH of a solution.

• They're used to give an <u>accurate value</u> of pH.

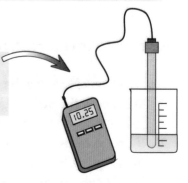

Experimentus apparatus...

Wizardry won't help you here, unfortunately. Most of this'll be pretty familiar to you by now,
but make sure you get your head down and know these techniques inside out so they're second
nature when it comes to any practicals. Once you've done that, feel free to go back to your wizardry.

Safety and Ethics

Before you start any experiment, you need to know what safety precautions you should be taking. And they depend on your method, your equipment, and the chemicals you're using.

Make Sure You're Working Safely in the Lab

1) Make sure that you're wearing sensible clothing when you're in the lab (e.g. open shoes won't protect your feet from spillages). When you're doing an experiment, you should also wear a lab coat to protect your skin and clothing, as well as safety goggles and gloves.

2) You also need to be aware of general safety in the lab, e.g. keep anything flammable away from lit Bunsen burners, don't directly touch any hot equipment, handle glassware carefully so it doesn't break, etc.

3) You should follow any instructions that your teacher gives you carefully. But here are some basic principles for dealing with chemicals and equipment...

Be Careful When You're Using Chemicals...

1) The chemicals you're using may be hazardous — for example, they might be flammable (catch fire easily), or they might irritate or burn your skin if it comes into contact with them.

2) Make sure you're working in an area that's well ventilated and if you're doing an experiment that might produce nasty gases (such as chlorine), you should carry out the experiment in a fume hood so that the gas can't escape out into the room you're working in.

3) Never directly touch any chemicals (even if you're wearing gloves). Use a spatula to transfer solids between containers. Carefully pour liquids between containers, using a funnel to avoid spillages.

4) Be careful when you're mixing chemicals, as a reaction might occur. If you're diluting a liquid, add the concentrated substance to the water (not the other way around) or the mixture could get very hot.

...and Equipment

1) Stop masses and equipment falling by using clamp stands. Make sure masses are of a sensible weight so they don't break the equipment they're used with, and use pulleys of a sensible length. That way, any hanging masses won't hit the floor during the experiment.

2) When heating materials, make sure to let them cool before moving them, or wear insulated gloves while handling them. If you're using an immersion heater to heat liquids, you should always let it dry out in air, just in case any liquid has leaked inside the heater.

3) If you're using a laser, there are a few safety rules you must follow. Always wear laser safety goggles and never look directly into the laser or shine it towards another person. Make sure you turn the laser off if it's not needed to avoid any accidents.

4) When working with electronics, make sure you use a low enough voltage and current to prevent wires overheating (and potentially melting) and avoid damage to components, like blowing a filament bulb.

You Need to Think About Ethical Issues In Your Experiments

1) Any organisms involved in your investigations need to be treated safely and ethically.

2) Animals need to be treated humanely — they should be handled carefully and any wild animals captured for studying (e.g. during an investigation of the distribution of an organism) should be returned to their original habitat.

3) Any animals kept in the lab should also be cared for in a humane way, e.g. they should not be kept in overcrowded conditions.

4) If you are carrying out an experiment involving other students (e.g. investigating the effect of exercise on pulse rate), they should not be forced to participate against their will or feel pressured to take part.

Safety first...

I know — lab safety isn't the most exciting topic. But it's mega important. Not only will it stop you from blowing your eyebrows off, it'll help you pick up more marks in the exam. And that IS worth getting excited about...

Setting Up Experiments

Setting up the equipment for an experiment correctly is <u>just as important</u> as making accurate measurements.

To Collect Gases, the System Needs to be Sealed

1) There are times when you might want to <u>collect</u> the gas produced by a reaction. For example, to investigate the <u>rate</u> of reaction.

2) The most accurate way to measure the volume of gas produced is to collect it in a <u>gas syringe</u> (p.234).

3) You could also collect it by <u>displacing water</u> from a measuring cylinder. Here's how you do it...

- Fill a <u>measuring cylinder</u> with <u>water</u>, and carefully place it <u>upside down</u> in a container of water. Record the <u>initial level</u> of the water in the measuring cylinder.

- Position a <u>delivery tube</u> coming <u>from</u> the reaction vessel so that it's <u>inside</u> the measuring cylinder, pointing upwards. Any gas that's produced will pass <u>through</u> the delivery tube and <u>into</u> the <u>measuring cylinder</u>. As the gas enters the measuring cylinder, the <u>water</u> is <u>pushed out</u>.

- Record the <u>level of water</u> in the measuring cylinder and use this value, along with your <u>initial value</u>, to calculate the <u>volume</u> of gas produced.

delivery tube   *collected gas*
measuring cylinder filled with water and upturned in a beaker of water
reaction mixture

If the delivery tube is underneath the measuring cylinder rather than inside it then some of the gas might escape out into the air.

4) This method is <u>less accurate</u> than using a gas syringe to measure the volume of gas produced. This is because some gases can <u>dissolve</u> in water, so less gas ends up in the measuring cylinder than is <u>actually produced</u>.

5) If you just want to <u>collect</u> a sample to test (and don't need to know the volume), you can collect it over water, as above, using a <u>test tube</u>. Once the test tube is full of gas, stopper it to store the gas for later.

You May Have to Identify the Products of Electrolysis

There's more about electrolysis on p.108-109.

1) When you electrolyse an <u>aqueous solution</u>, the products of electrolysis will depend on how reactive the ions in the solution are compared to the H^+ and OH^- ions that come from water.

2) At the <u>cathode</u> you'll either get a <u>pure metal</u> coating the electrode or bubbles of <u>hydrogen gas</u>.

3) At the <u>anode</u>, you'll get bubbles of <u>oxygen gas</u> unless a <u>halide ion</u> is present, when you'll get the <u>halogen</u>.

4) You may have to predict and identify what's been made in an electrolysis experiment. To do this, you need to be able to <u>set up the equipment</u> so that you can <u>collect</u> any gas that's produced. The easiest way to collect the gas is in a <u>test tube</u>.

5) Here's how to set up the equipment...

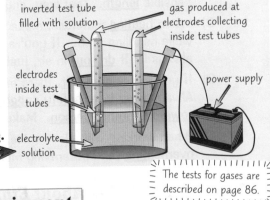

inverted test tube filled with solution   *gas produced at electrodes collecting inside test tubes*
electrodes inside test tubes
power supply
electrolyte solution

The tests for gases are described on page 86.

Make Sure You Can Draw Diagrams of Your Equipment

When you're writing out a <u>method</u> for your experiment, it's always a good idea to draw a <u>labelled diagram</u> showing how your apparatus will be <u>set up</u>. The easiest way to do this is to use a scientific drawing, where each piece of apparatus is drawn as if you're looking at its <u>cross-section</u>. For example:

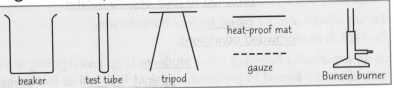

beaker   test tube   tripod   heat-proof mat   gauze   Bunsen burner

The pieces of glassware are drawn without tops so they aren't sealed. If you want to draw a closed system, remember to draw a bung in the top.

I set up my equipment — they had a blind date at the cinema...

Being a dab hand at setting up experiments won't just make your investigations more reliable. You might also be asked to comment on how an experiment's been set up in the exam. So best get learning. You'll thank me for it...

Heating Substances

Heating a reaction isn't as simple as wrapping it up in a lumpy wool jumper and a stripy scarf.
There's more than one way to do it, and you need to be able to decide on the <u>best</u>, and the <u>safest</u>, method.

Bunsen Burners Have a Naked Flame

Bunsen burners are good for heating things <u>quickly</u>. You can easily adjust how strongly
they're heating. But you need to be careful not to use them if you're heating <u>flammable</u>
compounds as the flame means the substance would be at risk of <u>catching fire</u>.

Here's how to use a Bunsen burner...

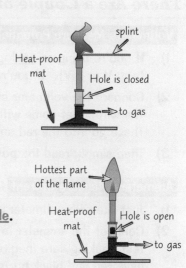

splint

Heat-proof
mat

Hole is closed

to gas

Hottest part
of the flame

Heat-proof
mat

Hole is open

to gas

- Connect the Bunsen burner to a gas tap, and check that the
  hole is <u>closed</u>. Place it on a <u>heat-proof mat</u>.

- Light a <u>splint</u> and hold it over the Bunsen burner. Now, turn on
  the gas. The Bunsen burner should light with a <u>yellow flame</u>.

- The <u>more open</u> the hole is, the <u>more strongly</u> the Bunsen burner
  will heat your substance. Open the hole to the amount you want.
  As you open the hole more, the flame should turn more <u>blue</u>.

- The <u>hottest</u> part of the flame is just above the <u>blue cone</u>,
  so you should heat things here.

- If your Bunsen burner is alight but not heating anything, make sure
  you <u>close</u> the hole so that the flame becomes <u>yellow</u> and <u>clearly visible</u>.

- If you're heating something so that the container (e.g. a test tube)
  is <u>in</u> the flame, you should hold the vessel at the <u>top</u>, furthest away
  from the substance (and so the flame) using a pair of <u>tongs</u>.

- If you're heating something <u>over</u> the flame (e.g. an evaporating dish), you should
  put a <u>tripod and gauze</u> over the Bunsen burner before you light it, and place the vessel on this.

The Temperature of Water Baths & Electric Heaters Can Be Set

1) A <u>water bath</u> is a container filled with water that can be heated to a <u>specific temperature</u>.
   A <u>simple</u> water bath can be made by heating a <u>beaker of water</u> over a <u>Bunsen burner</u> and monitoring the
   temperature with a <u>thermometer</u>. However, it is difficult to keep the temperature of the water <u>constant</u>.

2) An <u>electric water bath</u> will monitor and adjust the temperature for you. Here's how you use one:

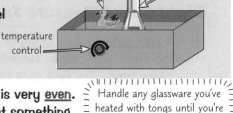

rubber duck
(optional)

reaction vessel

temperature
control

- <u>Set</u> the temperature on the water bath, and allow the water to <u>heat up</u>.

- Place the vessel containing your substance in the water bath
  using a pair of tongs. The level of the water outside the vessel
  should be <u>just above</u> the level of the substance inside
  the vessel. The substance will then be warmed to
  the <u>same temperature</u> as the water.

As the substance in the vessel is surrounded by water, the heating is very <u>even</u>.
Water boils at <u>100 °C</u> though, so you <u>can't</u> use a water bath to heat something
to a higher temperature than this — the water <u>won't</u> get <u>hot</u> enough.

> Handle any glassware you've
> heated with tongs until you're
> sure it's cooled down.

3) <u>Electric heaters</u> are often made up of a metal <u>plate</u> that can be heated to a certain temperature.
   The vessel containing the substance you want to heat is placed on top of the hot plate. You can heat
   substances to <u>higher temperatures</u> than you can in a water bath but, as the vessel is only heated from
   <u>below</u>, you'll usually have to <u>stir</u> the substance inside to make sure it's <u>heated evenly</u>.

A bath and an electric heater — how I spend my January nights...

You know, I used to have a science teacher who'd play power ballads when the Bunsen burners were alight and
sway at the front of the class like he was at a gig. You think I made that up, but it's true.

Working with Electronics

Electrical devices are used in a bunch of experiments, so make sure you know how to use them.

You Have to Interpret Circuit Diagrams

Before you get cracking on an experiment involving any kind of electrical devices, you have to plan and build your circuit using a circuit diagram. Make sure you know all of the circuit symbols on page 170 so you're not stumped before you've even started.

There Are a Couple of Ways to Measure Potential Difference and Current

Voltmeters Measure Potential Difference

1) If you're using an analogue voltmeter, choose the voltmeter with the most appropriate unit (e.g. V or mV). If you're using a digital voltmeter, you'll most likely be able to switch between them.

2) Connect the voltmeter in parallel (p.176) across the component you want to test. The wires that come with a voltmeter are usually red (positive) and black (negative). These go into the red and black coloured ports on the voltmeter. Funnily enough.

3) Then simply read the potential difference from the scale (or from the screen if it's digital).

Ammeters Measure Current

1) Just like with voltmeters, choose the ammeter with the most appropriate unit.

2) Connect the ammeter in series (p.175) with the component you want to test, making sure they're both on the same branch. Again, they usually have red and black ports to show you where to connect your wires.

3) Read off the current shown on the scale or by the screen.

> Turn your circuit off between readings to prevent wires overheating and affecting your results (p.171).

Multimeters Measure Both

1) Instead of having a separate ammeter and voltmeter, many circuits use multimeters. These are devices that measure a range of properties — usually potential difference, current and resistance.

2) If you want to find potential difference, make sure the red wire is plugged into the port that has a 'V' (for volts).

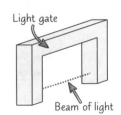

3) To find the current, use the port labelled 'A' or 'mA' (for amps).

4) The dial on the multimeter should then be turned to the relevant section, e.g. to 'A' to measure current in amps. The screen will display the value you're measuring.

Light Gates Measure Speed and Acceleration

1) A light gate sends a beam of light from one side of the gate to a detector on the other side. When something passes through the gate, the beam of light is interrupted. The light gate then measures how long the beam was undetected.

2) To find the speed of an object, connect the light gate to a computer. Measure the length of the object and input this using the software. It will then automatically calculate the speed of the object as it passes through the beam.

3) To measure acceleration, use an object that interrupts the signal twice in a short period of time, e.g. a piece of card with a gap cut into the middle.

4) The light gate measures the speed for each section of the object and uses this to calculate its acceleration. This can then be read from the computer screen.

Have a look at page 189 for an example of a light gate being used.

Light gate

Beam of light

Card interrupts the beam

A light gate is better than a heavy one...

After finishing this page, you should be able to take on any electrical experiment that they throw at you... ouch.

Investigating Ecosystems Data

Remember all those pages on investigating ecosystems back in <u>Chapter B3</u>? (Have a flick back to pages 38-39 if not.) Well here's a little <u>extra info</u> to help you get the most from your data.

Organisms Should Be Sampled At Random Sites in an Area

1) If you're interested in the <u>distribution</u> of an organism in an area, or its <u>population size</u>, you can take population samples in the area you're interested in using <u>quadrats</u> or <u>transects</u> (see pages 38-39).

2) If you only take samples from <u>one part</u> of the area, your results will be <u>biased</u> — they may not give an <u>accurate representation</u> of the <u>whole area</u>.

3) To make sure that your sampling isn't biased, you need to use a method of <u>choosing sampling sites</u> in which every site has an <u>equal chance</u> of being chosen. For example:

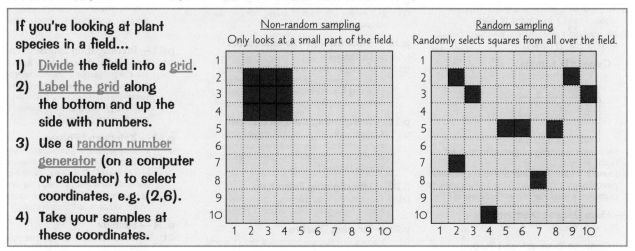

If you're looking at plant species in a field...
1) <u>Divide</u> the field into a <u>grid</u>.
2) <u>Label the grid</u> along the bottom and up the side with numbers.
3) Use a <u>random number generator</u> (on a computer or calculator) to select coordinates, e.g. (2,6).
4) Take your samples at these coordinates.

Non-random sampling — Only looks at a small part of the field.
Random sampling — Randomly selects squares from all over the field.

Percentiles Tell you Where in Your Data Set a Data Point Lies

1) Percentiles divide a data set into <u>one hundred equal chunks</u>. Each chunk is <u>one percentile</u> and represents <u>one percent</u> of the data.

2) The <u>value of a percentile</u> tells you <u>what percentage</u> of the data set has a <u>lower value</u> than the data points in that percentile. E.g. an <u>oak tree</u> is in the <u>90th percentile</u> for <u>height</u> in a forest. This means that <u>90%</u> of the <u>trees</u> in the forest are <u>shorter</u> than the oak tree.

3) Percentiles can be used to give a <u>better idea</u> of the <u>spread</u> of data than the <u>range</u> (which is just the difference between the lowest and highest data values — see page 225). For example:

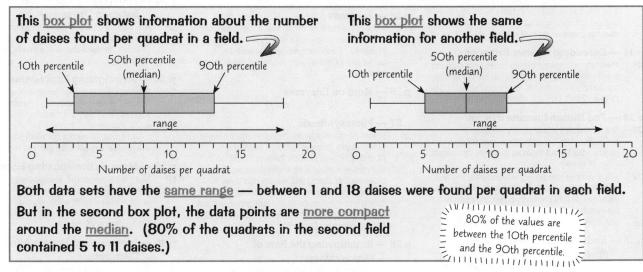

This <u>box plot</u> shows information about the number of daises found per quadrat in a field.
This <u>box plot</u> shows the same information for another field.

Both data sets have the <u>same range</u> — between 1 and 18 daises were found per quadrat in each field.

But in the second box plot, the data points are <u>more compact</u> around the <u>median</u>. (80% of the quadrats in the second field contained 5 to 11 daises.)

80% of the values are between the 10th percentile and the 90th percentile.

'Eeny, meeny, miny, moe' just doesn't cut it any more...

Sampling is an important part of an investigation. It needs to be done randomly, or the data won't be worth much.

Answers

p.1 — Cells and Genetic Material
Q1 As one long circular chromosome *[1 mark]* or in a plasmid *[1 mark]*.

p.2 — Cells and Microscopes
Q1 Select the lowest-powered objective lens *[1 mark]* and move the stage up so the slide is just underneath the objective lens *[1 mark]*. Looking through the lens, move the stage downwards until the specimen is nearly in focus *[1 mark]*. Adjust the height of the stage with the fine adjustment knob until the image is in focus *[1 mark]*.

p.3 — Genomes and Characteristics
Q1 The entire genetic material of an organism *[1 mark]*.
Q2 a) An organism's genotype is the combination of alleles it has for each gene *[1 mark]*.
b) An organism's phenotype is the characteristics that it displays *[1 mark]*.

p.4 — Genetic Diagrams
Q1 E.g.

	T	t
T	TT	Tt
t	Tt	tt

Proportion of offspring expected to be dwarf plants = 1 in 4.
[1 mark for correctly identifying the parents' genotypes as Tt, 1 mark for a correct genetic diagram, 1 mark for correct proportion.]

p.5 — More Genetic Diagrams
Q1 Ff and ff *[1 mark]*.

p.6 — Genome Research and Testing
Q1 E.g. the amniotic fluid surrounding the fetus could be sampled *[1 mark]* to obtain fetal DNA, which could be tested for genetic variants linked to a disorder *[1 mark]*.

p.7 — Genetic Engineering
Q1 It can improve the yield of the crop *[1 mark]*, because herbicide-resistant crops can be sprayed with herbicides to kill weeds without the crop being damaged *[1 mark]*.

p.9 — Health and Disease
Q1 A non-communicable disease is one which is not spread from one organism to another *[1 mark]*.

p.10 — How Disease Spreads
Q1 Any three from: e.g. in water / by air / by contact with infected surfaces / in body fluids / by animal vectors / in soil / in food *[1 mark for each correct answer, up to 3 marks]*.

p.11 — Defending Against Pathogens
Q1 Platelets prevent microorganisms from entering the blood through wounds in the skin *[1 mark]* by clumping together to form blood clots *[1 mark]*.

p.12 — The Human Immune System
Q1 E.g. antibodies disable the pathogen / antibodies 'tag' the pathogens, which helps phagocytes to find them so that they can engulf them *[1 mark]*.
Q2 Memory cells remain in the blood after the first infection with a pathogen *[1 mark]*. If the same pathogen enters the body again, they trigger the rapid production of antibodies so that the pathogen doesn't cause disease *[1 mark]*.

p.13 — Reducing and Preventing the Spread of Disease
Q1 Benefit: e.g. changing the type of plants that are grown stops the pathogens becoming established in an area since many pathogens are specific to a particular plant *[1 mark]*.
Cost: e.g. it may limit how profitable a farm is if it has to change farming practices for a different crop each year *[1 mark]*.

p.14 — Vaccinations
Q1 They produce antibodies *[1 mark]* that attack the antigens present on the cells within the vaccination *[1 mark]*.

p.16 — Culturing Microorganisms
Q1 a) A *[1 mark]*
b) diameter = 13 mm
radius = 13 ÷ 2 = 6.5 mm
$\pi r^2 = \pi \times 6.5^2$ *[1 mark]*
= 132.7... = 133 mm² *[1 mark]*
c) E.g. a disc soaked in sterile water *[1 mark]*.
d) To show that any difference in the growth of the bacteria is only due to the effect of the antibiotic *[1 mark]*.

p.17 — Non-Communicable Diseases
Q1 E.g. eating too much *[1 mark]*, not exercising regularly *[1 mark]*.

p.18 — More on Non-Communicable Diseases
Q1 E.g. increasing the price of cigarettes may mean that fewer people are able to afford them *[1 mark]*, which may lead to a decrease in the national prevalence of lung cancer *[1 mark]*.

p.19 — Interpreting Data on Disease
Q1 A bigger sample size makes it more likely that more of the different characteristics present in the whole population will be included in the sample *[1 mark]*.

p.20 — Investigating Pulse Rate
Q1 The time taken for the heart rate to return to its normal resting rate after exercise *[1 mark]*.

p.21 — Treating Disease
Q1 Many antibiotics are being misused *[1 mark]*, which has caused antibiotic-resistant strains of bacteria to become more common *[1 mark]*. This means that many antibiotics are less effective at killing the bacteria that cause bacterial infections *[1 mark]*.

p.22 — Treating Cardiovascular Disease
Q1 E.g. they can cause excessive bleeding if the person taking them is hurt in an accident *[1 mark]*.

p.23 — Developing New Medicines
Q1 In a double-blind trial, patients are randomly put into two groups — some receive the drug and some receive a placebo *[1 mark]*. Neither the patient nor the doctor knows whether the patient is getting the drug or a placebo until all of the results have been gathered *[1 mark]*.

p.25 — Enzymes
Q1 If the pH is too high or too low, it can interfere with the bonds holding the enzyme together *[1 mark]*. This changes the shape of the active site *[1 mark]* and denatures the enzyme *[1 mark]*.

p.26 — More on Enzymes
Q1 33 ÷ 60 = 0.55 cm³/s *[1 mark]*

p.27 — Photosynthesis
Q1 Plants produce glucose during photosynthesis. Some of this glucose is stored as starch *[1 mark]*. If you perform the starch test on a leaf grown without light, the leaf will not turn blue-black *[1 mark]* this means that there is no starch present in the leaf *[1 mark]*. As no starch has been made in the leaf grown without light, it shows that light is needed for plants to photosynthesise *[1 mark]*.

p.28 — Investigating the Rate of Photosynthesis
Q1 Plants release oxygen into the atmosphere when they photosynthesise *[1 mark]*, therefore the more a plant photosynthesises, the more oxygen it produces *[1 mark]*.

p.29 — Limiting Factors of Photosynthesis
Q1 The rate of photosynthesis increases with increasing light intensity/is directly proportional to light intensity *[1 mark]* up to a point at which the rate levels off *[1 mark]*.

p.30 — Diffusion, Osmosis and Active Transport
Q1 E.g. active transport requires energy and diffusion is passive *[1 mark]*. Active transport moves substances against a concentration gradient whereas diffusion is the movement of substances down a concentration gradient *[1 mark]*.

p.31 — Transport in Plants and Prokaryotes
Q1 Each branch of a plant's roots is covered in millions of root hair cells *[1 mark]*, which gives the plant a big surface area for absorbing water and mineral ions from the soil *[1 mark]*.

p.32 — Investigating Diffusion and Osmosis
Q1 That it is also 0.3 mol/dm³ *[1 mark]*. If the cells are surrounded by a solution with the same concentration as the fluid inside them, then water will not move in or out of the cells by osmosis *[1 mark]* and the cylinders won't lose or gain mass *[1 mark]*.

p.33 — Xylem and Phloem
Q1 Water evaporates and diffuses from a plant's surface, creating a slight shortage of water in the leaf *[1 mark]*. This draws more water up from the rest of the plant through the xylem vessels to replace it *[1 mark]*. This in turn means more water is drawn up from the roots *[1 mark]*.

p.34 — Stomata
Q1 Potassium ions are pumped into guard cells in response to light *[1 mark]*. This increases the solute concentration of the guard cells (which decreases the concentration of water molecules) *[1 mark]*. Water then moves into the guard cells by osmosis *[1 mark]*. This makes the guard cells turgid and the stoma opens *[1 mark]*.

p.35 — Transpiration Rate
Q1 percentage change $= \dfrac{217 - 262}{262} \times 100$
= –17.2% (to 3 s.f.)
[2 marks for correct answer, otherwise 1 mark for (217 - 262) / 262].

p.36 — Using a Potometer
Q1 E.g. light intensity *[1 mark]* / air movement *[1 mark]*.

p.37 — Ecosystems and Interactions Between Organisms
Q1 Any two from: e.g. temperature / moisture level / light intensity / pH of the soil / toxic chemicals *[1 mark for each correct answer, up to 2 marks]*.

p.38 — Investigating Ecosystems
Q1 Population size = (number in first sample × number in second sample) ÷ number in second sample previously marked
= (22 × 26) ÷ 4
= 143 crabs *[2 marks for each correct answer, otherwise 1 marks for correct working]*

p.39 — More on Investigating Ecosystems
Q1 Mark out a line in the area you want to study using a tape measure *[1 mark]*. Place quadrats at intervals / next to each other along the line *[1 mark]*. Count and record the organisms in each quadrat *[1 mark]*.

p.40 — Investigating Factors Affecting Distribution
Q1 The presence of bushy lichen indicates the air is clean *[1 mark]* because the lichen needs clean air / air with a low level of sulfur dioxide to grow *[1 mark]*.

Answers

p.41 — Food Chains and Food Webs
Q1 E.g. the number of hawks might increase because there will be more mice for them to eat *[1 mark]*. The amount of wheat might decrease because more will be eaten by the mice *[1 mark]*. The number of aphids might decrease because they would be competing with more mice for food *[1 mark]*. The number of humans might decrease because they would be competing with more mice for food *[1 mark]*.

p.42 — Making and Breaking Biological Molecules
Q1 a) simple sugars *[1 mark]*
b) amino acids *[1 mark]*

p.43 — Testing for Biological Molecules
Q1 Proteins are present *[1 mark]*.

p.44 — Cycles in Ecosystems
Q1 E.g. not as much CO_2 in the air is being used for photosynthesis *[1 mark]*. Microorganisms involved in the decomposition of the dead trees release CO_2 into the atmosphere through respiration *[1 mark]*.

p.45 — More on Cycles in Ecosystems
Q1 a) By evaporation / transpiration *[1 mark]*.
b) By providing them with fresh water *[1 mark]*.

p.47 — Respiration
Q1 glucose + oxygen $\rightarrow$ carbon dioxide + water *[1 mark for correct reactants, 1 mark for correct products.]*

p.48 — More on Respiration
Q1 Ethanol and carbon dioxide *[1 mark]*.
Q2 E.g. aerobic respiration produces much more ATP than anaerobic respiration *[1 mark]*.

p.49 — The Cell Cycle and Mitosis
Q1 The cell grows larger *[1 mark]*, increases the amount of its subcellular structures *[1 mark]* and duplicates its DNA *[1 mark]*.

p.50 — Microscopy
Q1 They've allowed us to see the internal structures of cells in more detail *[1 mark]*, which has allowed scientists to develop explanations as to how the structures are related to their functions *[1 mark]*.

p.51 — More Microscopy
Q1 actual size = measured size ÷ magnification
= 7×10^{-1} mm (or 0.7 mm) ÷ 400 *[1 mark]*
= 0.00175 mm *[1 mark]*
(× 1000) = 1.75 µm *[1 mark]*

p.52 — Sexual Reproduction and Meiosis
Q1 During fertilisation, a male gamete fuses with a female gamete to form a zygote/fertilised egg *[1 mark]*. Gametes need half the chromosome number so that the zygote/fertilised egg ends up with the full number of chromosomes, and not twice as many *[1 mark]*.

p.53 — Stem Cells
Q1 The tips of plant shoots contain meristem tissue *[1 mark]*. Meristems produce unspecialised cells that are able to divide and form any cell type in the plant *[1 mark]*. This means the plant is able to produce all the different specialised cells it needs in order to grow into a new plant *[1 mark]*.

p.55 — Exchange of Materials
Q1 Surface area:
(1 × 1) × 2 = 2
(4 × 1) × 4 = 16
2 + 16 = 18 µm² *[1 mark]*
Volume:
1 × 1 × 4 = 4 µm³ *[1 mark]*
So the surface area to volume ratio is 18 : 4, which is 9 : 2 in its simplest form *[1 mark]*.
(In this question the ratio has been simplified down to the smallest whole numbers. It's not in the form n : 1 because then n would not be a whole number.)

p.56 — Human Exchange Surfaces
Q1 E.g. they have a large surface area / they have a moist lining for dissolving gases / they have very thin walls / they have a good blood supply *[1 mark]*.

p.57 — The Circulatory System
Q1 the right ventricle *[1 mark]*

p.58 — Blood Vessels
Q1 They have a big lumen to help the blood flow despite the low pressure *[1 mark]* and they have valves to keep the blood flowing in the right direction *[1 mark]*.
Q2 E.g. networks of capillaries carry blood to every cell in the body to exchange substances with them *[1 mark]*. They have permeable walls, so that substances can easily diffuse in and out of them *[1 mark]*. Their walls are only one cell thick, which increases the rate of diffusion *[1 mark]*.

p.59 — Blood
Q1 haemoglobin *[1 mark]*
Q2 Any three from: e.g. red blood cells have a large surface area to volume ratio for absorbing oxygen / They don't have a nucleus, which allows more room for carrying oxygen / They contain haemoglobin, which can combine with oxygen in the lungs and release it in body tissues / They're small and flexible so they can easily pass through tiny capillaries.
[1 mark for each, up to 3 marks].

p.60 — The Nervous System
Q1 brain *[1 mark]*, spinal cord *[1 mark]*

p.61 — Reflexes
Q1 Impulses are sent from taste receptors on the tongue along a sensory neurone to the CNS *[1 mark]*. The impulse is transferred across a synapse to a relay neurone *[1 mark]* via the release of neurotransmitters *[1 mark]*. It is then transferred across another synapse to a motor neurone *[1 mark]* and travels along the motor neurone to the effectors — the salivary glands *[1 mark]*.

p.62 — Hormones and Negative Feedback
Q1 Endocrine glands secrete hormones *[1 mark]*. These act as chemical messengers *[1 mark]* and travel in the bloodstream *[1 mark]* to effectors *[1 mark]*. These have receptors so they can respond to the hormone *[1 mark]*.

p.63 — Hormones in Reproduction
Q1 LH stimulates the release of an egg/ovulation *[1 mark]*. It also stimulates the remains of the follicle to secrete progesterone *[1 mark]*.

p.64 — Hormones for Fertility and Contraception
Q1 The hormones FSH and LH *[1 mark]* can be injected by women with naturally low FSH levels *[1 mark]* to stimulate ovulation *[1 mark]*.

p.65 — More on Contraception
Q1 E.g. oral contraceptives can have unpleasant side-effects / she might find it difficult to remember to take a pill every day *[1 mark]*.
Q2 Any two from: e.g. IUDs are more effective. / IUDs are longer acting / there's less chance of IUDs not working as they are intended *[1 mark for each, up to 2 marks]*.

p.66 — Homeostasis and Blood Sugar Level
Q1 When blood glucose level is too low, the pancreas secretes glucagon into the bloodstream *[1 mark]*. Glucagon makes the liver turn stored glycogen into glucose *[1 mark]*. The liver then releases this glucose into the bloodstream *[1 mark]*.

p.67 — Diabetes
Q1 In type 1 diabetes, the person doesn't produce insulin *[1 mark]*, whereas in type 2 diabetes, the person still produces insulin but they are resistant to it/don't respond properly to it *[1 mark]* or don't produce enough of it *[1 mark]*.

p.69 — Natural Selection and Evolution
Q1 Some of the musk oxen may have had a genetic variant/allele which gave them thicker fur *[1 mark]*. Those musk oxen would have been more likely to survive and reproduce *[1 mark]* and so pass on their genetic variants/alleles for thicker fur *[1 mark]*. This process of natural selection may have continued over many generations, leading to all musk oxen having thick fur *[1 mark]*.

p.70 — Evidence for Evolution
Q1 By mutations *[1 mark]*.
Q2 Fossils can show what organisms that lived a long time ago looked like *[1 mark]*. Arranging them in chronological/date order shows how organisms gradually changed/developed *[1 mark]*.

p.71 — Selective Breeding
Q1 He should choose the bean plants that are best at surviving the drought *[1 mark]* and breed them with each other *[1 mark]*. He should then continue this process over several generations *[1 mark]*.

p.72 — Classification
Q1 E.g. organisms may be very similar physically but have many genetic differences / belong to different species *[1 mark]*.

p.73 — Biodiversity
Q1 E.g. chemicals used in agriculture may pollute water sources *[1 mark]*, affecting organisms which rely on the water for survival *[1 mark]*.

p.74 — More on Biodiversity
Q1 E.g. captive breeding programmes in zoos can be used to increase the number of Siberian tigers *[1 mark]*. Some of these individuals can then be released into the wild *[1 mark]*.

p.75 — Maintaining Biodiversity
Q1 E.g. undiscovered plant species may contain new medicinal chemicals *[1 mark]*. If these plants are allowed to become extinct we could miss out on valuable medicines *[1 mark]*.

p.77 — States of Matter
Q1 a) In a solid, the particles are held by strong forces *[1 mark]* in fixed positions in a regular lattice arrangement *[1 mark]*. The particles don't move but vibrate about their positions *[1 mark]*.
b) In a gas, there's almost no force of attraction between the particles *[1 mark]*. The particles are far apart from each other *[1 mark]*. The particles move constantly with random motion and travel in straight lines *[1 mark]*.
c) In a liquid, there are weaker forces of attraction between the particles than there are in a solid *[1 mark]*. The particles move constantly with random motion *[1 mark]* but they do tend to stick closely together *[1 mark]*.

p.78 — Changing State
Q1 a) solid *[1 mark]*
b) liquid *[1 mark]*
c) liquid *[1 mark]*
d) gas *[1 mark]*

p.79 — Chemical Formulas
Q1 12 *[1 mark]*

p.80 — Chemical Equations
Q1 $2Fe + 3Cl_2 \rightarrow 2FeCl_3$ *[1 mark]*
Q2 a) water $\rightarrow$ hydrogen + oxygen *[1 mark]*
b) $2H_2O \rightarrow 2H_2 + O_2$
[1 mark for correct reactants and products, 1 mark for a correctly balanced equation.]

Answers

p.81 — Endothermic and Exothermic Reactions
Q1 a) exothermic *[1 mark]*

b)

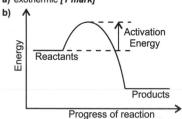

[1 mark for correct shape, 1 mark for correctly labelled axes, 1 mark for correctly labelled products, reactants and activation energy.]

p.82 — Bond Energies
Q1 Energy required to break original bonds:
$(1 \times N \equiv N) + (3 \times H–H)$
$= 941 + (3 \times 436) = 941 + 1308$
$= 2249 \, kJ/mol$ *[1 mark]*
Energy released by forming new bonds:
$(6 \times N–H)$
$= 6 \times 391 = 2346 \, kJ/mol$ *[1 mark]*
Overall energy change:
$2249 – 2346 = –97 \, kJ/mol$ *[1 mark]*

p.83 — The Evolution of the Atmosphere
Q1 Green plants and algae reduced the level of carbon dioxide *[1 mark]* and increased the level of oxygen *[1 mark]* in atmosphere by carrying out photosynthesis *[1 mark]*.

p.84 — Combustion and Air Pollution
Q1 E.g. carbon monoxide *[1 mark]* and soot *[1 mark]*.

p.85 — Greenhouse Gases and Climate Change
Q1 Any three from: e.g. polar ice caps melting / sea levels rising / coastal erosion / changing rainfall patterns / some regions may have too much or too little water / it may be difficult to produce food / there may be an increase in the frequency and severity of storms *[1 mark for each, up to 3 marks]*.

p.86 — Reducing Pollution and Tests for Gases
Q1 E.g. governments can put a cap on the amount of greenhouse gases that a business can emit and issue licences for set amounts of emissions up to this point *[1 mark]*. They can also impose taxes on companies according to the amount of greenhouse gases that they emit to encourage them to cut down on emissions *[1 mark]*.

p.87 — Potable Water
Q1 Any two from: e.g. to force dissolved gases out of the water / to remove ions that react with oxygen to form insoluble oxides / to encourage aerobic bacteria to break down organic matter *[1 mark for each, up to 2 marks]*.

p.89 — The History of the Atom
Q1 In the plum pudding model, the atom is a ball of positive charge with electrons spread throughout it *[1 mark]*.

p.90 — The Atom
Q1 In the nucleus *[1 mark]*.
Q2 nuclear radius, atomic radius, simple molecule, nanoparticle *[2 marks for all 4 correct, 1 mark if up to 2 are incorrect]*.

p.91 — Atoms, Ions and Isotopes
Q1 a) Bromine-79: 35 protons, 35 electrons and (79 – 35 =) 44 neutrons *[1 mark]*.
Bromine-81: 35 protons, 35 electrons and (81 – 35 =) 46 neutrons *[1 mark]*.
b) 35 + 1 = 36 electrons *[1 mark]*

p.92 — The Periodic Table
Q1 2 *[1 mark]*
Q2 Potassium and sodium are both in Group 1. Potassium and calcium are in different groups. So the chemical properties of potassium should be closer to those of sodium than calcium *[1 mark]*, because elements in the same group have similar chemical properties *[1 mark]*.

p.93 — Electronic Structure
Q1 2.8.8.1 or

[1 mark]

p.94 — Metals and Non-Metals
Q1 Any three from: e.g. metals tend to be shiny / good conductors of heat / good at conducting electricity / have high melting/boiling points / tend to have high densities *[1 mark for each, up to 3 marks]*.

p.95 — Group 1 Elements
Q1 As you go further down the group, the outer electron is further away from the nucleus *[1 mark]*. This means the attraction between the nucleus and the electron decreases, so the electron is more easily removed. This results in an increase in reactivity *[1 mark]*.

p.96 — Reactions of Group 1 Elements
Q1 lithium *[1 mark]*
Q2 $2Rb + 2H_2O \rightarrow 2RbOH + H_2$ *[1 mark for correct reactants and products, 1 mark for correctly balanced equation.]*

p.97 — Group 7 Elements
Q1 Bromine would be a solid at this temperature *[1 mark]*. The melting points of the halogens increase as you go down the group, so at the melting point of chlorine, bromine would still be solid *[1 mark]*.
Q2 $2Na + I_2 \rightarrow 2NaI$
[1 mark for correct reactants and products, 1 mark for correctly balanced equation.]

p.98 — Displacement Reactions of Group 7
Q1 bromine water *[1 mark]*

p.99 — Group 0 Elements
Q1 Xenon has a higher boiling point than neon *[1 mark]*.
Q2 Argon has a full outer shell *[1 mark]* so is electronically stable and does not readily lose or gain electrons *[1 mark]*.

p.100 — Ionic Bonding
Q1 K_2O *[1 mark]*

p.101 — Ionic Compounds
Q1

[1 mark for arrow showing electron transferred from potassium to bromine, 1 mark for correct outer shell electron configurations, 1 mark for correct charges.]

p.103 — Metallic Bonding and Reactivity
Q1 a) E.g. copper is a good electrical conductor *[1 mark]* as it contains delocalised electrons which are able to carry an electrical current *[1 mark]*.
b) The layers of atoms in a metal can slide over each other whilst still being held together by electrons *[1 mark]*.

p.104 — Ionic Equations and Reactions of Metals
Q1 Lead would not displace zinc from zinc chloride solution, as it's lower than zinc in the reactivity series/it's less reactive than zinc *[1 mark]*.
Q2 $Mg_{(s)} + Fe^{2+}_{(aq)} \rightarrow Fe_{(s)} + Mg^{2+}_{(aq)}$ *[1 mark for correct reactants and products, 1 mark for correctly balanced equation.]*

p.105 — More Reactions of Metals
Q1 E.g. copper / silver *[1 mark]*

p.106 — Extracting Metals
Q1 Iron is less reactive than carbon *[1 mark]* so you could extract iron from its ore by reducing it with carbon *[1 mark]*.

p.107 — Oxidation and Reduction
Q1 $Cl_2 + 2e^- \rightarrow 2Cl^-$
[1 mark for correct reactants and products, 1 mark for a correctly balanced equation.]

p.108 — Electrolysis
Q1 a) chlorine gas/Cl_2 *[1 mark]*
b) zinc atoms/Zn *[1 mark]*

p.109 — Electrolysis of Aqueous Solutions
Q1 chlorine gas *[1 mark]*

p.110 — Covalent Bonding
Q1 NH_3 *[1 mark]*

p.111 — Simple Covalent Substances
Q1 The intermolecular forces between molecules of O_2 are weak *[1 mark]* and don't need much energy to break, therefore they have low boiling points *[1 mark]*.

p.112 — Homologous Series and Alkanes
Q1
```
  H  H  H
  |  |  |
H-C--C--C-H
  |  |  |
  H  H  H
```
[1 mark]
Q2 a) E.g. $C_{10}H_{22}$ is more viscous than C_5H_{12} / C_5H_{12} is less viscous than $C_{10}H_{22}$ *[1 mark]*.
b) E.g. $C_{10}H_{22}$ has a higher boiling point than C_5H_{12} / C_5H_{12} has a lower boiling point than $C_{10}H_{22}$ *[1 mark]*.
c) E.g. $C_{10}H_{22}$ is less flammable than C_5H_{12} / C_5H_{12} is more flammable than $C_{10}H_{22}$ *[1 mark]*.

p.113 — Fractional Distillation of Crude Oil
Q1 Short-chain hydrocarbons have weak intermolecular forces between them *[1 mark]* so have low boiling points *[1 mark]*. This means they condense towards the top of the column where it is cooler *[1 mark]*.

p.114 — Uses of Crude Oil
Q1 C_3H_6 *[1 mark]*

p.116 — Polymers
Q1 E.g. doesn't melt when heated, strong, hard, stiff *[1 mark for each, up to 4 marks]*.

p.117 — Giant Covalent Structures
Q1 Similarities: any two from, e.g. giant covalent structure / covalent bonding / high melting point *[1 mark for each similarity, up to 2 marks]*. Differences: any two from, e.g. diamond is colourless, graphite is black / graphite conducts electricity, diamond doesn't / carbon atoms form 4 covalent bonds in diamond, and 3 in graphite *[1 mark for each difference, up to 2 marks]*.
Q2 E.g. a single layer of carbon atoms *[1 mark]* which each form three covalent bonds *[1 mark]*.

p.118 — Bulk Properties of Materials
Q1 Charged particles/electrons or ions that are free to move *[1 mark]*.

p.119 — Types of Materials
Q1 Any two from: e.g. fibreglass / concrete / carbon fibre *[1 mark for each correct material, up to 2 marks]*.

Answers

p.120 — Materials and their Uses
Q1 E.g. glass would be the best choice *[1 mark]*. The equipment shouldn't soften or melt below 300 °C, so LDPE and poly(propene) are poor choices *[1 mark]*. Aluminium is fairly reactive, so could react with the chemicals *[1 mark]*.

p.121 — Reuse and Recycling
Q1 E.g. metal ores are non-renewable, so recycling metals is important to conserve finite resources of the metal *[1 mark]*. Also, non-recycled material has to be disposed of in landfill sites, which take up space and can pollute the surroundings *[1 mark]*.

p.122 — Life Cycle Assessments
Q1 Any four from: e.g. the energy required to extract the raw materials / whether the raw materials are renewable or not / whether other harmful emissions are produced / whether the waste products are harmful or not / how environmentally friendly the cars are to dispose of *[1 mark for each, up to 4 marks]*.

p.123 — Nanoparticles
Q1 The molecule with a diameter of 0.2 nm *[1 mark]*.

p.124 — Uses of Nanoparticles
Q1 Any three from: e.g. catalysts / to deliver drugs / lubricant coatings / tiny electrical circuits / antibacterial materials / sun creams / deodorants / stronger plastics *[1 mark for each, up to 3 marks]*.

p.126 — Purity and Mixtures
Q1 The sample melts over a range of temperatures *[1 mark]*. The melting point is lower than that of pure aspirin *[1 mark]*.

p.127 — Chromatography
Q1 During paper chromatography, the molecules of each chemical in the sample move between the stationary phase and the mobile phase *[1 mark]*. The mobile phase moves through the stationary phase over the course of the experiment, and anything that's dissolved in it will move with it *[1 mark]*. The distance a compound moves through the stationary phase depends on how long it spends dissolved in the mobile phase compared to on the stationary phase *[1 mark]*. Since different compounds will interact differently with the mobile phase and the stationary phase, they'll move different amounts through the stationary phase, and so be separated from each other *[1 mark]*.

p.128 — Interpreting Chromatograms
Q1 a) Rf = $\dfrac{\text{distance travelled by solute}}{\text{distance travelled by solvent front}} = \dfrac{4.8}{6.0}$ *[1 mark]*
= 0.80 *[1 mark]*

b) E.g. spray the paper with ninhydrin solution / put the paper in a jar containing a few iodine crystals *[1 mark]*.

p.129 — Separating Mixtures
Q1 E.g. slowly heat the solution to evaporate off some of the water *[1 mark]*. Stop heating once some of the water has evaporated / once copper sulfate crystals start to form *[1 mark]*. Allow the solution to cool *[1 mark]*. Filter the crystals out of the solution and dry them in a warm place / desiccator / drying oven *[1 mark]*.

p.130 — Relative Mass
Q1 a) A_r of H = 1.0 and A_r of O = 16.0
M_r of H_2O = (2 × 1.0) + 16.0 = 18.0 *[1 mark]*

b) A_r of Li = 6.9, A_r of O = 16.0 and A_r of H = 1.0
So M_r of LiOH = 6.9 + 16.0 + 1.0 = 23.9 *[1 mark]*

c) A_r of H = 1.0, A_r of S = 32.1 and A_r of O = 16.0
M_r of H_2SO_4 = (2 × 1.0) + 32.1 + (4 × 16.0) = 98.1 *[1 mark]*

Q2 A_r of K = 39.1, A_r of O = 16.0 and A_r of H = 1.0
M_r of KOH = 39.1 + 16.0 + 1.0 = 56.1 *[1 mark]*
$\dfrac{39.1}{56.1}$ × 100 = 69.7% *[1 mark]*

p.131 — Conservation of Mass
Q1 The mass of the reaction vessel will decrease *[1 mark]*. The reactants are a solid and a liquid, so will be contained inside the vessel *[1 mark]*, but, during the reaction, hydrogen gas is formed which will escape from the vessel, so its mass will no longer be accounted for *[1 mark]*.

p.132 — The Mole
Q1 moles = mass ÷ M_r = 90 ÷ 18.0 = 5.0 moles *[1 mark]*

Q2 mass = moles × M_r
= 0.200 × 119.0 = 23.8 moles *[1 mark]*

Q3 M_r = mass ÷ moles = 87.0 ÷ 0.500 = 174 *[1 mark]*

p.133 — Calculations Using Balanced Equations
Q1 M_r(KBr) = 39.1 +79.9 = 119.0
M_r(Br_2) = 79.9 × 2 = 159.8 *[1 mark]*
moles of KBr = mass ÷ M_r = 23.8 ÷ 119 = 0.200 moles *[1 mark]*
From the equation, 2 moles of KBr react to produce 1 mole of Br_2. So 0.200 moles of KBr will produce (0.200 ÷ 2 =) 0.100 moles of Br_2 *[1 mark]*.
So mass of Br_2 = 0.100 × 159.8 = 16.0 g *[1 mark]*.

p.134 — Calculations Using Moles
Q1 A_r(B) = 10.8 M_r(F_2) = 2 × 19.0 = 38.0 *[1 mark]*
Moles of B = 86.4 ÷ 10.8 = 8.0
Moles of F_2 = 228 ÷ 38.0 = 6.0
Divide by the smallest (2) gives a ratio of B : F_2 of 4 : 3 *[1 mark]*.
The balanced equation gives a ratio of B : F_2 of 2 : 3, so F_2 must be the limiting reactant *[1 mark]*.

p.135 — Acids, Alkalis and Concentrations
Q1 a) Concentration = 2.7 ÷ 0.03 = 90 g/dm³ *[1 mark]*

b) sulfuric acid + sodium hydroxide → sodium sulfate + water *[1 mark]*

p.136 — Quantitative Tests and Standard Solutions
Q1 volume = 300 ÷ 1000 = 0.300 dm³ *[1 mark]*
mass = concentration × volume = 24 × 0.300 = 7.2 g *[1 mark]*

p.137 — Titrations
Q1 The indicator will have just changed colour *[1 mark]*.

Q2 E.g. to increase the accuracy of your result *[1 mark]* and to spot any anomalous results *[1 mark]*.

p.138 — Titration Calculations
Q1 Moles of KOH = 0.150 × (22.5 ÷ 1000)
= 0.003375 *[1 mark]*
From the reaction equation, 1 mole of KOH reacts with 1 mole of HNO_3, so 0.003375 mol of KOH reacts with 0.003375 mol of HNO_3 *[1 mark]*.
Concentration of HNO_3
= (0.003375) ÷ (25.0 ÷ 1000)
= 0.135 mol/dm³ *[1 mark]*

p.140 — Acids, Alkalis and pH
Q1 a) acidic *[1 mark]*

b) The pH has increased by 3 so the H^+ concentration would decrease *[1 mark]* by a factor of 1000 *[1 mark]*.

p.141 — Strong and Weak Acids
Q1 A strong acid dissociates completely in water *[1 mark]*. A weak acid only dissociates a small amount in water *[1 mark]*.

p.142 — Reactions of Acids
Q1 $2HCl + CaCO_3 \rightarrow CaCl_2 + H_2O + CO_2$
[1 mark for correct reactants and products, 1 mark for a correctly balanced equation.]

p.143 — Making Salts
Q1 E.g. React the iron oxide with the nitric acid. Keep on adding base until all the acid has been reacted and the base is in excess — at this point, no more iron oxide will react and it will sink to the bottom of the flask *[1 mark]*. Filter out the excess solid using filter paper and collect the solution of salt and water *[1 mark]*. Gently evaporate off some of the water from your salt solution and leave to allow the salt to crystallise *[1 mark]*. Scrape the salt onto a piece of fresh filter paper and leave it to dry *[1 mark]*.

p.144 — Rates of Reactions
Q1 B, because the granules have a higher surface area to volume ratio than the solid piece *[1 mark]*. This means that the water particles will have more area to work on which increases the frequency of collisions *[1 mark]*.

p.145 — Reaction Rates and Catalysts
Q1 A catalyst is a substance that increases the rate of reaction *[1 mark]*, without being chemically changed or used up in the reaction *[1 mark]*.

Q2 E.g.

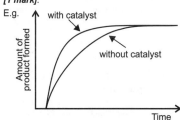

[1 mark for the curve with the catalyst starting with a steeper gradient than the curve without the catalyst, 1 mark for the curve with the catalyst flattening off before the curve without the catalyst, 1 mark for both curves flattening off at the same level.]

p.146 — Measuring Reaction Rates
Q1 Any one from: e.g. add Na_2CO_3 to a flask containing HCl *[1 mark]* and take readings of the mass of the flask at regular intervals *[1 mark]* using a mass balance *[1 mark]*. / Add Na_2CO_3 to a flask containing HCl *[1 mark]* and take regular readings of the volume of gas released *[1 mark]* using a gas syringe/by collecting the gas over water in a measuring cylinder *[1 mark]*.

Answers

p.147 — Finding Reaction Rates from Graphs

Q1 a) E.g.

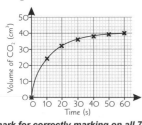

[1 mark for correctly marking on all 7 points, 1 mark for choosing a sensible scale for the axes, 1 mark for drawing a line of best fit.]

b) E.g.

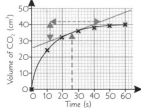

change in y = 42 − 30 = 12,
change in x = 44 − 12 = 32,
rate = (change in y) ÷ (change in x) = 12 ÷ 32
= 0.38 cm³/s
[1 mark for drawing a tangent at 26 s, 1 mark for correctly calculating a change in y from the tangent, 1 mark for correctly calculating a change in x from the tangent and 1 mark for a rate between 0.28 cm³/s and 0.48 cm³/s.]

p.148 — Dynamic Equilibrium

Q1 E.g. a reversible reaction is one where the products can react with each other to produce the reactants *[1 mark]*.

Q2 Dynamic equilibrium is when the forwards and backwards reactions in a reversible reaction occur at the same rate *[1 mark]*.

Q3 Temperature, *[1 mark]* pressure *[1 mark]* and concentration *[1 mark]*.

p.149 — Changing the Position of Equilibrium

Q1 The position of equilibrium will shift to the right (towards the products) *[1 mark]*. The forward reaction is endothermic, so when the temperature is increased the equilibrium position will move to the right to absorb the excess heat *[1 mark]*.

Q2 Decreasing the pressure would shift the equilibrium position to the left (towards the reactants) *[1 mark]* as there are more moles of gas on the reactant side than on the products side *[1 mark]*. So the yield of SO_3 would decrease *[1 mark]*.

p.151 — Waves

Q1 7.5 ÷ 100 = 0.075 m *[1 mark]*
wave speed = frequency × wavelength,
so frequency = wave speed ÷ wavelength
= 0.15 ÷ 0.075 *[1 mark]* = 2 Hz *[1 mark]*

p.152 — Wave Experiments

Q1 E.g. attach a variable power supply to a dipper and place it in a ripple tank filled with water to create waves *[1 mark]*. Place a cork in the water and time how long it takes to bob up 10 times *[1 mark]*. Divide this time by 10 to give the period of the wave *[1 mark]*. 1 ÷ the period gives the frequency of the wave *[1 mark]*.

p.153 — Reflection and Refraction

Q1 $v = f\lambda$ *[1 mark]* and the frequency of the wave cannot change (it stays the same) *[1 mark]*. So the wavelength must decrease if speed decreases *[1 mark]*.

p.154 — Reflection and Refraction Experiments

Q1 Draw around one prism on a piece of paper and trace the path of a light ray as it enters and leaves the prism *[1 mark]*. Draw the refracted ray by connecting the ends of the other two rays with a straight line *[1 mark]*. Draw the normals at the points where the ray enters and leaves the prism *[1 mark]*. Mark and measure the angles of incidence and refraction for the ray entering and leaving the prism *[1 mark]*. Repeat with the second prism using the same initial angle of incidence *[1 mark]*.

p.155 — The Electromagnetic Spectrum

Q1 X-rays, visible light, microwaves *[1 mark]*.

Q2 A change in the nucleus / radioactive decay *[1 mark]*.

p.156 — Energy Levels and Ionisation

Q1 An electron/electrons can move up to a higher energy level / leave the atom *[1 mark]*.

Q2 Gamma radiation is ionising *[1 mark]*, which can lead to mutations of cells and their abnormal growth *[1 mark]*.

p.157 — Uses of EM Radiation

Q1 An alternating current of a set frequency in an electric conductor causes charges to oscillate *[1 mark]*, creating an oscillating electric and magnetic field (an EM wave) of the same frequency — a radio wave *[1 mark]*.

p.158 — More Uses of EM Radiation

Q1 Any two from: e.g. sterilising medical instruments / sterilising food / cancer treatment / medical imaging *[1 mark for each, up to 2 marks]*.

p.159 — Absorbing and Emitting Radiation

Q1 Star A is hotter *[1 mark]*. The hotter an object it is, the higher its principal frequency *[1 mark]*.

p.160 — The Greenhouse Effect

Q1 E.g. carbon dioxide / methane / water vapour *[1 mark for each, up to 3 marks]*.

Q2 E.g. they add more greenhouse gases to the atmosphere *[1 mark]*. The extra greenhouse gases increase the amount of radiation absorbed *[1 mark]* and re-emitted back towards Earth *[1 mark]*. This causes the temperature of the Earth's surface to gradually increase *[1 mark]*.

p.162 — Energy Stores and Transfers

Q1 Energy is transferred electrically *[1 mark]* from the chemical energy store of the battery *[1 mark]* to the kinetic energy store of the motor *[1 mark]*.

p.163 — Conservation of Energy and Power

Q1 $E = P \times t$ = 4.8 × 1000 = 4800 J
t = 2 × 60 = 120 s *[1 mark]*
Rearrange $E = P \times t$ for P:
$P = E \div t$ = 4800 ÷ 120 *[1 mark]* = 40 W *[1 mark]*

Q2 t = 45 minutes = 45 ÷ 60 = 0.75 hours *[1 mark]*
Calculate energy in kWh:
$E = P \times t$ = 4.0 × 0.75 *[1 mark]* = 3 kWh *[1 mark]*
At 14p per kWh, a load of drying costs:
3 × 14p = 42p *[1 mark]*

p.164 — Efficiency and Sankey Diagrams

Q1 efficiency = useful energy transferred ÷ total energy transferred
= 225 ÷ 300 *[1 mark]* = 0.75 *[1 mark]*
0.75 × 100 = 75% *[1 mark]*

p.165 — Energy Resources

Q1 Any two from: e.g. biofuels / wind / the Sun / hydroelectricity / the tides *[1 mark for each, up to 2 marks]*.

p.166 — Renewable Energy Resources

Q1 E.g. solar power produces no pollution when being used *[1 mark]* but production can't be increased to meet extra demand *[1 mark]*.

p.167 — Trends in Energy Use

Q1 Any two from: e.g. it is a clean energy resource / it is reliable / it provides lots of jobs *[1 mark for each, up to 2 marks]*.

p.168 — The National Grid

Q1 In an alternating current (a.c.) supply, the current is constantly changing direction *[1 mark]*. In a direct current (d.c.) supply, the current always travels in the same direction *[1 mark]*.

Q2 Live — 230 V *[1 mark]*, Neutral — 0 V *[1 mark]*, Earth — 0 V *[1 mark]*.

p.170 — Circuits — The Basics

Q1 time = charge ÷ current = 28 800 ÷ 8.0 *[1 mark]*
= 3600 s (= 1 hour) *[1 mark]*

p.171 — Resistance and $V = I \times R$

Q1 resistance = p.d. ÷ current = 230 ÷ 5.0 *[1 mark]*
= 46 Ω *[1 mark]*

p.172 — Resistance and I-V Characteristics

Q1 a)

[1 mark for a straight line through the origin.]

b)

[1 mark for correct shape that passes through the origin.]

p.173 — Circuit Devices

Q1 E.g.

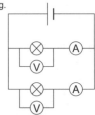

[1 mark for drawing an LDR, an ammeter and a battery in series, 1 mark for drawing a voltmeter in parallel with the LDR.]

p.174 — Energy and Power in Circuits

Q1 11 × 60 = 660 seconds *[1 mark]*
1.5 × 10³ = 1500 W
energy transferred = power × time
= 1500 × 660 *[1 mark]*
= 990 000 J *[1 mark]*

p.175 — Series and Parallel Circuits

Q1 R = 2 + 2 + 2 = 6 Ω *[1 mark]*

p.176 — More on Series and Parallel Circuits

Q1 3.5 V *[1 mark]*

p.177 — Investigating Series and Parallel Circuits

Q1 E.g.

[1 mark for drawing a closed circuit containing at least two bulbs in parallel with a cell, 1 mark for drawing a voltmeter in parallel with each bulb and an ammeter in series with each bulb.]

p.178 — Permanent and Induced Magnets

Q1 At the poles *[1 mark]*.

Q2 E.g. permanent magnets produce their own magnetic fields but induced magnets become magnets when they're in a magnetic field *[1 mark]*. When taken away from a magnetic field, an induced magnet will lose its magnetisation, but a permanent magnet will remain magnetised *[1 mark]*.

Answers

p.179 — Electromagnetism

Q1 E.g.

[1 mark for concentric circles, 1 mark for arrows on field lines in the correct direction.]

p.180 — The Motor Effect

Q1 Thumb — direction of the force *[1 mark]*. First finger — direction of the magnetic field *[1 mark]*. Second finger — direction of the current *[1 mark]*.

Q2 35 cm = 0.35 m *[1 mark]*
magnetic field strength
= force ÷ (current × length of conductor)
= 9.8 ÷ (5.0 × 0.35) *[1 mark]* = 5.6 T *[1 mark]*

p.181 — Electric Motors

Q1 E.g. in a fan/blender to make the blades move / in electric toothbrushes to move the bristles / in hair dryers to move the fan blades *[1 mark]*.

Q2 Any two from: e.g. decrease the current / decrease the number of turns on the coil / decrease the magnetic field strength. *[1 mark for each, up to 2 marks]*

p.182 — Transformers

Q1 Step-down transformer *[1 mark]*.

Q2 p.d. across secondary coil
= (p.d. across primary coil × current in primary coil) ÷ current in secondary coil *[1 mark]*
= (6.5 × 4.0) ÷ 5.0 *[1 mark]*
= 5.2 V *[1 mark]*

p.184 — Forces and Newton's Third Law

Q1 When the ball hits the wall, it exerts a force on the wall. There is an equal and opposite force on the ball from the wall (Newton's third law) *[1 mark]*. This means that the ball is pushed in the opposite direction, away from the wall, and so bounces back *[1 mark]*.

p.185 — Mass and Weight

Q1 weight = mass × gravitational field strength
mass = weight ÷ gravitational field strength *[1 mark]*
= 820 ÷ 10 *[1 mark]* = 82 kg *[1 mark]*

p.186 — Scalars and Vectors

Q1 Scalar quantities only have a size whereas vector quantities also have a direction *[1 mark]*. E.g. distance is a scalar quantity, whereas displacement is a vector quantity *[1 mark]*.

p.187 — Calculating Speed

Q1 First convert minutes into seconds:
2.0 × 60 = 120 s *[1 mark]*
average speed = distance ÷ time
= 660 ÷ 120 *[1 mark]*
= 5.5 m/s *[1 mark]*

Q2 54 km/hr ÷ (60 × 60) = 0.015 km/s
0.015 km/s × 1000 = 15 m/s *[1 mark]*
distance = average speed × time
= 15 × 24 *[1 mark]* = 360 m *[1 mark]*

p.188 — Acceleration

Q1 initial speed = 0 m/s, final speed = 5.00 m/s,
acceleration = g = 10 m/s^2,
distance = (final speed^2 − initial speed^2) ÷ (2 × acceleration) *[1 mark]*
= (25 − 0) ÷ (2 × 10) *[1 mark]*
= 1.25 m *[1 mark]*

p.189 — Investigating Motion

Q1 Use the light gates to time how long it takes the object to pass between the two light gates *[1 mark]*. Measure the distance between the two light gates *[1 mark]*. Divide the distance by the time taken for the object to travel between the two light gates *[1 mark]*.

Q2 Using a stopwatch introduces human errors like reaction times, which aren't present with light gates *[1 mark]*. This matters more for short intervals, as the reaction time is a larger proportion of the interval being timed *[1 mark]*.

p.190 — Distance-Time Graphs

Q1 E.g.

[1 mark for a continuous line that initially curves upwards, 1 mark for the line to finish straight with a positive gradient.]

p.191 — Velocity-Time Graphs

Q1 E.g.

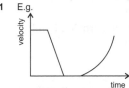

[1 mark for line which is initially horizontal, then becomes a straight line with a negative gradient, continuing until it meets the time axis, 1 mark for showing the line then continuing horizontally along the time axis, and 1 mark for then showing the line curving upwards.]

p.192 — Free Body Diagrams and Forces

Q1

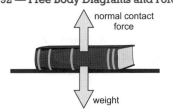

normal contact force

weight

[1 mark for arrows pointing in the right direction and labelled correctly, 1 mark for arrows being the same length.]

p.193 — Forces and Scale Drawings

Q1

5 N

Resultant force

12 N

Resultant force = 13 N
[1 mark for a correct scale drawing, 1 mark for correct resultant force.]

p.194 — Newton's First Law and Circular Motion

Q1 The resultant force is 0 N *[1 mark]*.

Q2 The force acts along the string/along the radius of the stone's circular path towards the centre of the circle *[1 mark]*. It is always at right angles to the line of motion of the stone *[1 mark]*.

p.195 — Momentum and Newton's Second Law

Q1 momentum = mass × velocity
= 220 000 × 250 *[1 mark]*
= 55 000 000 kg m/s *[1 mark]*

Q2 First, convert quantities to the correct units:
45 g = 0.045 kg
10.8 ms = 0.0108 s *[1 mark]*
Then calculate the change in momentum:
change in momentum
= momentum after − momentum before
= (mass of ball × final velocity of ball)
− (mass of ball × initial velocity of ball)
= (0.045 × 36) − (0.045 × 0) *[1 mark]*
= 1.62 kg m/s *[1 mark]*
resultant force = change of momentum ÷ time taken
= 1.62 ÷ 0.0108 *[1 mark]*
= 150 N *[1 mark]*

p.196 — Conservation of Momentum

Q1 Total momentum before collision
= (2.0 × 1.5) + (3.0 × 0) *[1 mark]*
= 3 kg m/s *[1 mark]*
The total momentum before the collision is equal to the total momentum after the collision.
Total momentum after collision
= total mass of trolleys × final velocity
3 = (2.0 + 3.0) × velocity
velocity = 3 ÷ (2.0 + 3.0) *[1 mark]*
= 0.6 m/s *[1 mark]*

Q2 Take 'to the right' to be positive.
Total momentum before collision
= (20 × 3) + (20 × (−2))
= +20 kg m/s *[1 mark]*
The total momentum before the collision is equal to the total momentum after the collision *[1 mark]*.
Total momentum after the collision
= (20 × −1) + (20 × velocity)
20 = −20 + (20 × velocity)
40 = (20 × velocity)
velocity = 40 ÷ 20 *[1 mark]*
= 2 m/s to the right *[1 mark]*

p.197 — Newton's Second Law and Inertia

Q1 The empty trolley has a smaller inertial mass *[1 mark]*, so less force is needed to change its velocity/stop it *[1 mark]*.

p.198 — Reaction Times

Q1 E.g. click a mouse button *[1 mark]* when a computer screen changes colour *[1 mark]*.

Q2 (final speed)^2 − (initial speed)^2
= 2 × acceleration × distance
(final speed)^2 = 2 × 10 × 0.162 + 0 *[1 mark]*
= 3.24
final speed = $\sqrt{3.24}$ = 1.8 m/s *[1 mark]*
time = change in speed ÷ acceleration
= 1.8 ÷ 10 *[1 mark]* = 0.18 s *[1 mark]*

p.199 — Stopping Distances

Q1 Work done by brakes = energy transferred from the kinetic energy store of the car *[1 mark]*.
Energy in the kinetic store of the car
= 0.5 × mass of car × (speed of car)^2
= 0.5 × 1000 × 25^2 *[1 mark]*
= 312 500 J *[1 mark]*
Work done by brakes
= braking force × braking distance = 312 500 J
Rearrange equation for braking distance:
braking distance = 312 500 ÷ braking force
= 312 500 ÷ 5000 *[1 mark]*
= 62.5 m
So the braking distance ~ 60 m *[1 mark]*

Answers

p.200 — Vehicle Safety

Q1 A large deceleration means that there is a large change in momentum in a short amount of time *[1 mark]*. This means that there must be a large force acting on the car and its passengers *[1 mark]*. These large forces can cause injuries to the passengers / cause the brakes to overheat / cause the car to skid *[1 mark]*.

Q2 The foam compresses when the cyclist's head hits an obstacle. This increases the time it takes for the cyclist's head to come a stop *[1 mark]*. This reduces the force acting on the cyclist's head, which reduces the risk of injury *[1 mark]*.

p.201 — Work Done and Energy Transfers

Q1 For the book to stop, it will need to do work against friction. The work done will be equal to the energy initially in its kinetic energy store. work done = force × distance, so
distance = work done ÷ force *[1 mark]*
= 1.25 ÷ 5.0 *[1 mark]* = 0.25 m
[1 mark]

p.202 — Kinetic and Potential Energy Stores

Q1 gravitational potential energy
= mass × gravitational field strength × height
= 0.80 × 10 × 1.5 *[1 mark]* = 12 J *[1 mark]*

Q2 kinetic energy = 0.5 × mass × speed²
= 0.5 × 4.9 × (2.0)² *[1 mark]*
= 9.8 J *[1 mark]*

p.203 — Energy Transfers and Power

Q1 As the ball falls, energy is transferred mechanically from its gravitational potential energy store to its kinetic energy store *[1 mark]*. When the ball hits the ground, some energy is transferred away by sound waves *[1 mark]*. The rest of the energy is carried away by heating to the thermal energy stores of the ball, the ground and the surroundings *[1 mark]*.

Q2 power = energy transferred ÷ time,
so energy transferred = power × time *[1 mark]*
5.0 minutes = 5.0 × 60 = 300 s
energy transferred = 12 × 300 *[1 mark]*
= 3600 J *[1 mark]*

p.205 — Developing the Model of The Atom

Q1 a) The centre of an atom is a tiny, positively charged nucleus *[1 mark]*. This is made up of protons and neutrons and is the source of most of the atom's mass *[1 mark]*. Most of the atom is empty space *[1 mark]*. Electrons orbit the nucleus at different distances *[1 mark]*.

b) The diameter of an atom is around 1×10^{-10} m *[1 mark]*. The size of a nucleus is 100 000 times smaller than this *[1 mark]*.

p.206 — Isotopes and Radioactive Decay

Q1 C *[1 mark]*

p.207 — Penetration Properties and Decay Equations

Q1 $^{238}_{92}U \longrightarrow \,^{234}_{90}Th \,+\, ^{4}_{2}He$

[1 mark for the correct representation of uranium, 1 mark for correct alpha particle symbol (He or α) and mass and atomic numbers and 1 mark for the correct mass and atomic numbers for thorium.]

p.208 — Activity and Half-life

Q1 10 × 24 = 240 hours
The number of half-lives in 240 hours is
240 ÷ 60 = 4 half-lives *[1 mark]*
Initially, activity = 2000 Bq
after 1 half-life, activity = 2000 ÷ 2 = 1000
after 2 half-lives, activity = 1000 ÷ 2 = 500
after 3 half-lives, activity = 500 ÷ 2 = 250
after 4 half-lives, activity = 250 ÷ 2 = 125
The activity after 4 half-lives = 125 Bq *[1 mark]*

p.209 — Dangers of Radioactivity

Q1 E.g. Radiation can cause minor damage to a cell that causes it to mutate / radiation can cause cells to divide uncontrollably / causes cancer *[1 mark]*. Radiation can also kill a cell completely *[1 mark]*.

p.210 — Half-life and Uses of Radiation

Q1 Gamma radiation can penetrate through tissue, so it can be detected outside the body with the radiation detector *[1 mark]*. It is also causes less damage inside the body than alpha and beta would *[1 mark]*.

p.212 — Density

Q1 E.g. use a mass balance to find the mass of the object *[1 mark]*. Fill a eureka can with water to just below the spout, then immerse the object in the can *[1 mark]*. Collect the water displaced by the object in a measuring cylinder as it flows out of the spout and record its volume *[1 mark]*. Then calculate the density of the object using density = mass ÷ volume *[1 mark]*.

Q2 volume in m³ = 75 ÷ (100³)
= 7.5×10^{-5} m³ *[1 mark]*
density = mass ÷ volume
= $(4.5 \times 10^{-2}) \div (7.5 \times 10^{-5})$ *[1 mark]*
= 600 kg/m³ *[1 mark]*

p.213 — The Particle Model of Matter

Q1 Solids are generally denser than liquids, which are generally denser than gases *[1 mark]*. The forces between the particles are greatest in solids and weakest in gases *[1 mark]*. This means that the particles are closest together in solids and furthest apart in gases *[1 mark]*.

p.214 — More on the Particle Model of Matter

Q1 There are less frequent collisions between particles and the container walls in a given amount of time, resulting in a lower overall force exerted on the container wall *[1 mark]*. The particles have a lower momentum, so they each exert a smaller force on the container walls during collisions *[1 mark]*. A lower force results in a lower pressure of the gas *[1 mark]*.

p.215 — Specific Heat Capacity

Q1 change in internal energy = mass × specific heat capacity × change in temperature, so:
change in temperature = change in internal energy ÷ (mass × specific heat capacity)
[1 mark]
= 1680 ÷ (0.20 × 420) *[1 mark]* = 20 °C *[1 mark]*

p.216 — Specific Latent Heat

Q1

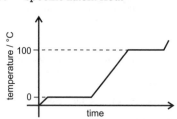

[1 mark for showing the line as flat at 0 °C, 1 mark for showing the line as flat at 100 °C, 2 marks for drawing a straight line with a positive gradient for temperatures below 0 °C, between 0 and 100 °C , and above 100 °C.]

p.217— Forces and Elasticity

Q1 extension of the spring
= 0.20 – 0.16 = 0.04 m *[1 mark]*
Rearrange force = extension × spring constant
So spring constant = $\dfrac{\text{force}}{\text{extension}}$ = $\dfrac{3.0}{0.04}$ *[1 mark]*
= 75 N/m *[1 mark]*

p.218 — Investigating Hooke's Law

Q1 First calculate the extension of the spring:
extension = 1.3 – 1.2 = 0.1 m *[1 mark]*
energy stored in a stretched spring
= 0.5 × spring constant × (extension)²
= 0.5 × 54 × 0.1² *[1 mark]* = 0.27 J *[1 mark]*

Index

Index

Index

Index